750/

see p. 38
for a good time at Day's

D1020282

CULTURE: *Man's Adaptive Dimension*

CONTRIBUTORS

ROBERT ASCHER, *Cornell University*

ERNST CASPARI, *University of Rochester*

EARL W. COUNT, *Hamilton College*

BENSON E. GINSBURG, *University of Wisconsin*

A. IRVING HALLOWELL, *University of Pennsylvania*

CHARLES F. HOCKETT, *Cornell University*

RALPH L. HOLLOWAY, JR., *Columbia University*

ERICH KAHLER, *Princeton University*

R. KUTTNER

WILLIAM S. LAUGHLIN, *University of Wisconsin*

M. F. ASHLEY MONTAGU, *Columbia University*

CULTURE

Man's Adaptive Dimension

EDITED BY

M. F. ASHLEY MONTAGU

New York OXFORD UNIVERSITY PRESS 1968

PRINTED IN THE UNITED STATES OF AMERICA

Foreword

Man alone among the forms of animated nature is the creature that has moved into an adaptive zone which is an entirely learned one. This is the zone of *culture,* the man-made, the learned, part of the environment. Man's basic needs must still be physically satisfied. He must eat, drink, sleep, rest, exercise, eliminate, and avoid noxious and dangerous stimuli. But even here the manner in which man satisfies his basic needs is largely culturally determined, and to a much greater extent than is customarily understood. Thanks to the work of cultural anthropologists it is now clear that virtually the full range of possible ways in which man is capable of responding to the challenges of the environment has been exploited by him in all his manifold variety.

Man's adaptability is equalled only by his educability, and the two are, of course, developmentally and dynamically interrelated. In the evolution of man cultural adaptability has been at a high premium and, correspondingly, so has his ability to learn, his educability. Educability is, indeed, the outstanding species characteristic of man. The evolution of culture and the development of educability are species traits which have proceeded integratively in the evolution of man, man considered not merely as a cultural creature, but also as an organic being. In an earlier collection of papers on this subject, *Culture and the Evolution of Man* (New York, Oxford University Press, 1962), it was shown that culture affected not only man's social evolution but also his physical evolution in a process of reciprocating interactive feedback. In this process cultural challenges put a high selective premium upon those individuals possessing the necessary abilities to respond successfully—that is to say, those carrying the necessary genes. Thus, in the evolution of man cultural and genetic development have proceeded interdependently.

Furthermore, it is important to observe that man evolved as the creature he has become not merely because of a peculiar genetic endowment, but because the pressure of his way of life, throughout his two million or more years of evolution, gave his genetic development a selective direction which it could never otherwise have achieved.

The most important setting of human evolution is the human cultural environment. That setting will not only continue to be the principle *mise-en-scène* of man's future development, but it will increasingly be his chief and most important means of adapting himself to the complexities of the world he has created. Hence, it is important to understand not only what human culture is, how it acts, but also how it came about. And not only for its own sake, or simply because it is so extraordinarily interesting, but principally because the understanding such knowledge of man's nature confers will enable us more intelligently to control and direct our future development. If culture is man's past working upon the present to create the future, it is today more than ever necessary to understand the manner in which he got to be the way he is now, in order that we shall the better be able to make him what he ought to be. Toward that end the contributions gathered together in the present volume are dedicated.

A. M.

Princeton, N.J.
July 1967

Contents

CULTURE: *Man's Adaptive Dimension*

Culture and Evolution

ERICH KAHLER

I

The terms "Culture" and "Evolution" are by no means self-evident. They have been understood in different ways, and the variety of these meanings reflects a variety of human experiences in different historical situations. A brief survey of the diverse uses of the words will show how the meaning of the terms kept broadening, and then, as a re-active consequence, narrowed down into more specific connotations.

The word "Culture" derives from Latin *cultura* and *cultus,* which mean care, cultivation, but carry a variety of connotations, from "training," "fostering," "adornment," to "worship," and "cult." Both words were used originally in an attributive, functional sense, desig-nating cultivation *of something.* In fact, *cultura* occurs first in the composite form *agri cultura,* agriculture, tilling, cultivation of the soil, and traces of this origin persist up to the Middle Ages when occasion-ally the worship of God is referred to as *agricultura Dei,* "agricult" of God. The meaning of *cultura* broadens through diverse applications: Cicero speaks of *cultura animi,* cultivation of the mind, which he identifies with philosophy; but gradually *cultura animi* ceased to be so restricted and came to signify cultivation of arts and letters, of intel-lectual capacities in general. Thus, the common feature of all kinds of cultivation was brought to the fore, namely control and organization, refinement and sublimation of nature.

In this way, the various attributive, functional uses of *cultura* and *cultus* fused into the general and substantive term "Culture," as we still apply it when we oppose culture to barbarism, or when we call a person a "cultivated man." This change from an attributive to a sub-stantive significance implies a turn from the representation of *cultura,* cultivation, as an *activity* (cultivating something, cultivating oneself —*cultivare se ipsum*) to the concept of *culture as an established con-dition,* a state of being cultivated.

NOTE: First given as a lecture at the 1960 Graduation Colloquium of the Albert Ein-stein School of Medicine in New York.

From *The Centennial Review,* Vol. V, No. 3, Summer 1961, pp. 239–59. Reprinted by permission.

In this capacity as a specific condition of man, a state of being, the term "Culture" became synonymous and interchangeable with other terms, such as *humanitas,* humanity, that is, the condition worthy of a human being, as compared with that of the animal; or *civilitas,* civility, and *urbanitas,* urbanity, the condition fitting a city dweller and citizen, as against that of a peasant, a boor. The Roman Empire, and the Latin countries, which originated in Roman provinces and followed the Roman tradition, issued from and centered on a dominating city. The country at large was considered subservient to the city, and city life was the standard of life, in contradistinction to Germany, where the cities developed late, after and within the framework of a universal Empire, and where, due to the persistent rusticality of the nobility, cities never achieved such a predominant position as in the West. Until very late, Germany never had a capital city. These differences seem to me to explain the eventual prevalence of the term "Civilization" in the West and of "Culture" in Germany. The German notion and high valuation of culture, *Kultur,* evolved from the concepts of German philosophy. *Kultur* was identified with *Bildung,* the cultivation of inner life, of mental and spiritual capacities, and held superior to Western "Civilization" which was understood as a complex of outer forms: nicety of manners and development of technological and socio-political institutions.

From the sixteenth century on, a new concept of culture began to form. In the wake of the rise of modern nations and territorial states, political thinkers started to differentiate the various national customs and institutions, and to speculate about the national donominators of such specific customs and institutions. The theorist of the French monarchy, Jean Bodin, in his *Six Livres de la République,* 1576, inaugurated the notion of different forms of republic as *organisms,* growing and decaying like natural organisms and peculiarly distinct according to character and climate. He thereby anticipated the modern theories of Spengler and Toynbee. Later, Montesquieu, in his *Esprit des Lois,* 1748, and Voltaire, in his *Essai sur les Moeurs,* 1757, spoke of *"le génie du peuple,"* genius of the people, its *"esprit général,"* general spirit, its *"genre de vie,"* which may be adequately rendered by "style of life" or "way of life." I need not recount the whole genealogy of this notion which in the nineteenth century led up to the concept of "cultures" as specific forms of life of ethnic communities, or of epochs. As far as I can see, the Swiss historian, Jakob Burckhardt, in the middle of the nineteenth century, was the first to apply this concept of *a* culture to specific studies in his *Kultur der Renaissance* and his *Griechische Kulturgeschichte.* Likewise, modern anthropologists have adopted the term "Culture" in this specific sense for the tribal groups which they explore.

The shift from the concept of culture as a general human condition to the concept of culture as a particular style of life of ethnic groups, in short, from culture to *a* culture, involves another important change of outlook. Culture seen as a general state and stage of human existence carried a *value* connotation which it lost when it was understood as merely a different style of life. Culture as a value was equivalent to superiority over the state of plain nature, over barbarism and bestialism; it was an intellectual and moral criterion to measure the worth and dignity of individuals and peoples. It meant improvement, refinement, enlightenment, and this, in turn, implied development.

Thus, originally, *cultura,* culture, was *synonymous with development,* and—this is most important to note—development in the sense of *progress,* of betterment of the human condition.

II

Here we have arrived at the problem of *development,* or *evolution.* Both words denote fundamentally the same: development means literally unwrapping, evolution means unfolding. There is only one difference: evolution has come to be the more general, development the more specific, term.

The story of the concept of development in its broader sense of evolution is, as far as the human domain is concerned, identical with the history of history, which cannot be retraced in detail within the limits of this paper. Suffice it to recall the main phases.

Ancient thinking and society were founded on a stable image of the universe. The concept of evolution was arrested in the bud; it was itself, paradoxical as this may sound, static; it was implicit in the appreciation of culture. Even Aristotle who, because of his concept of *entelechy,* is held to be the initiator of the idea of evolution and who indeed regarded the different realms of organic nature, the vegetal, the animal, and the human, as consecutive evolutionary stages, considered only one as the essential premise of the other, but did not assume a real transformation of one into the other. To him, any organic being or genus was created separately by a touch of the deity. Nor did there yet exist among the ancients, at least before the Hellenistic period, any notion of an historical evolution of humanity. The Greeks and the Romans did not realize actual history, integral history, that is, history as that single, unique, and unrepeatable flow of happenings passing through and beyond the individual peoples, history as the comprehensive record of the career of man. To them, the human world was either rooted in eternity, or it was believed to be recurrently created and destroyed, in a circular movement. Accordingly, their conception of change and evolution was still very shallow and was limited by the notion of a periodical recurrence of events.

The experience of actual evolution was inaugurated by the Jews, who came to visualize history as the road of man from a primal state of *unconscious innocence,* which he lost through his fall, to an ultimate state of *consciously achieved innocence* in the Kingdom of God to be established at the end of time. To be sure, this progression of human history may still appear as a circular movement in that it seems to return to the original situation. But, in fact, the situation at which it is aimed lies on a new level, on the level of consciousness. This makes the crucial difference: it establishes the uniqueness of the whole process. The messianic prophecy of Judaism led up to Christianity, and the belief in a sacrificial help of the divine savior transformed the Judaic road toward a humanly achieved innocence into a road to divine salvation. So, in the Christian era, evolution was equivalent to man's gradual preparation for salvation. Through the Judaeo-Christian concepts, then, human destiny was dynamized; it was made into a process, into one, unique evolutionary process. This evolutionary process made explicit what was merely implied in the ancient concepts of culture: the notion of betterment and sublimation. Again, development meant improvement, accomplishment of a higher and happier state of man.

Finally, when at the end of the Middle Ages, the rule of the Christian dogma crumbled and human reason supplanted God, rationalism inherited from Christian theology the concept of history as man's road to perfection. To be sure, the established definite end, as expected in the kingdom of God, had vanished and was replaced by the indefinite goal of a Kingdom of Reason: evolution was no longer a road to a distinct redeeming event but became an unending approach to secular betterment and happiness through the rational, scientific, and technological improvements of man's living conditions. The goal was split into gradual steps; it came to merge with the road itself, with *Progress* explicit, its ends moving along with it. The emphasis shifted from the final being to infinite becoming.

Since the late nineteenth century, and increasingly in the twentieth, the belief in human progress began to wane. Or, to be more exact, what dwindled away was the hope that the scientific and technological improvement of *material* conditions would by itself bring about an improvement of man's *inner* condition, that is to say, make him better and happier. Long before the turn of the century, men of vision had seen the dark reverse of our expanding rational enlightenment, the growing collectivization and dehumanization which technological progress was carrying with it. They foresaw what was to happen in the great crises of the twentieth century: the abrupt slump of humanity from an overstrained civilization into a new, rationalized barbarism. The hopes of the rationalistic generations turned into bitter disillusionment with progress, and since evolution had always been identified with progress, the notion of evolution went down together with the idea of progress.

There were other factors which brought evolution into disrepute. In the domain of history, it was the hypertrophy of historicism itself that discredited the very idea of history as a coherent evolution of man: the overgrowth of newly discovered factual material obscured the broad lines of development and made historians apprehensive of "generalizations." Or, more exactly, it was not so much the growth of factual material in itself, but rather the failure of historians to integrate the new facts into a general concept of human evolution, due to the scientistic ambition and positivistic tendency of modern historiography. As a reaction against the great philosophical and social conceptions of the post-Kantian era, in the first half of the nineteenth century, a sweeping distrust of uncritical speculation set in. Such a reaction was certainly justified to a certain degree, but, as usual, it was carried to the opposite extreme; it led to an attitude that was just as uncritical. Under the influence of scientistic positivism, all criterion of facts was lost; historical research arrived at what I would call a democracy of facts, a total equality of facts, which invalidated the distinction between essential and non-essential. Where could a broad evaluation of facts derive from when no general view was left of the historical process? Any clear statement of a development became impossible; it simply disappeared under its qualifications. Eventually, this tendency resulted in scientific, basically anti-historical, theories of history, such as Spengler's and Toynbee's, which split the process of human evolution into so many "philosophically contemporaneous" cultures in order to abstract from them "laws of history" equivalent to laws of nature. The constructions of these "cultures" or "civilizations" are no less uncritically speculative than the old philosophical systems.

Spengler and Toynbee are only the most conspicuous exponents of the anti-historical and anti-evolutional trend that developed since the beginning of our century and pervades all studies in the human domain. It manifests itself in this country in the Great Books movement, in the principles and practices of the New Criticism, in the purely descriptive methods of the American school of anthropology and its opposition to the evolutional theories of the French anthropologists Durkheim and Lévy-Bruhl. Here, in anthropology, too, the anti-evolutionist tendency is due to radical positivism.

In biology the concept of evolution, modified though it has been, could never be given up, just as the historical point of view is the only one from which geology, the structure of the earth, can be understood. But even in paleobiology anti-evolutionism left its traces. The German paleontologist, Edgar Dacqué, a very learned and imaginative man, came out with a theory that was meant to reverse the whole course of evolution of living forms. In his book *Urwelt, Sage und Menschheit,* 1924, he contended that from the beginning of life there existed different genetically unrelated types, or type groups (*Typkenkreise*) which gradually developed into the various animal forms. Like these, man too has existed, rudimentarily, from the outset as a distinct genetic type. Of course, Dacqué could not deny that man had to go through various animal stages before reaching his human form. But this he explained by the theory that the specific circumstances and environments of the different paleontological periods imposed on genetically independent types certain seemingly homogeneous structural forms and organs, structural fashions as it were: from the Cambrian to the Devonian the dominant form was fish; in the Permian the various species were wearing amphibian, so to speak; from the Permian to the Cretaceous they changed to reptile; with the Eocene it was mammals; and later the dominant form was ape.[1] As a residue of the phenomenon, Dacqué mentions the fauna of Australia where the most diverse species of higher mammals seem to imitate the form of a lower type of mammal, the marsupial: the marsupial badger, the opossum, the kangaroo, the phalanger, the Australian bear (koala), all of them appear as different versions of the marsupial form.

But even this hypothesis does not fundamentally invalidate the fact of evolution. The assumption of several original types instead of a single, common one would indicate nothing else than the existence of many parallel evolutions; and in regard to the concept of human evolution, it does not make much difference whether one calls a reptile a reptile, or man in the temporary disguise of a reptile.

III

The main source of the trend, indeed the intellectual fashion, of anti-evolutionism was, as I said, disillusionment with progress and the identification of evolution with progress. It seems to me that in order properly to understand what evolution means, it is necessary to put an end to this confusion and clearly to distinguish evolution from progress. The first point I want to make is that *there was no progress, but there was evolution*. Progress implies a value statement; evolution denotes a plainly factual process.

Progress means improvement. In the human domain it was understood as an improvement not only of living conditions, but of human life; in other words, an advancement not only of material circumstances, but of happiness and morality, or, to put it more modestly, of action according to reason. Evidently, these high expectations of the era of enlightenment have not been fulfilled. Biological theories also identified evolution with progress inasmuch as they took it to be a succession of steps leading up to the human being as its peak, if not its definite end. Indeed, Julian Huxley, even today, seems to assume that the human individual is the final perfection of evolution. In the face of our present situation, this appears to me a rather questionable human presumption. So when we speak of evolution today, we do better, I think, to eliminate the notion of progress which cannot be divested of its original, plainly optimistic meaning.

But if not progress, what is evolution? First of all, we should take into account that in science recent experiences and findings have initiated a trend of thought that runs diametrically counter to the fashion of anti-evolutionism. Our picture of nature has become thoroughly dynamic, that is to say, nature no longer appears, as it did appear to scientists up to the nineteenth century, as a static, eternally immutable sphere; it has revealed itself as a *process*. Not only does it, as modern physics has shown, in its entirety consist of processes; it is in itself and as a whole, and it has always been, a process. Astronomy today considers itself a historical science, while biological nature has been seen as a process for a long time, ever since Buffon and Lamarck. To be sure, the research of one and a half centuries has produced a picture of the history of life which makes it appear no longer as a straight line development, but rather as a tree-like growth of multifarious ramifications. The most important change, however, that has taken place in our scientific views with respect to the problem of evolution is the fact that the gap has begun to close, the barriers are crumbling, between the inorganic and the organic stages of nature.

When we take all these experiences together, then, the history of the universe, the history of the earth, the history of life, and the history of man, all emerge as so many sections and stages of *one* unique, or, to put it more cautiously, peculiar happening. This overwhelming happening which started from the universe and has this very moment ar-

rived at the here and now where we sit reflecting about it, this process, viewed in its entirety, shows undeniably a definite direction.
Mind you, I say *direction,* and by this I do not mean a *plan,* transcen-
dental or otherwise. Here again a strict distinction has to be made. A
direction in the sense of *trend* does not necessarily imply direction in
the sense of *guidance* or *providence* or *design*. I see a direction, but I
would not venture to say anything about the origin or cause of such
direction. This direction is what permits us to speak of evolution. Indeed, the most superficial glance at what happened from the amoeba
to man, from Neanderthal man to a human condition which produced personalities like Buddha and Jesus, Dante and Shakespeare,
Newton and Einstein, this simple glance at the career of life and of
man compels us to assume some sort of evolution.

But again, what is this evolution? What is the nature of this happening? When we ask biologists, we hardly get one clear-cut answer;
we get many partial answers concerning functional or structural features. Gaylord Simpson, for instance, enumerates all sorts of criteria of
evolution (he calls it "progress"), such as "the tendency for life to
expand, to fill in all the available spaces in the livable environments,"
"improvement in adaptation," "control over the environment," "increasing structural complication," "progress in individualization,"
etc.[2] In all this, he is very anxious to remain "objective" with regard
to man, that is to say, not to look at evolution from a pre-established
point of view of man as the goal or climax of evolution. He refuses to
accept the criterion of "increasing approximation to man"; indeed, he
finds certain partial aspects which show man not exactly at the top,
for instance: "If one group had to be picked as most dominant now,
it would have to be the insects," which implies a rather narrow,
purely physical concept of dominance.[3] However, he cannot help listing man in almost all respects within the highest range of evolution;
indeed, he declares on the grounds of evidence: "Man *is* the highest
animal. The fact that he alone is capable of making such a judgment
is in itself part of the evidence that this decision is correct." He goes
even farther by stating that man is an animal ". . . in which, although organic evolution continues on its way, a fundamentally new
sort of evolution has also appeared," the basis of which "is a new sort
of heredity, the inheritance of learning."[4] Actually, however, he stops,
as most biologists do, at the threshold of this new kind of evolution,
at the point where *Homo sapiens* began his career on his own plane
which is history and which entails psychic, mental, and social developments, entirely new dimensions of development, by far surpassing
the heredity of learning. Julian Huxley is more specifically positive in

that he does not hesitate, as I said before, to make the bold assertion that the human individual not only is, but *"will continue to be* the highest product of evolution."[5] Evolution he defines as an increase in complexity, ". . . greater control, greater independence or self-regulation, greater, but at the same time more harmonious complexity of organization, greater range of knowledge or available experience."[6]

IV

I will now venture an interpretation of my own, taking into consideration both the biological and the historical spheres, but disregarding the genetical and functional aspects of the problem. When we view the record of the history of life and the history of man from a vantage point, looking only at the succession of forms up to now, evolution appears as a gradual, but consistent *extension of scope, extension of range of being,* with all the growing differentiation, organization, concentration, with all the variation and intensification of experience that go with it. Such extension of range of being seems equivalent to a process of *interiorization,* which means transference and transformation of outer functions into inner functions, an increasing incorporation of external and extensive world contents into internal and intensive organism. Actually, the process consists of two processes, approximating what the Stoics called *diastole* and *systole* distension and concentration. Only through distension can new world contents be appropriated and integrated.

Let me concretely exemplify this assumption. To begin with, life itself is such a concentration, interiorization, intensification of physical elements: the successive formation of molecule and cell. The process continues in the transformation of living forms: in the development leading from sporiferous plants, which multiply through detached spores, to flowering plants, propagating through internal generation, and in the animal sphere, correspondingly, from ovipara to mammals —this, even Gaylord Simpson stresses as being one of the most firmly established evolutionary traits: "The mammals are . . . the highest animals in this particular respect and the case is clear-cut and indisputable, from the protection and uniformity of internal gestation through most highly perfected post-natal care including provision of nearly uniform and highly nutritious food from the mother."[7] Parallel developments are: the shift of the body supports from exoskeleton (shells, as with arachnids, insects, crustaceans, testaceans) to endoskeleton (inner bone structure of the vertebrates; the bony fishes are the latest among fishes); furthermore, the gradual interiorization of metabolism, and the formation of a central nervous system; the advance from the metamorphosis of metabolic plants and animals to the immediate generation in higher forms. In all these instances, external processes and relations have become inner functions and systems and have been more and more closely integrated in an expanding organic system.

Integration, in this process, goes hand in hand with differentiation——integration, not only internally, of the various differentiating, specializing parts and organs, and of the organism as a whole, but also, correspondingly, externally, of an ever wider and more differentiated world. Increasing differentiation of the organic system means correlatively an expansion of scope, an extension and amplification of relationship and control. So we have here a two-way process of expansion and concentration, and it is hardly possible to make out which originated which.

The same development can be shown in the specifically human sphere, the sphere of history, in which this evolution was carried on, and carried over from the physical to the psychic, mental, and the more and more predominant social level. External, magical and mythical, relationships of the human being with external, divine powers gradually turned into interiorized connections of rational ideas and concepts; the visually pictured, diversely animate universe of participation and religion passed over into an inner realm of human reason organizing exploratory experiences. External dependencies were replaced by man's growing feeling of inner autonomy, by judgment, choice, man's control of himself and of his world. The rise of human consciousness corresponds to the unfolding of his counterpart, an ever more abundant and diversified world. We see that this again is as much a process of differentiation, elaboration of distinctive intellectual faculties, as it is a process of integration, of incorporating an ever vaster phenomenal territory.

When we finally compare the state of human knowledge and of man's technological mastery of nature in the first centuries of the modern era with the one we witness today, we notice a further step in the same direction. The mechanistic universe of Newtonian physics was linked together by outer, grossly material, and sensorily conceivable forces; modern physics faces a universe not moved, but perpetually moving by itself and in itself, a universe in which matter is identical with energy, and which is approachable only by increasingly speculative means of understanding. Today, infinitely subtler methods of intellectual grasp correspond to a hitherto unparalleled extension of the objective orbit of human contemplation and manipulation. I need not emphasize the advance of our technological control of nature, which has reduced our globe to a single room as it were, and has taken us to the verge of interplanetary communications. Modern biology and medicine have penetrated into the microsphere of genes and hormones and enzymes, and have begun to elucidate the subtle interconnections within the organic whole; modern psychology has entered into the sphere of the unconscious. A similar process may be observed in the modern arts, in their reaching beyond the range of portrayal of individual, tangibly "objective" forms, of individual narrative, of sensuous *melos,* into abstract fundamentals of form as such, of phenomenal appearance as such, existence as such, sound relations as such.

V

What I have stated just now requires, however, some specification which introduces a new aspect into the problem of evolution. This new aspect concerns the *relation between individual and group,* and that is, *between different levels of existence.* It seems to me that without a clarification of this relationship it is impossible properly to understand what evolution means in our present situation. For my statement must be qualified to the effect that *the tremendous recent expansion of human reach, and incorporation of world contents in human consciousness, applies to man as a whole, but no longer to the human individual.* When Julian Huxley characterizes evolution as an increase of complexity and organization of complexity, greater control, greater independence or self-regulation, greater range of knowledge, etc., it appears more than evident that this may be said of man, but hardly of the human individual in his present condition. The human individual today shows, on the contrary, a blatant *de*crease of control, independence, self-regulation, and range of knowledge; and this *de*crease on the *individual* level appears to be correlative with the *in*crease on the *collective* level.

A. L. Kroeber in his essay, "The Concept of Culture in Science," distinguishes sharply the different "levels of organization" or "levels" pure and simple, the physico-chemical, the biological or organic, the social and cultural. And he rightly rejects the practice of nineteenth century science of applying the categories of one level to another level, or, more specifically, to reduce the terms of the higher levels to the supposedly basic ones of the physio-chemical level. "Gravitation," he says, "electrical conductivity, and element valence apply to organic bodies as well as to inorganic ones. But principals or laws such as these are the only ones which apply to inorganic bodies; and yet they do not to any serious degree explain the specific organic phenomena of hereditary repetition, of conception and death, of adaptability. These specifically organic processes *conform* to established physiochemical processes; they cannot be *derived* from them." So the different levels are to a certain degree autonomous while they are still in certain respects ". . . dependent on the subjacent ones and of support to the independent overlying ones." [8]

While sharing this view in general, I am inclined to assume a much closer connection between the various levels of existence. It was utterly wrong, of course, to derive the specific phenomena of one level from those of another level, but if we want to understand the real nature of any entity or being we cannot sharply separate one level from another, we cannot confine ourselves to considering one level strictly apart from its subjacent and overlying ones. We do not live as individuals *in* society or *in* a nation as within an overarching, delimitable space. We *are* this society, this nation to a large degree; we form part of it, and it forms part of us, down indeed to our physical being. We are, all of us, any entity or being is, *existing on different levels at the same time. Existence is a multilevel affair.* As a body, I am a natural organization of lower beings, living, moving, changing, growing and decaying beings, namely the *cells.* Any change or disturbance in this organization, or even in the organization of the cells themselves, has most powerful and serious effects on what we may consider the essence or quintessence of the physical system, the *psyche.* This is, after all, recognized in the psychosomatic theory and in recent psychiatry. The psyche, in turn, has a well-established influence on the *mind.* All such dependence, however, does not invalidate the fact that the functioning or operation on each specific level has its own distinct and, to a certain degree, autonomous character. We must also realize that all influence effective between different levels is a two-way process: it works upward as well as downward. There is a mutual interaction going on between mind, psyche, body, and so forth.

A similar interrelationship prevails between individual and group, and this interrelationship is crucial in regard to our specific concern. As a psycho-intellectual being, as a person and an individual, I move in a constantly interactive relationship with social units, with communities and collectives; the fundamental difference between these two kinds of social unit cannot and need not be elaborated within the present context. What matters is that, socially too, I live on different levels at the same time, in closest interdependence and interaction between my self and the various groups to which I belong. In point of fact, I am part of the groups, and the groups are part of my very self.

I simply do not exist without them; and whenever anything changes in the groups, my personal self is affected by it. Accordingly, when we study social or psychic evolution, it is no use considering social forms and individual psyche separately, since they both move together and transform together, in constant interrelationship with each other. Whenever the one changes, the other changes with it, and the nature of the relationship changes too. What develops is not the group *per se,* or the individual *per se,* but the combination and the relationship of both, and we have to study both with regard to each other. Therefore, we cannot gain a complete picture of human processes if we deal with psychology without considering sociology, or conversely study sociology, or for that matter, any human conditions, happenings, and activities, without including psychology.

I said that the individual psyche changes with the change of social forms and *vice versa,* and that the nature of the relationship changes also. But along with the interrelated developments an even more important change has taken place. Evolution is, as I have attempted to show, a process of extension of scope. Now in the course of this process it happened at certain points that *the emphasis, the point of gravity of events, shifted from one level to another.* Just as with the emergence of *Homo sapiens* the emphasis has moved from body to mind, and evolution proper had turned into human history, in a similar way, in our age, since the nineteenth century, the point of gravity of events appears to have shifted from the individual to the collective level. And while on the collective level man has immensely expanded his reach, the individual, through this very process, has shrunk in independence, self-regulation, power of control, and range of knowledge. The fact that the technological and intellectual scope of humanity has advanced far beyond the capacity of the individual mind, and that individual consciousness is less and less able to keep pace with the growing extent and complexity of happenings and with what I would call collective consciousness—namely, the vast corpus of our present, ever moving, ever changing knowledge—this tragic inadequacy of the individual is one of the basic causes of our human crisis.

VI

Now how does *culture* fit into this picture? What role and meaning has it in the process of evolution?

Our historical survey of the term Culture has shown us four different concepts: 1) culture as a *human condition,* which implies a *value* (this is what we mean when we speak of a "cultivated man"); 2) the *value-free* concept of culture as a *specific way of life, style of life, of a people,* or, to use Kroeber's definition, as the *totality of customs and ways of life of a people*; 3) culture as an *ethnic entity pure and simple,* in which sense the term is generally used by modern anthropologists; and 4) culture is a *regionally meta-ethnic entity,* a concept that has been introduced by Leo Frobenius and Oswald Spengler and has been taken over by Toynbee for the construction of some of his civilizations.

These different concepts of culture are, as we have seen, manifestations of different evolutionary stages; they reflect the growth of human self-realization. The realization of the diversity, and the diverse organic coherence, of ethnic groups presupposes the Judaeo-Christian realization of a common humanity above and in all of them. In the pre-Christian, pre-Helenistic, pre-Stoic era, each particular ethnic community identified humanity with itself. There is not too much difference between the attitude of peoples like the Zuñi, Déné, Kiowa, who by these tribal names naively designate human beings as equivalents of themselves, and the Greek and Roman identification of strangers with barbarians. Culture, to the Greeks and the Romans, was the antithesis of barbarism, the advance on barbarism.

The ancient concept of *culture as a human condition and a value,* as an enlightened, sensitized, humane state, a most desirable state of the human being, as *paideia,* in the Greek sense, is still valid today; to express it we have no better word. *Culture in the sense of style of life, or the totality of customs,* seems to me a superfluous synonym. Why not say style of life, or customs? This is simpler, it means what it says. What concerns us closely, however, is the concept of *a* culture, *culture as an independent entity,* as a being in itself. Here we have the choice between identifying a culture with an *ethnic community,* or the posting of *meta-ethnic cultures* comprehending various ethnic groups.

For Spengler and Toynbee the concept of man as a coherent entity hardly exists in any clearly stated form. Toynbee at least substitutes for it his theological superstructure which in a way unifies, or is expected retroactively to unify, the various civilizations, dead or alive. But both of them, Spengler and Toynbee, break up the coherence of human evolution in history into the isolated units of their "philosophically contemporaneous," meta-ethnic civilizations. What remains of a common human quality are the well-known parallelisms, the historical "laws of nature." (We may leave aside Spengler's occasional characterization of man as the "technological beast of prey.")

Careful analysis would show, indeed has shown in critical studies by a number of scholars, the precariousness of these theories.

Since the whole of nature in its broadest perspective comes to be seen as a historical process, history proper must be understood as a unique section of a unique cosmic happening; it must be understood as the history of the organic genus, Man. Accordingly, we have first to explore the uniqueness of the process of human history, the uniqueness of its place within the larger, comprehensive whole of nature, and the uniqueness of its stages and ramifications, before we may be able to recognize the real, the *genotypical homologies* prevailing among its different subdivisions and sub-processes. We have first to establish what specific stage each subdivision represents within the whole of human history, and only over against this coherence of historical consecution and diversity can we try to find out very cautiously what the different subdivisions, or variations, of the one historical process may have in common. If, however, we start from seeking general laws we are prone to crude simplifications and fallacies. An apparently identical phenomenon may have a fundamentally different significance in this and that specific unit according to their different origins, their different relations to the whole, the different evolutionary stages they represent. In studying history, we have to use a method diametrically opposite to that of Spengler and Toynbee; we have to strive for ever more subtle differentiation and grasp of the unique.

The unreliability and superficiality of "general laws" as derived from "philosophical contemporaneity" are furthermore increased if one chooses as units "civilizations" which first have to be established in order to yield their general laws. Such a procedure carries the danger of begging the question, namely, the temptation to shape the civilizations according to the general laws they are supposed to demonstrate. But apart from this ambiguity of Spengler's and Toynbee's concepts, their views must be considered inadequate in that they confine the historical processes to one single level, whereas, as I have tried to show, these processes move on different levels at the same time, and involve changes not only from stage to stage, but from level to level.

For all these reasons, I would prefer to stick to the units which human evolution itself has developed, the ethnic communities. Here again, I would not be inclined merely to equate these ethnic communities with "cultures." Culture and community are not exactly the same thing. It seems to me that the cultures and the communities have the same relationship to each other as the psyche or the character of an individual person has to his body. I would equate the culture of an ethnic entity in its subjective, inward aspect with the *psyche,* in its objective, outward aspect with the *character,* of an ethnic community.

There are, however, certain turning points in the historical process where cultures become independent of the place and community in which they originated. When an old people declines, and when, after its climatic flowering and absorption of world contents to capacity, its physical power begins to disintegrate, something takes off; the spirit, the transcending form as it were, the residual character of this people, detaches itself from its specific origins, survives spiritually and fecundates new forces. Only such a transcending form of life that disengages itself from its specific origins and becomes a spiritual being of its own, influencing other units, merging with others, and carried farther by others even after its originator may have died down and dissolved, only such an independent entity may be seen as a culture, or civilization, *per se,* clearly distinguished from the people from which it has emerged. As seen in this aspect, cultures are not identical with their originating peoples and historical spheres; they are their offspring, their spiritual spores as it were. They mature very late and come into being as detached, separate units of history only in the ultimate stages of their originators. In this capacity, as independent entities, intermediate between ethnic communities and man, they represent and carry evolution.

The first cultures, or civilizations, of that kind, the first that were explicitly recognized as meta-ethnic, were those arising from the Greek and the Jewish peoples: *Hellenism* and *Christianism.* The very fact that they were so recognized indicates that they represent historical units of a higher order, involving a new stage, a new level of consciousness. Other examples are, within the European orbit, *Latinism,* the survival of Roman tradition, and in the Oriental sphere, *Buddhism* and *Islam.* The historical process entails a gradual shift to broader units, and at the same time to higher levels of consciousness. The process starts with peoples. Peoples are the unit which, in a relay as it were, carry the evolutionary process and develop, in their inner and outer forms, their psychic and social forms, man's specific quality and consciousness. Gradually, the widening scope produces new and broader units which later take over and lead the essential process.

In our time, we are witnessing the gradual detachment and independent global spread of what we may identify as our *Western civilization.* Whether this Western civilization still means culture, in the original sense of the term, is, however, an open question.

Notes

1. In the paleozoic period, Dacqué says, when the salamander form was the "style of the epoch," even the first reptiles, or better those types that were on the point of becoming reptiles, appeared in the attire of the salamander. Later, the first flying vertebrates were just winged reptiles.

2. George Gaylord Simpson, *The Meaning of Evolution* (Yale University Press, 1951), pp. 240ff.

3. Simpson, p. 246.

4. Simpson, p. 285ff.

5. T. H. Huxley and Julian Huxley, *Touchstone for Ethics 1893–1943* (New York, 1947), p. 33.

6. Huxley, p. 146.

7. Simpson, pp. 257ff.

8. A. L. Kroeber, "The Concept of Culture in Science," in *The Nature of Culture* (University of Chicago Press, 1952), pp. 120ff.

The Human Revolution

CHARLES F. HOCKETT AND ROBERT ASCHER

This essay [1] attempts to set forth the story of the emergence of the first humans from their prehuman ancestors. A special feature is that we have tried to incorporate the various steps and stages of the evolution of language into the total picture.[2]

We dedicate this essay to the memory of Paul Fejos, whose encouragement, over a number of years, played an important part in bringing the work to fruition.

The inquiry into human origins is a collective task to which hundreds of investigators have contributed. Virtually none of the proposals in the present paper are our own. Even for the ways of thinking about the evidence that seem to be fruitful, we are completely indebted to our predecessors. We do accept responsibility for the particular way in which we have chosen among alternative theories, and for the way in which we have tied them together. We believe that the time is ripe for a synthesis of this sort, if only as a clear point of departure for the further investigation of both method and detail.

The term "revolution" in our title is not intended to be flamboyant. A revolution is a relatively sudden set of changes that yield a state of affairs from which a return to the situation just before the revolution is virtually impossible. This seems to be the sense of the word intended by V. Gordon Childe (1936) when he speaks of the "Neolithic evolution" and of the "Urban Revolution." But these two revolutions were experienced by our fully human ancestors. The sec-

NOTE: The present article, submitted to *Current Anthropology* on May 21, 1963 represents a departure from traditional CA treatment in that it was first sent to 7 scholars of whom the following responded with comments: Weston La Barre, Frank B. Livingstone and George G. Simpson. Authors Hockett and Ascher then wrote a reply and the whole (article, 3 comments and reply) was sent for CA treatment to 57 scholars of whom the following responded with written comments: George A. Agogino, Ray Lee Birdwhistell, Alan Lyle Bryan, John Desmond Clark, Carleton S. Coon, Earl W. Count, Robert Cresswell, A. Richard Diebold, Theodosius Dobzhansky, R. Dale Givens, Gordon W. Hewes, Ilse Lehiste, Margaret Mead, Ashley Montagu, Hans G. Mukarovsky, John E. Pfeiffer, Bernard Pottier, Adolph Schultz, Henry Lee Smith, Jr., James L. Swauger, George L. Trager, Eugene Verstraelen, and Roger W. Wescott. The comments written for publication are printed in full as are the replies of the authors.

From *Current Anthropology*, Vol. 5, No. 3, 1964, pp. 135–68. Reprinted by permission.

ond could not have occurred had it not been for the first. The first could not have taken place had it not been for an even earlier extremely drastic set of changes that turned nonhumans into humans. These drastic changes, as we shall see, may have required a good many millions of years; yet they can validly be regarded as "sudden" in view of the tens of millions of years of mammalian history that preceded them.

For the reconstruction of human evolution we have evidence of two sorts, plus certain firm and many tentative principles of interpretation.

One kind of evidence is the archeological, fossil, and geological record. The fossil record of our own ancestry is still disappointingly sparse for the bulk of the Miocene and Pliocene. It seems unlikely that such records can ever be as complete as we might wish. But techniques of interpretation improve, and we suspect that the archeological record, in particular, holds an as yet unrealized potential.

The second kind of evidence is the directly observable physical structure and ways of life of ourselves and of our nearest nonhuman cousins, the other hominoids of today. Chimpanzees, gorillas, orangutans, gibbons, siamangs, and humans have ultimately a common ancestry not shared with any other living species. We shall refer to their most recent common ancestors as the *proto-hominoids*. Since all the hominoids of today constitute continuations of the proto-hominoids, we can attempt to reconstruct something of the physical structure and of the lifeways of the common ancestors by comparing those of the descendants. Such an effort at reconstruction must at the same time propose realistic courses of development from the ancestral group down to each of the directly observable descendant groups, and must make proper provision for those strains known only through fossils or archeological remains.

The method is very much like the comparative method in historical linguistics—and, as a matter of fact, it was first devised in the latter context, only subsequently transferred to the domain of biological evolution.[3] The term "comparative" appears also in "comparative morphology" (or "comparative anatomy"); we must therefore emphasize that the method of which we are speaking applies not only to gross anatomy but also to the fine-scale phenomena dealt with in biochemistry, and not only to structure but also to behavior.

In any domain of application, a comparative method shares with all other historical methods the fact that it can yield reliable results only insofar as one can be sure of certain key *irreversible* processes. Given information about stages *A* and *B* in the history of a single system, we can posit that stage *A* preceded stage *B* if and only if the change from *A* to *B* is the sort that happens, while a change from *B* to *A* is impossible or highly improbable. In historical linguistics, the requisite irreversibility is afforded by sound change. The philologists of the late 19th century were correct when they characterized sound change as slow, constant, inexorable, and beyond conscious control; for, as we shall see later, it is a necessary by-product of a crucial design feature of all human language, and could not be eliminated save by altering language into something unrecognizable. Whenever sound change leads to the repatterning of the phonological system of a language—and this has happened about 100 times in English between King Alfred's day and our own (Hockett 1958:457) [4]—the consequences ramify through every part of the language; soon the results are so scattered, so subtle, and from the point of view of effectiveness of communication so *trivial,* that a return to the state of affairs before the repatterning has, in effect, probability zero.

The situation in biological evolution is much more complicated, with no simple analogue for sound change. Is a particular organ in a particular species (living or fossil) vestigial or incipient? Is the swimming bladder of current teleosts a former lung, or is the lung of lungfishes, a one-time swimming bladder? Evolutionists are plagued by such questions. The answers are often obtainable, but not through any simple formula. A new fossil does not automatically resolve the dispute, since one's opinion as to lines and directions of development will affect one's notions as to how the new fossil is to be fitted into the picture.

For the *mechanisms* of change we are in less trouble. We have now a good understanding of genetics, and also of the traditional transmission of lifeways. The latter was once believed to be exclusively human, but this is not so. At least for land mammals and for birds, genetics and tradition work in a constant dialectic complementation, neither being wholly responsible for anything (Hochbaum 1955; Dobzhansky 1956; 1962). We are also clearer about a point that used to be quite obscure: the domain (so to speak) within which these two mechanisms operate is not the individual but the community, which has a gene pool, a distribution of phenotypes, and a repository of lifeways, and which, as a functioning unit, faces the problems of survival (Simpson 1958).

The greatest pitfall in evolutionary thinking stems from the keenness of hindsight.[5] For example, we know that long ago, over a long period of time, our own ancestors abandoned the trees for the ground and developed effective machinery for bipedal locomotion. This seems beyond dispute, because the pre-hominoid primates were arboreal and we ourselves are bipedal ground walkers. But when we ask *why* this change, we must remember that our ancestors of the time were not striving to become human. They were doing what all animals do: trying to stay alive.

Thus, in searching for causes of the change we must look to conditions pertaining at the time. There are only two possibilities. The conditions at the time may have been such that minor variations in gait and posture had no bearing on survival. We should then class the change that actually did take place as fortuitous. Or, the conditions of life at the time may have positively favored selection for bipedal locomotion and upright posture. If this is what happened, then the change was adaptive. By definition, a change that was neither adaptive nor fortuitous would lead to the extinction of the strain that underwent it, and in the present instance we know that that did not happen.[6]

The most powerful antidote for the improper use of keen hindsight is a principle that we shall call "Romer's Rule," after the paleontologist A. S. Romer who has applied it so effectively—without giving it any name—in his own work. We phrase this rule as follows:

The initial survival value of a favorable innovation is conservative, in that it renders possible the maintenance of a traditional way of life in the face of changed circumstances.

Later on, of course, the innovation may allow the exploration of some ecological niche not available to the species before the change; but this is a consequence, not a cause.

One of Romer's examples concerns the evolution of Devonian lungfishes into the earliest amphibians (1959:93–94; 1958 *passim*). The invasion of the land was feasible only with strong fins (which in due time became legs). But strong fins were not developed "in order to" invade the land. The climate of the epoch was tempestuous; the water level of the pools in which the lungfishes lived was subject to sudden recessions. There was thus selection for those strains of lungfishes which, when stranded by such a recession, had strong enough fins to *get back to the water*. Only much later did some of their descendants come to stray ashore most of the time.

It is worthy of note that Romer's Rule is not anti-teleological. We are permitted to speak in terms of purposeful behavior whenever we are dealing with a system that incorporates negative feedback.[7] Individual organisms, and certain groupings of organisms (the kinds we call "communities"), are such systems. There is nothing wrong in asserting that a stranded Devonian Lungfish tried his best to get back to the water. We are forced, however, to distinguish carefully between purposes and *consequences,* and we are not allowed to ascribe "purposefulness" to any such vague and long-continuing process as "evolution."

No principle, no matter how universal, answers all questions. Romer's Rule cuts as keenly as any razor ever devised by Occam to expose, excise, and discard unworkable pseudo-explanations. Yet it is applicable, in a sense, only after the fact. For example, in this paper we follow majority opinion and trace man's ancestry back to a point of separation from the ancestors of the great apes, the gibbons, and the siamangs. Having assumed this, we elaborate one of Romer's own suggestions as to how some of the early developments may have come about. Suppose, however, that new fossil finds should convince us that man is actually more closely related to some other group of surviving primates (Coon 1962: ch. 5). We should then be confronted by a different set of putative historical facts requiring explanation; but we should evoke the same Rule as we sought that explanation. The Rule does not tell us which line of descent to postulate.

THE PROTO-HOMINOIDS

From the location, date, and morphology of the fossil dryopithecine *Proconsul* we infer that the proto-hominoids lived in East Africa in the Middle or Lower Miocene or, at the earliest, in the Upper Oligocene (Oakley 1962).[8] This does not mean that *Proconsul* himself—in any of the strains of species so far identified—was a proto-hominoid; indeed, he is not a good candidate as an ancestor of the gibbons and siamangs, to whom, by definition, the proto-hominoids were ancestral. But *Proconsul* was clearly an *early* hominoid, and at the moment he is the best fossil evidence available for the date and provenience we seek.

The proto-hominoids inherited certain crucial capacities from their totally tree-dwelling ancestors.[9] It is the arboreal pattern that developed the keen accomodative vision characteristic of the higher primates, de-emphasized the sense of smell, turned forelimbs into freely movable arms with manipulative hands, and built brains somewhat larger than the average for land mammals.

The balance of the characterization we are about to give—what Count (1958) would call a "biogram" of the proto-hominoids—derives mainly from the comparative method applied to what we know of the hominoids of today (Schultz 1961 in a superb review;

Sahlins 1959; Hediger 1961; Chance 1961; Spuhler 1959; Altmann 1962; Bartholomew and Birdsell 1953; Coon 1962). We shall not give all the evidence in detail. Furthermore, for the sake of vividness we shall allow some interpolations of a degree of precision that may be unwarranted. The proportion of guesswork in each statement will, we think, be fairly obvious.

Like most of their descendants, the proto-hominoids were hairy. Like all of them, they were tailless. They were smaller than we are, though not so small as present-day gibbons, whose size has decreased as an adaptation to brachiation. They had mobile facial muscles; they had neither mental eminence nor simian shelf (nor mastoid processes); they had large interlocking canines, and could chew only up and down; their tooth pattern was $\frac{2:1:2:3}{2:1:2:3}$. It seems likely that there was little sexual dimorphism, although on this the comparative evidence is conflicting. The chromosome count was somewhere in the forties.

They lived in bands of from ten to thirty, consisting typically of one or a very few adult males plus females and offspring. They had a roughly defined nucleated territoriality: that is, the territory within which the members of a band moved about had only roughly demarcated boundaries, but centered on the specific arboreal sites in which they built their nests.[10] The total population was probably never very great, nor very dense, from the proto-hominoids all the way down to the first true humans.[11]

They were expert climbers and spent much of their lives in the trees of the tropical or subtropical forests which were their habitat, certainly building their nests in the trees and sleeping there. Like rodents, they climbed up a tree head first; unlike rodents, they climbed down stern first. They slept at night, from dusk to dawn, which in the tropics means nearer to one-half of each twenty-four-hour period than to the one-third characteristic of ourselves in recent times. They were active during the day. Some activities, particularly the constant search for food, led them not only among the trees—in which they may have brachiated, but with no great expertness—but also quite regularly to the ground below. On the ground, they could stand with a semi-upright posture (erect enough to raise their heads above shoulder-high grass to look about), and they could sit with arms free for manipulative motions; they could walk on all fours and could run on their feet, but bipedal walking was infrequent and awkward.

Occasionally they would pick up a stick or stone and use it as a tool. Judging from modern chimpanzees,[12] they may have reshaped such tools slightly, using nothing but their hands and teeth to do so, and may have carried a tool for a short distance for immediate use, thereafter discarding it. They carried other things too, in mouth or hands or both, in connection with nest-building; and at least the females, perhaps on occasion the males, carried infants.

Their diet was largely vegetarian, supplemented by worms and grubs, and sometimes by small mammals or birds that were injured or sick and thus unable to escape. (We might call this *"very* slow game.") They scavenged the remains of the kills of carnivores whenever they could. Unlike all other mammals except the Dalmation coach hound, their bodies produced no uricase; hence uric acid was not converted into allantoin before secretion in the urine, and had a chance to accumulate in the bloodstream. The structural formula of uric acid is something like that of caffein and, like the latter, it seems to be a mild brain stimulant. Since this type of purine metabolism is shared by all the hominoids, it can hardly explain our own unusual brilliance; but it may help to account for the generally high level of hominoid intelligence as compared with other primates and other mammals (Coon 1962:172 and references cited).

The males had the pendulous penis typical of the primates. Copulation was effected exclusively with the dorsal approach common to land mammals in general. Gestation required about thirty weeks. The uterus was single-chambered, and twinning was as rare as it is for us today. The placenta was of the single-disc type. The young required and received maternal care for many months. Mammary glands were pectoral; nursing females held infants to their breast in their arms, though doubtless the infant clung to the mother's fur also. The eruption of permanent teeth began perhaps at two and one-half or three. Menarche was at eight or nine years; general growth stopped for both sexes at nine or ten. The females showed a year-round menstrual cycle rather than a rutting season. Inbreeding within the band was the rule. The life-span was potentially about thirty years, but death was largely from accident, disease, or predation, or a combination of these, rather than old age. Corpses were abandoned, as were members of the band too sick, injured, or feeble to keep up with the rest, and were disposed of by predators or scavengers. Adult males were sexually interested in females and "paternally" interested in infants, but without any permanent family bond, and without any jealousy when they were themselves sexually satisfied.

Relations with adjacent bands were normally hostile to neutral, rarely if ever friendly; yet there was surely enough contact to provide for some exchange of genes. Social differentiation within the band turned largely on age and sex, secondarily on physical strength. In case of conflict of interest within the band, the huskiest adult males normally got their way. Collective activities required intragroup coordination, effected by various forms of communication—patterns of body motion, pushing and prodding, changes of body odor, and vocal signals. The conventions of these forms of communication were transmitted in part genetically, but in some part by tradition, acquired by the young through guided participation in the ways of the group. This implies also a certain capacity to learn from experience, and to pass on any new skills thus acquired to other members of the band by teaching and learning, rather than merely by slow genetic selection. But we may assume that usually there was very little new in any one lifetime thus to be learned or passed on.

A kind of activity called *play* is widespread among land mammals, and obviously intensified among primates; we can be sure that the proto-hominoids indulged in it, at least before maturity (Kroeber 1948:27–30; Altman 1962 and references cited). It is very hard to characterize play precisely, beyond saying that it resembles one or another serious activity without being serious. Play at fighting, observable for example among dogs, goes through much the same gross motions as true fighting but the participants receive no injury. Sexual play has the general contours of courtship, but ends short of coitus or with mock coitus. We suspect that play is *fun,* for any species that manifests it, and that that is the immediate motive for indulging in it. But play is also genuinely pedagogical, in that the young thereby get needed practice in certain patterns of behavior that are biologically important for adult life.

The proto-hominoids did not have the power of speech. The most that we can validly ascribe to them in this respect is a call system similar to that of modern gibbons. Even this ascription may be stretching the comparative evidence somewhat. It is not hard to assume that a line of continuity from the proto-hominoids to the gibbons should have maintained such a call system essentially unchanged. It is also quite reasonable, as we shall see, to explain the evolution of a call system into language among our ancestors. The difficulty is to account for the apparently less highly developed vocal-auditory signaling of the great apes. Our hypothesis for the proto-hominoids suggests that the communicative behavior of the great apes may be somewhat more subtle and complex than has yet been realized. Be this as it may, we posit a call system for the proto-hominoids because we know no other way to proceed.[13]

The essential design features of a call system are simple. There is a repertory of a half-dozen or so distinct signals, each the appropriate vocal response—or the vocal segment of a more inclusive response—to a recurrent and biologically important type of situation. Among gibbons, one such situation is the discovery of food; another is the detection of danger; a third is friendly interest and the desire for company. A fourth gibbon call apparently does nothing but indicate the whereabouts of the gibbon that emits it: this call keeps the band from spreading out too thin as it moves through the trees. One can guess at other possible situations appropriate for a special call: sexual interest; need for maternal care; pain. Band-to-band differences in calls may help to distinguish friend from alien.

A single call may be varied in intensity, duration, or number of repetitions, to correlate with and give information about the strength of the stimulus which is eliciting it. However, the signals of a call system are *mutually exclusive* in the following sense: the animal, finding himself in a situation, can only respond by one or another of the calls or by silence. He cannot, in principle, emit a signal that has some of the features of one call and some of another. If, for example, he encounters food and danger at the same time, one of these will take precedence: he is constrained to emit either the food call or the danger call, not some mixture of the two.

The technical description of this mutual exclusiveness is to say that the system is *closed*. Language, in sharp contrast, is *open* or *productive*: we freely emit utterances that we have never said nor heard before, and are usually understood, neither speaker nor hearer being aware of the novelty.

A call system differs from language in two other ways, and perhaps in a third.[14] (1) Gibbons do not emit, say, the food call unless they have found food (or, perhaps, are responding to the food call from another gibbon, as they approach for their share of it). Furthermore, the gibbon that finds food does not go back to headquarters and report; he stays by the food as he emits the call. A call system does not have *displacement*. Language does: we speak freely of things that are out of sight or are in the past or future—or even nonexistent. (2) The utterances of a language consist wholly of arrangements of elementary signaling units called *phonemes* (or *phonological components,* to be exact), which in themselves have no meanings but merely serve to keep meaningful utterances apart. Thus, an utterance has both a structure in terms of these meaningless but differentiating elements, and also a structure in terms of the minimum meaningful elements. This design feature is *duality of patterning*. A call system lacks it, the differences between any two calls being global. (3) Finally, the detailed conventions of any one language are transmitted wholly by the traditional mechanism, though, of course, the capacity to learn a language, and probably the drive to do so, are genetic. On this score we are still in ignorance about the gibbons. Regional differences in gibbon calls have been noted, but various balances between tradition and genetics can yield that. We believe it safer to assume that proto-hominoid call systems were passed down from generation to generation largely through the genes, tradition playing a minor role.[15] This assumption is the conservative one—it gives us more to try to explain in later developments than would any alternative.

This completes our characterization of the proto-hominoids, which can now serve as point of departure for the story of our own evolution.

OUT OF THE TREES

Some of the descendants of the proto-hominoids moved out of the trees and became erect bipeds. Romer's description (1959:327) of how this may have begun affords another example of the application of the Rule we ascribe to him.[16]

Geological evidence suggests that at one or more times during the East African Miocene a climatic change gradually thinned out the vegetation, converting continuous tropical forest into open savannah with scattered clumps of trees. As the trees retreated, some bands of hominoids retreated with them, never abandoning their classical arboreal existence; their descendants of today are the gibbons and siamangs. Other bands were caught in isolated groves of slowly diminishing extent. In due time, those bands whose physique made it possible for their members to traverse open country to another grove survived; those that could not do this became extinct. Thus, for those bands, the survival value of the perquisites for safe ground travel was not at all that they could therefore begin a new way of life out of the trees, but that, when necessary, they could make their way to a place where the traditional arboreal way of life could be continued. The hominoids that were successful at this included those ancestral to the great apes and to ourselves.

Sometimes the band forced to try to emigrate from a grove would be the total population of that grove. More typically, we suspect, population pressure within a diminishing grove would force bands into competition over its resources, and the less powerful bands would be displaced. Also, when a migrating band managed to reach another grove, it would often happen that the new grove was already occupied, and once again there would be competition. Thus, in the long run, the trees would be held by the more powerful, while the less powerful would repeatedly have to get along as best they could in the fringes of the forest or in open country. Here is a double selective process. The trees went to the more powerful, provided only that they maintained a minimum ability to traverse open country when necessary: some of these successful ones were ancestral to the great apes of today. Our own ancestors were the failures. We did not abandon the trees because we wanted to, but because we were pushed out.

We are speaking here of displacements and movements of whole bands, not of individual animals. There is one thing that surely accompanied any band whenever it moved: the essential geometry of its territoriality. At any halt, no matter how temporary, whether in the trees, under the trees, or in open country, some specific site became, for the nonce, "home base"—a GHQ, a center, a focus, relative to which each member of the band oriented himself as he moved about. Headquarters was the safest place to be, if for no other reason than the safety of numbers. In a later epoch—though doubtless earlier than will ever be directly attested by archeology—headquarters among our own ancestors came to be crudely fortified, as by a piled ring of stones;[17] it became the place where things were kept or stored; in due time it became house, village, fort, city. But earliest of all it was *home*. The tradition for this sort of territoriality is much older than the proto-hominoids, and has continued unbroken to the present day.

It is at this point in our story that we must stop referring to our ancestors as "hominoids" and start calling them "hominids." Of course, all hominids are hominoids; but we have now seen the sorting-out of the pre-apes from the pre-humans, and when we wish to speak exclusively of the latter the appropriate term is "hominid."

CARRYING

It is no joke to be thrown out of one's ancestral home. If the next grove is only a few miles away, in sight, then one has something to aim for; but sooner or later movements must have taken place without any such visible target. Treeless country holds discomforts and dangers. There may not be much food, at least not of a familiar sort. There may be little available water, for the trees tend to cluster where the water is more abundant. And there are fleet four-footed predators, as well as herbivorous quadrupeds big and strong enough to be dangerous at close quaters. One cannot avoid these other animals altogether, since their presence often signals the location of water, or of food fit also for hominid consumption. The quest for food must be carried on constantly, no matter how pressing may be the drive to find a new grove of trees in which to settle. It is a wonder that any of the waifs of the Miocene savannah survived at all. Enormous numbers of them must have died out.

The trick that made survival possible for some of them was the trick of *carrying*. The proto-hominoids, as we have seen, probably carried twigs and brush to make nests, and certainly carried infants. Also, they had fine arms and hands usable for carrying as well as for climbing, grasping, and manipulating; and the comparative evidence suggests that they occasionally picked up sticks or stones to use as tools. These are the raw-materials for the kind of carrying to which we now refer. But it takes something else to blend them into the new pattern. In the trees, hands are largely occupied with climbing. The infant-in-arms grabs onto the mother when the latter needs her hands for locomotion. The twig being taken to the nest is transferred to the mouth when the hand cannot at the same time hold it and grasp a tree branch. One puts down one's ad-hoc tool when one has to move.

The conditions for carrying are no better on the ground than in the trees if the hand must revert to the status of a foot. But if bipedal locomotion is at all possible, then the hand is freed for carrying; and the survival value of carrying certain things in turn serves to promote a physical structure adapted to bipedal locomotion.

Two sorts of ground carrying in the hands may have been extremely early; there seems to be no way of determining which came first. One is the carrying of crude weapons; the other is the transportation of scavenged food.[18]

The earliest ground-carrying of weapons may well have been a sort of accident. Imagine an early hominid—perhaps even a prehominid hominoid sitting on the ground and pounding something (a nut, say) with a handy stone. A predator approaches. Our hero jumps up and runs away as best he can on two legs—there are no trees nearby to escape into—but keeps his grasp on the stone for no better reason than that he does not need his hand for anything else. Cornered, he turns, and either strikes out at the predator with the hand that holds the stone, or else throws it. The predator falls or runs off, and whatever in our hero's genes or life experience, or both, has contributed to his behavior stands a chance of being passed on to others.

The first carrying of scavenged food back to headquarters (instead of consuming it on the spot) may also have been a sort of accident. A scavenging hominoid is eating the remains of a predator's kill where he has found it, and is surprised by the predator who is coming back to make another meal from the same kill. The hominoid runs off towards headquarters, still holding a piece of meat in his hand. In due time, he or his successors develop the habit of carrying the spoils off without waiting for the predator to turn up.

As described, these two early kinds of hand-carrying involve movements of a single animal *within* the band's territory. The carrying-along of things as the whole band moves is another matter, and probably a later development. Surely the earliest carrying of this latter sort was of unshaped weapons of defense. Yet other things might have been taken along. Extra food would be a great rarity, but if some were taken along because no one happened to be hungry as a movement began, it would be important if the band reached a particularly barren region. Water-carrying would have been extremely valuable—primates in general have to drink at least once a day, in contrast to some mammalian species which can store up several days' supply. Short hauls of small quantities of water cupped in the large leaves of tropical plants may have been quite early; large-scale water transport as a whole band moves must have been a great deal later, since it requires technologically advanced containers.

The side-effects of carrying things in the hands are of incalculable importance. We have already seen that its immediate practical value helped to promote bipedal walking, which in turn selected both for carrying and for an upright posture that renders bipedal walking mechanically more efficient. A less obvious consequence is that carrying made for a kind of behavior that has all the outward earmarks of what we call "memory" and "foresight": one lugs around a heavy stick or stone despite the absence of any immediate need for it, as though one were remembering past experiences in which having it available was important and were planning for possible future encounters of the same kind. Taking scavenged meat back to headquarters without waiting for the predator to return to his kill also looks like foresight. We do not mean to deny the validity of the terms "memory" and "foresight." The point is that the outward earmarks surely came first, and only over a long period of time *produced* the psychological characteristics to which these terms refer.[19]

A third consequence of carrying and of wandering was a change in dietary balance. The first tools to be carried were defensive weapons. Often enough, no doubt, the use of these weapons against a predator, even if successful, would only scare him off. But sometimes the predator would be killed. Why waste the meat? We can also suppose that the wandering Miocene or Pliocene hominids occasionally found themselves in open country where no suitable plant food was available. Herbivorous animals could eat the grass; quadruped predators could eat the grazers; and the hominids, if they were lucky, could eat the grazers or the predators, or else starve. Thus the hunted became the hunters, and weapons of defense became weapons of offense.[20]

The gradual increase of meat in the diet had important consequences of its own, to which we will turn after noting one further direct consequence of hand-carrying.

The use of the hands for carrying implied that the mouth and teeth, classically used for this by land mammals, birds, and even reptiles, were freed for other activities. It can quite safely be asserted that if primate and hominid evolution had not transferred from mouth to hand first the grasping and manipulating function and then the carrying function, human language as we know it would never have evolved. What were the hominids to do with their mouths, rendered thus relatively idle except when they were eating? The answer is: they chattered.[21]

Remember that the proto-hominoids are assumed in this account to have had a call system, and that that system would not have been lost by the stage we have now reached. The hunting of dangerous animals is a challenge even with advanced weapons. With primitive weapons there is a great advantage if it can be done collaboratively. But this calls for coordination of the acts of the participants. Their hands hold weapons and are thus unavailable for any complicated semaphor. Their visual attention must be divided between the motions of the quarry and those of the other participants. All this favors an increase in flexibility of vocal-auditory communication.

Other factors also favor such an increase. Meat is a highly efficient and compactly packaged food, as compared with uncultivated plants. A small kill may not go very far, but with collective hunting larger quarry were caught. After such a large kill, there is often more food than can be consumed even by all the direct participants in the hunt. Sharing the food among all the members of the band comes about almost automatically, in that when the hunters themselves are sated they no longer care if the rest take the leavings. Thus the sharing of meat makes for the survival of the whole band. Collective hunting, general food-sharing, and the carrying of an increasing variety of things all press towards a more complex social organization, which is only possible with more flexible communication. These same factors also promote what we vaguely call the "socialization" of the members of the band.[22]

Another development bearing on the quality, if not the degree, of hominid socialization must have taken place during this same period.

At some point during the slow morphological shift to efficient upright posture, the frontal approach for copulation must have first become anatomically possible, and it was doubtless immediately exploited. It may even be imagined that, for certain strains of the hominids at certain times, the expansion of the gluteus maximus rendered the dorsal approach so awkward that the invention of the frontal approach had the conservative value required by Romer's Rule. Humans have never shown much tendency to confine themselves to this position for intercourse, but it does seem to be universally known, and is almost exclusively human.[23] Just how this change may have affected hominid lifeways is not clear. Our guess is that it changed, for the adult female, the relative roles of the adult male and of the infant, since after the innovation there is a much closer similarity for her between her reception of an infant and of a lover. This may have helped to spread the "tender emotions" of mammalian mother-infant relations to other interpersonal relationships within the band, ultimately with such further consequences as the Oedipus complex.

OPENING OF THE CALL SYSTEM

We have seen a changing pattern of life that would be well served by a vocal-auditory communicative system of greater complexity and subtlety. Now a call system can become more flexible, within limits, through the development of totally new calls to fit additional types of recurrent situation. But it cannot take the first step towards language as we know it unless something else happens: through a process about to be described, the closed system becomes open.

Let us illustrate the way in which this can come about by describing what may occasionally happen among the gibbons of today— although, to be sure, such an occurrence has never been observed. Suppose a gibbon finds himself in a situation characterized by both the presence of food and the imminence of danger. The factors are closely balanced. Instead of emitting either the clear food call or the unmistakable danger call, he utters a cry that has some of the characteristics of each. Among gibbons such an event is doubtless so rare and unusual that the other members of the band have no way of interpreting it; thus, the consequences are negligible. But if we suppose that the early weapon-carrying hominids had a somewhat richer call system (though still closed), functioning in a somewhat more complex social order, then we may also assume that this type of event happened occasionally, and that sooner or later the other members of a band responded appropriately, therefore handling an unusually complex situation more efficiently than otherwise. Thus reinforced, the habit of *blending* two old calls to produce a new one would gain ground.

Indeed, we really have to believe that this is what happened, because the phenomenon of blending is the only logically possible way in which a closed system can develop towards an open one.[24] Let us represent the acoustic contours of one inherited call arbitrarily with the sequence of letters *ABCD* and those of another with *EFGH*. All we mean by either of these representations is that each call possesses two or more acoustic properties in which primate ears could focus attention; it does not matter just how many such acoustic properties are involved nor just what they are. Suppose that *ABCD* means "food here," while *EFGH* means "danger coming." Finding both food and danger, the hominid comes out with *ABGH*. If this new call becomes established, then the 2 old calls and the new one are all henceforth *composite*, instead of unanalyzable unitary signals. For, in *ABCD*, the part *AB* now means "food" and the part *CD* means "no danger"; in *EFGH*, *EF* now means "no food" and *GH* means "danger"; while *ABGH* means "food and danger" because *AB* and *GH* have acquired the meanings just mentioned. One might eventually even get *EFCD*, obviously meaning "no food and no danger."

It must be asked whether this mechanism of blending can really turn a closed system into an open one. The answer is that it can start the transformation (while no other known mechanism can), but that further developments must follow. Consider the matter for a moment in a purely abstract way. Suppose the initial closed system has exactly ten calls, and that each is blended with each of the others. After the blending, there are exactly 100 calls. From one point of view, a repertory of 100 calls—or of 1,000, or of ten million—is just as closed as is a system of 10 calls. A second point of view is more important. Each of the hundred possible calls now consists of 2 parts, and each part recurs in other whole calls. One has the basis for the habit of *building* composite signals out of meaningful parts, whether or not those parts occur alone as whole signals. It is this habit that lies at the center of the openness of human languages. English allows only a finite (though quite large) number of sentences only two words long. But it allows an unlimited number of different sentences because there is no fixed limit on how long a sentence may be.

Surely the opening-up of the closed call system of our ancestors required literally thousands of years, just as all the other developments on which we have touched came about at an extremely leisurely pace. It is irrelevant that the production of a single blend, or the momentary accidental carrying of a stick or stone in the hand, is a brief episode. A potentially crucial type of event can recur numberless times with no visible effect, or with effect on a band that later becomes extinct for unrelated reasons, for every one occurrence that has minuscule but viable consequences. When the opening-up of the formerly closed call system was finally achieved, the revolutionary impact on subsequent developments was as great as that of hand-carrying.

For one thing, the detailed conventions of an open system cannot be transmitted wholly through genes. The young may emit some of the calls instinctively. But they are also exposed to various more or less complex composite calls from their elders, and are obliged to infer the meanings of the parts, and the patterns by which the parts are put together to form the whole signals, from the acoustic resemblances among the calls they hear and from the behavioral contexts in which they are uttered. (To this day, that is how human infants learn their native language.) Thus, the development of an open system puts a premium on any capacity for learning and teaching that a species may have, and selects for an increase in the genetic basis for that capacity.

If the conventions of a system have largely to be learned before the system can be efficiently used, then much of that learning will eventually be carried on away from the contexts in which the utterances being practiced would be immediately relevant. We recall the general mammalian phenomenon of play. The development of an open, largely traditionally transmitted, vocal-auditory communicative system means that *verbal play* is added to play at fighting, sexual play, and any other older categories. But this, in turn, means that situations are being talked about when they do not exist—that is, it means the addition of displacement to the design features already at hand. Speaking of things which are out of sight or in the past or future is very much like carrying a weapon when there is no immediate need for it. Each of these habits thus reinforces the other.

What was formerly a closed call system has now evolved into an open system, with details transmitted largely by tradition rather than through the genes, and with the property of displacement. Let us call such a system *pre-language*. It was still not true language, because it lacked the duality of patterning of true language. Nothing like pre-language is known for sure in the world today.[25] Any hominid strain that developed its vocal-auditory communication only to this stage has become extinct. If we could hear the pre-language of our forerunners, it would probably not sound like human speech. It would sound much more like animal calls, and only very careful analysis would reveal its language-like properties.

The development of openness, with the various consequences already mentioned, either accompanied or paved the way for some radical developments in tool habits. We imagine that tool *manufacture*—as over against the using and carrying of tools—received its single greatest impetus from this source. If carrying a weapon selects for foresight, shaping a rough weapon into a better one indicates even greater foresight. The manufacturing of a generalized tool—one designed to be carried around for a variety of possible uses—and the development of tools specialized for use in the making of other tools, certainly followed the inception of pre-language. Weapon-making and tool-shaping are further activities at which the young can play, as they learn their communicative system and other adult ways by playing with them.

We must suppose that the detailed conventions of pre-language underwent changes, and became differentiated from one band to another, much more rapidly than had the earlier call system from which it sprang (though perhaps much more slowly than languages change today). Both of these points are implied by the increased relative role of tradition as over against genetics. New blends were not uncommon. They introduced new patterns for combining elements into whole signals, and old patterns became obsolete. Any such innovation of detail spread naturally to all members of the band in which it occurred, but not readily, if at all, from one band to another. If a band fissioned into two bands—this must have happened repeatedly throughout hominoid and hominid history—the "daughter" bands started their independent existence with a single inherited pre-language, but innovations thereafter were independent, so that in course of time the two daughter bands came to have two "mutually unintelligible" pre-languages. This is exactly—except for rate of change—what has happened to true human languages in recent millennia; we must assume that the phenomena of change and of divergence are as old as the emergence of pre-language.

THE INCEPTION OF DUALITY

Something else had been happening during prehominid and hominid evolution up to this point. In apes, the glottis lies very close to the velum, and articulatory motions anything like those involved in human language are structurally awkward. The development of upright posture, with the completion of the migration of the face from the end to the ventral side of the head, turns the axis of the oral cavity to a position approximately at right angles to the pharynx, and introduces a marked separation of glottis from velum (Spuhler 1959; DuBrul 1958). Hundreds of generations of chattering, first in a call system and then in pre-language, increases the innervation of the vocal tract and enriches the cortical representation of that region. The stage is set for the development of the kinds of articulatory motions familiar today.

Now, neither of these changes leads directly and inevitably to duality of patterning. Indeed, the first change is in no sense logically required if duality is to develop; in a way, it was fortuitous, since it was a by-product of changes taking place for a totally different set of selective reasons. In another species with a different earlier history, duality might use some other apparatus. If early primate history had for some reason promoted precision of control of the sphincter, and of the accumulation and discharge of intestinal gas, speech sounds today might be anal spirants. Everything else about the logical design of human language could be exactly as it actually is. The failure to distinguish in this way between the logically possible and the historically actual has led many investigators astray: they infer, for example, that our ancestors could not have had language until the articulatory apparatus had evolved to what it is now. They then interpret fossil jaws in invalid ways—and offer inadequate explanations of why the speech parts should have changed their morphology as they actually have during the Pleistocene.[26]

However, the two changes described above did set the stage in a certain way. The hominids were in a state in which, if duality did develop, the machinery used for it was in all probability going to be the kind of articulatory motions we still use.

We can envisage the development of duality as follows. Pre-language became increasingly complex and flexible, among the successful strains of hominids, because of its many advantages for survival. The constant rubbing-together of whole utterances (by the blending mechanism described earlier) generated an increasingly large stock of minimum meaningful signal elements—the "pre-morphemes" of pre-language. Lacking duality, however, these pre-morphemes had to be holistically different from one another in their acoustic contours. But the available articulatory-acoustic space became more and more densely packed; some pre-morphemes became so similar to others that keeping them apart, either in production or in detection, was too great a challenge for hominid mouths, ears, and brains. Something had to happen, or the system would collapse of its own weight. Doubtless many overloaded systems did collapse, their users thereafter becoming extinct. In at least one case, there was a brilliantly successful "mutation": pre-morphemes began to be listened to and identified not in terms of their acoustic gestalts but in terms of smaller features of sound that occurred in them in varying arrangements. In pace with this shift in the technique of detection, articulatory motions came to be directed not towards the generation of a suitable acoustic gestalt but towards the sufficiently precise production of the relevant smaller features of sound that identified one pre-morpheme as over against others.

With this change, pre-morphemes became true morphemes, the features of sound involved became phonological components, and pre-language had become true language.

Although brilliant and crucial, this innovation need not have been either as sudden or as difficult as our description may seem to imply. With openness, but as yet without duality, the hearer is already required to pay attention to acoustic detail, rather than merely to one or another convenient symptom of a whole acoustic gestalt, if he is to recognize the constituent pre-morphemes of a composite call and thus react appropriately to the whole call. In a pure call system, the beginning of a call may be distinctive enough to identify the whole call; the rest does not have to be heard. In pre-language, one cannot predict from the beginning of a call how it will continue and end. This clearly paves the way for duality. It is then, in one sense, but a small step to stop regarding acoustic details as *constituting* morphemes and start interpreting them as *identifying* or *representing* morphemes.[27]

Here, as for all the other developments we have mentioned, we must remember Romer's Rule. The ultimate consequences of the inception of duality have been enormous. But the immediate value of the innovation was conservative. It rendered possible the continued use of a thoroughly familiar type of communicative system in a thoroughly familiar way, in the face of a gradual but potentially embarrassing increase in the complexity of the system.

The emergence of true language from a closed call system, by the steps and stages we have described, should properly be thought of not as a replacement of one sort of communicative system by another, but rather as the growth of a new system within the matrix of the old one. Certain features of the proto-hominoid call system are still found in human vocal-auditory behavior, but as accompaniments to the use of language rather than as part of language. The proto-hominoids could vary the intensity, the pitch, and the duration of a single call. We still do this as we speak sentences in a language: we speak sometimes more loudly, sometimes more softly, sometimes in a higher register and sometimes in a lower, and so on. Also, we use certain grunts and cries (*uh-huh, huh-uh, ow!*) that are not words or morphemes and not part of language. These various *paralinguistic* phenomena, as they are called (Trager 1958; Pittinger, Hockett, and Danchy 1960), have been reworked and modified in many ways by the conditions of life of speaking humans, but their pedigree, like that of communicative body motion, is older than that of language itself.

The phenomenon of sound change, mentioned briefly at the outset of this paper, began immediately upon the transition from prelanguage to true language, continues now, and will continue in the future unless our vocal-auditory communication crosses some currently unforeseeable Rubicon. The phonological system of a language has almost as its sole function that of keeping meaningful utterances apart. But a phonological system is a delicately balanced affair, constantly being thrown into slight disbalance by careless articulation or channel noise and constantly repatterning itself in a slightly altered way. It is perfectly possible, in the course of time, for two phonemes to fall together—that is, for the articulatory-acoustic difference between them to disappear. Obviously, this changes the machinery with which morphemes and utterances are distinguished. The interest this holds for us is that it affords an example of the workings of Romer's Rule in a purely cultural context instead of a largely genetic one.

What happens seems to be about as follows. A particular phonemic difference is slowly eaten away by sound change, to the point that it is no longer reliable as a way of keeping utterances apart.[28] This is the "changed circumstances" of Romer's Rule. The speakers of the language develop, by analogy, a way of paraphrasing any utterance that would be potentially ambiguous if uttered in the traditional way. The paraphrase is the "innovation" of the Rule. The value of the paraphrase is that the speakers can thereby continue to speak in largely the same way they learned from their predecessors. The innovation is minor and trivial, but effective in that if the phonemic contrast disappears entirely, ease of communication is in no way impaired. The inevitable and continuous process of sound change never reduces the machinery of a language to zero. A compensation of some sort is developed for every loss of contrast.

CHRONOLOGY

We have now outlined a plausible evolutionary sequence leading from the proto-hominoids to our earliest truly human ancestors. For we assert that as soon as the hominids had achieved upright posture, bipedal gait, the use of hands for manipulating, for carrying, and for manufacturing generalized tools, and language, they had become men. The human revolution was over. Two important questions remain. How long did the changes take? How long ago were they completed?

It is certain that the changes we have talked about did not begin before the time of the proto-hominoids. But at present we have no way of knowing how much later than that was their inception. Conceivably the hominids of the Middle or Upper Pliocene, though already separated from the pongids, were very little more like modern man than were the proto-hominoids.

On the other hand, we are convinced that all the crucial developments of which we have spoken had been achieved by about one million years ago—that is, by the beginning of the Pleistocene.

The most important evidence for the date just presented is the *subsequent* growth of the brain, attested by the fossil record. The brain of *Australopithecus* is scarcely larger than that of a gorilla. But from about three-quarters of a million years ago to about forty thousand years ago, the brain grew steadily. Part of this increase reflects an overall increase in body size (Spuhler 1959; Washburn 1959:27; Coon 1962: Table 27). Allowing for this, there is still something to be explained. Was the increase in relative size fortuitous or adaptive?

It is utterly out of the question that the growth was fortuitous. A large brain is biologicaly too expensive. It demands a high percentage of the blood supply—12% in modern man, though the brain accounts for only about 2% of the body's volume (Coon 1962:77–78)—and all that blood, in an upright biped, must be pumped uphill. It requires an enlarged skull, which makes for difficulty during parturition, particularly since the development of upright posture resculptures the pelvis very badly for childbirth. This cost cannot be borne unless there are compensations.

We must therefore assume that if a species has actually developed a bigger and more convoluted brain, with a particularly sharp increase in the forebrain, there was survival value in the change. For our ancestors of a million years ago the survival value of bigger brains is obvious if and only if they had *already* achieved the essence of language and culture. Continued growth would then be advantageous up to a certain maximum, but thereafter unprofitable because it made for excessive difficulties in other respects but yielded no further usable gain in brainpower.

The archeological and fossil record supports our date, or even suggests that we have been too conservative. Until recently, the earliest obviously shaped tools that had been dug up were not quite so ancient, but they implied an earlier period of development that was not directly attested. Now, however, we have the direct evidence of at least crudely shaped stone tools in association with hominid fossils from Bed I at Olduvai, for which a maximum date of one and three-quarters million years ago is seriously proposed (Leakey, Curtis, and Evernden 1962). What is more, the Australopithecines show the typically human reduction in the size of the canine teeth, formerly used for cutting and tearing; and this reduction could not have been tolerated had the hominids not developed tools with which to perform such operations.

It might be suggested that, although all other crucial innovations of the human revolution were as early as we have proposed, the inception of duality may have been later. There are two reasons why we think that duality is just as old as the rest.

One side-effect of brain growth is that the top of the head is pushed forward to form a forehead. We do not see why this should in itself entail a recession of the lower part of the face, to yield the essentially flat perpendicular human physiognomy which, with minor variations, now prevails. In terms of the balancing of the head above an upright body, perhaps the recession of the snout and the decrease in its massiveness are useful. If cooking is a sufficiently old art, then perhaps this external predigestion of food at least rendered possible the reduction in size of teeth and jaws. But it seems to us that these factors still leave room for a further influence: that of the habit of talking, in a true language that uses the kinds of articulatory motions that are now universal, requiring precise motions of lips, jaw, tongue, velum, glottis, and pulmonary musculature. If true language can be assumed for our ancestors of a million years ago, then it is old enough to have played a role in the genetically monitored evolutionary changes in what we now call the "organs of speech." And if this is correct, then "organs of speech" is no metaphor but a biologically correct description.

Our other reason for believing that duality of patterning, and the modern type of sound-producing articulatory motions, are very old, turns on time, space, and degrees of uniformity and diversity. The fossil record shows that the human diaspora from East Africa cannot be much more recent than the Middle Pleistocene. This means that several hundred thousand years have been available for a genetic adaptation to a wide variety of climates and topographies. Yet man shows an amazingly small amount of racial diversity—far less, for example, than that of dogs, which has come about in a much shorter span of time. (Of course, the difference in generation span between men and dogs must be taken into account; but when one allows liberally for this the comparison, though less striking, still seems valid.)

There is this same striking lack of diversity in certain features of language. Though we have no fossils, our observations of the languages of today, and of those few attested by written records during the past few millennia, have some relevance. Almost every type of articulation known to function in any language anywhere recurs in various other languages, with no significant pattern of geographical distribution.[29] Phonological systems—as over against individual speech sounds—show much less variety than could easily be invented by any linguist working with pencil and paper (Hockett 1963; Ferguson 1963). This uniformity precludes the independent invention of duality of patterning, and of modern articulatory motions, in two or more parts of the world. The crucial developments must have taken place once, and then spread. The innovations could have been either recent or ancient, except for an additional fact: in every language, the phonological raw materials are used with remarkable efficiency (see footnote 27). This speaks for great antiquity, since we cannot imagine that such efficiency was an instant result of the appearance of the first trace of duality.

True diversity is found in more superficial aspects of language, and in all those other phases of human life where tradition, rather than genetics, is clearly the major mechanism of change and of adaptation. We are thus led to a familiar conclusion. The human revolution, completed before the diaspora, established a state of affairs in which further change and adaptation could be effected, within broad limits, by tradition rather than genetics. That is why human racial diversity is so slight, and it is why the languages and cultures of all communities, no matter how diverse, are elaborations of a single inherited "common denominator."

ADDITIONAL PLEISTOCENE CHANGES

The further consequences of the human revolution include, in the end, everything that we have done since. Only a few of the more striking (and earlier) of these subsequent developments need to be mentioned here.

Language and culture, as we have seen, selected for bigger brains. Bigger brains mean bigger heads. Bigger heads mean greater difficulty in parturition. Even today, the head is the chief troublemaker in childbirth. This difficulty can be combatted to some extent by expelling the fetus relatively earlier in its development. There was therefore a selection for such earlier expulsion. But this, in turn, makes for a longer period of helpless infancy—which is, at the same time, a period of maximum plasticity, during which the child can acquire the complex extra-genetic heritage of its community. The helplessness of infants demands longer and more elaborate child care, and it becomes highly convenient for the adult males to help the mothers. Some of the skills that the young males must learn can only be learned from the adult males. All this makes for the domestication of fathers. This, together with the habit of paying attention to past experiences and future contingencies (which we have seen arising in the context of play, of tool-carrying, of the displacement of pre-language, and of tool-making), promotes male jealousy. The seeds of this may have been earlier, but it now becomes eminently reasonable for a male to reserve a female, even when he is not sexually hungry, that she may be available when the need arises.

In the developments just outlined we can also see contributing sources for the complex restrictions and rituals with which human sexual relations are hedged about. These include not only all the rules of exogamy and endogamy and the varying principles controlling premarital and extramarital relations, but also the whole matter of taste —some individuals of the opposite sex are attractive, others unattractive, according to criteria learned from one's community. Any male past puberty, and any female between menarche and menopause, can, in a matter of seconds, stand a good chance of launching a new human. But child care requires time and energy thereby unavailable for other important activities. From this stem such varied modern institutions as celibate orders and beauty contests.

Among the proto-hominoids the band leaders were the strongest adult males. Language, in particular, changes this. The oldest members of the band, strong or feeble, are valued because they have had time to learn more. They are repositories of information on which the community can call as it is needed (Sahlins 1959). This use of the elderly as encyclopedias perhaps helps to select for a greater life span, though the pedomorphism discussed earlier may also have played a part in bringing about this result. Certainly the increased social utility of the elderly promotes a protection of the old and feeble by the young and strong; it may contribute to doing something positive about the disposal of the dead.

As soon as the hominids had achieved a reasonably effective bipedal *walking* gait—not running, which is useful only for fast coverage of short distances [30]—they had the basic wherewithal for migrating slowly throughout all the continental territory to which they could adapt their lifeways. For the invasion of some climatic zones, protection against the cold is necessary. There are various physiological ways of doing this (Coon 1962:62–68), but the hominids developed an additional device: clothing.

The Chinese variety of *Pithecanthropus* [31] used fire for warmth. By his epoch, then, the hominid invasion of cold climates had begun. But we suspect that clothing was a much earlier invention, already available when it was first needed for warmth.

Clothing serves roughly three functions: protection, as against the cold; modesty and vanity; and *carrying*. The last of these functions was, we suggest, the one of earliest relevance. If one's way of life rests on hand-carrying, and if the number and variety of things to be carried is increasing to the point of awkwardness, then the invention of a device that helps one carry things has the conservative survival value required by Romer's Rule. The first clothing-as-harness may have been nothing more than a piece of vine pulled from the trees and draped over the shoulder or around the waist. Later, when the hominids were regularly killing small animals, the hides—useless as food —might have been put to this use. A hide cannot be eaten, but if one is hungry enough there is some nourishment to be obtained by chewing at it. Almost as early as the first use of hides as harness, it may have been discovered that a hide that has been chewed is more flexible and comfortable to wear than one that has not. This way of processing hides was still widespread only yesterday.

It is unlikely that any direct archeological evidence of these posited early clothing developments will ever turn up. But if clothing of sorts is actually that ancient, then it was already available, with only minor modifications, when it was first needed to help explore ecological niches characterized by cold. It may even be old enough to have played a part in permitting the development of the relative hairlessness characteristic of all strains of *Homo sapiens* today.

ABSTRACT

Except for an introductory discussion of methodology, this paper is an effort at a narrative account of the evolution of our ancestors from proto-hominoid times to the earliest fully human stage.

Notes

1. Earlier versions of this paper were read: Wednesday, 27 February 1963, at The University of Toronto, as the last of the 1962–63 Lecture Series of the

Presidential Committee on Linguistics (under the title "Language and Man: The contribution of Linguistics to our Understanding of Human Behaviour"); Saturday, 30 March 1963, at The Northeast Anthropological Conference held in Ithaca, New York; Saturday, 27 April 1963, at The Buffalo English Linguistics Project, University of Buffalo; and Friday, 10 May 1963, at a Supper Conference of The Wenner-Gren Foundation for Anthropological Research, in New York City. Many comments from members of these audiences have been incorporated into the present version. We wish especially to acknowledge valuable suggestions from David Stout of The University of Buffalo and from Allan R. Holmberg of Cornell University.

2. Most paleoanthropologists have either ignored language or have tried to infer from a fossil skull or jaw that its owner could, or could not, have had "articulate speech." Childe (1936; 1951 edition: 29) fell into this error, as has Kelemen (1948); for a brief discussion, see Hockett (1956). Other examples are cited in Coon (1962:259 fn. 1, 299 fn. 5), where Coon shows his own healthy skepticism of such inferences. The basis of the trouble is that "articulate speech" does not mean anything. Bryan (1963) falls into the same trap.

Some recent discussions (e.g., Critchley 1960) try to deal with the emergence of language merely in terms of the contrast between "sign" and "symbol"; intentionally or not, these treatments give the impression that our ancestors acquired language in a single enormous leap. Anyone aware of the intricacy of design of every human language knows that such a leap was impossible; there had to be steps and stages. The contrast between "sign" and "symbol," first carefully discussed by Langer (1942), then adopted and developed by White (e.g., 1949, 1959), is too gross to serve. In White's version, the definition of the distinction is ultimately circular. A more elaborate itemization of design features found in human and animal communication will be found in Hockett (1959, 1960a, 1960b, 1963a). Stuart A. Altmann, of the Department of Zoology, University of Alberta, is currently engaged in making even more subtle discriminations in this area.

3. The first comparative grammar was published in 1799 (Bloomfield 1933: ch. 1; see also Pederson 1931). The mutual stimulation of biologists and linguists at the time of Darwin is briefly discussed by Greenberg (1959). In the literature of the last few decades we fail to find any discussion of the comparative method that properly highlights the necessary differences in its applications to language, to human lifeways other than language, and in genetics and phylogeny. The authors are attempting to fill this hiatus in a forthcoming article; the remarks in the next few paragraphs of the present paper are only suggestive.

4. For the nature of sound change see Hockett (1958: chs. 52–54) and Bloomfield (1933: chs. 20–21).

5. When it comes to human evolution there is another dangerous pitfall: that of anthropomorphizing the rest of nature or (equally dangerous) of interpreting the difference between ourselves and the rest of nature in physically and biologically impossible terms. In the discussion of man's place in nature there is no place for mentalism or vitalism. The only valid assumption is that of *physicalism:* life is part of the inorganic world and subject to all the laws of physics; man is an animal and subject to all the laws of biology (Bloomfield 1936; Hockett 1948). Anthropologists still fall constantly into the error of contrasting the "cultural" and the "biological"; even Dobzhansky (1962) chooses the unfortunate terms "organic" and "superorganic" (through what he says with

these terms is good). It is equally misleading to speak of "natural" versus "artificial" selection. Such pairings of terms are survivals of the mind-body dualism of an earlier day in the intellectual history of the West; they should be extirpated.

6. By "extinction" we mean exclusively what Coon (1962:31) calls "utter extinction without issue"; the use of the same word for "extinction through successive evolution" is misleading, stemming from and lending support to an almost word-magical handling of the term "species."

7. Especially since Wiener (1948), it has come to be recognized that purposeful behavior can be described as the behavior of mechanisms with certain physical properties, and that organisms are such mechanisms. On the basic assumption of physicalism (see fn. 5), we are required to speak of "purpose" only when we know, or can reasonably assume, that we are dealing with a system with the requisite physical structure. The teleological proposals in evolutionary theory, dealt with and disposed of so well by Simpson (1949: 1951 paperback edition ch. 2), do not meet these requirements.

8. *Propliopithecus,* from the Fayum Oligocene, looks like a possible ancestral gibbon rather than a pre-proto-hominoid; if so, then the proto-hominoids had to be earlier than *Proconsul* (Coon 1962:196).

9. Apparently this suggestion was first made by Smith (1913).

10. Students of primate behavior use the terms "band" and "troop" in technically distinct ways. Without prejudice for the subtle distinctions thus indicated, we have found it more convenient to use the term "band" throughout in a generic sense. The kind of territoriality described here is coming to be distinguished from other varieties (for instance, from the perimeter-defending territorial behavior of many birds) by the use of the term "core area." On nests: Nissen (1931); Bingham (1932); Bolwig (1959); Carpenter (1938); Hooton (1942:14–15, 155, 78–80, 124–25).

11. This is important because of the Sewall Wright effect. If the population size range is correct, random genetic drift was operative. The development of similar but independent gene pools, and the occasional gene flow across population lines, worked in favor of the selection of those mutations important for the survival of the entire population. Such circumstances favor more rapid adaptive change.

12. Crucial recent observations by Jane Goodall were reported to us orally by L. S. B. Leakey (see fn. 17).

13. Although we draw largely on Carpenter's account of gibbon calls (1940), vocal-auditory signaling of the sort that qualifies as a call system is widespread among land mammals; e.g., among prairiedogs, whose system has been partly described (King 1955). Hediger (1961) writes—using nontechnical terms that require to be properly interpreted: "Five elements of speech that by purely theoretical reasoning have been found to be the most essential are in fact contained in all animal systems of communication investigated up to date and receive added differentiation in the course of evolution, in accordance with the requirements imposed by the respective living conditions. These are the five sounds or signals: (a) warning signal (enemy), (b) mating and territorial possession, (c) mother-and-child contact, (d) social contact, (e) announcement of food." And Schultz (1961): "Without the hearing of sounds, produced by their own kind, monkeys and apes would never have become the intensely social animals that they are. Sounds of a surprising variety serve continually for the contact between the members of a group, for the orientation of mother and young, for the

information of the entire group about possible danger, and, last but not least, for scaring enemies of different or the same species and even for warning rival groups away from the territories already occupied. . . . The orgies of noise, indulged in especially by howlers, guerezas, gibbons, siamangs, and chimpanzees, seemingly so repetitious and meaningless, are probably at least as informative to the respective species as most after-dinner speaking is to *Homo sapiens.*"

14. Of the thirteen design features described in Hockett (1960*b*), the following are shared by gibbon calls and language, hence presumably also by the call system of the proto-hominoids: vocal-auditory channel; broadcast transmission and directional reception; rapid fading (combatted by repetition in the case of gibbon calls); interchangeability; total feedback; specialization; semanticity; arbitrariness; discreteness. Hence we need not deal with any of these properties in the sequel.

15. It is exceedingly difficult to phrase a statement of this kind in such a way as to avoid misunderstanding. We are *not* sorting out various features of structure and behavior and saying: genes are responsible for these, tradition is responsible for those. Both mechanisms of transmission contribute to everything—but with great variation in the balance and the precise nature of the interplay between the two. The best discussion we know of this is Dobzhansky (1956).

16. We elaborate Romer's brief suggestion considerably. See also Oakley (1961).

17. In a lecture at Cornell University, Wednesday, 26 March 1963, L. S. B. Leakey showed a slide of a ring of stones unearthed at a very early East African site; in conversation, he scoffed at the traditional notion that our ancestors had no homes until they moved into caves.

18. On the latter, Hewes (1961) is particularly convincing.

19. This interpretation insists on the correctness of what has been called the "exogenic" rather than the "endogenic" theory as to the basic (though not the only) direction of causal connections in evolution (Hewes 1961:689). Our treatment is in general accord with Washburn's recent proposals (1959; 1960), which are also exogenic.

20. It has often been proposed that the first non-scavenged meat was "slow game" (Coon 1962:80). We agree on the importance of slow game, except in one respect: the adventures that served as crucial impetus making for the carrying of weapons must have been adventures with fast and dangerous creatures, not slow and harmless ones. Once weapon-carrying was established, the weapons would obviously be used on slow game too—perhaps even predominantly so.

One other factor promoting meat in the diet should be mentioned. Oakley (1961:190) points out that a desiccating climate (of the sort that would thin out the forest) may have induced a change in intestinal flora and fauna, rendering the utilization of certain vegetable foods less efficient and thus increasing the hunger for protein.

21. Some of our guesses at the lifeways of the proto-hominoids are based on observations of modern baboons (Washburn and DeVore 1961), whose conditions of life seem to be somewhat similar. But in at least one respect there is a sharp difference: the baboons carry on their affairs in a strikingly silent way. Their vocal sounds are rare.

22. We do not imply that there was no sharing of food or "socialization" before collective hunting. The suckling of the young is a kind of food-sharing;

a food call is indicative of food-sharing; scavenged meat hauled back to head-quarters, perhaps long before any use of weapons for hunting, may have been shared. The developments outlined in the text are a matter of intensification and elaboration.

23. The pygmy chimpanzee, the porcupine, the hamster, and the two-toed sloth are variously known or reputed to share the human habit (Coon 1962: 161). Hewes also comments on it (1961:696). The guess given here as to its consequences among the hominids is, as far as we know, our own.

24. This is not quite true. Continuously variable features of a single call—say pitch, or volume, or duration—could become associated with continuously variable features of a type-situation, so that, in time, a specific uttering of the danger call could quite precisely specify "danger of degree seventeen, due north, three hundred yards away." The openness of a system that had de-veloped in this way would be logically like that of bee dances (von Frisch 1950; Lindauer 1963), which is quite unlike that of human language.

25. But many animal communicative systems have not yet been adequately studied. There is some hint that the song systems of certain passerine birds may prove to have just the array of design features that characterized pre-language (Lanyon 1960). Of course, this would not necessarily mean that the birds in question are on their way towards the development of true language.

26. See references cited in the first paragraph of fn. 2.

27. In recorded human history a somewhat similar transformation is ob-servable in the evolution of Chinese characters. The earliest characters were holistically different from one another to the eye—any visual resemblances be-tween constituent parts of different characters were unsystematic and accidental. But as the system developed, and a larger and larger number of characters had to be devised, it became impossible to keep on inventing completely dif-ferent new shapes; instead, new characters came to be built by putting together pieces drawn from old ones. But this incipient "duality," as an economy mea-sure, never developed as far as it has in languages (i.e., spoken languages). Thousands of characters in use today are built out of hundreds of recurrent parts; the tens of thousands of morphemes in any language are built out of a mere double handful of phonological components, used with amazing effi-ciency.

28. A possible example in current American English is medial posttonic *t* versus *d*: *matter* and *madder,* or *petal* and *pedal,* or *atom* and *Adam,* are acoustically very close in the speech of many people, and absolutely identical for some. When this leads to misunderstanding, the speaker repeats with clearer articulation, or paraphrases.

29. Coarticulated stops are commonest in west Africa, but recur in New Guinea. Clicks seen to be the least widespread: they are found only in south and east Africa, largely in languages known to be related to one another.

30. A point emphasized by Washburn in a talk at the Wenner-Gren Foundation for Anthropological Research, Spring 1960.

31. Here and throughout we have used the taxonomic terms of Simpson (1945) and LeGros Clark (1955).

COMMENTS

WESTON LA BARRE
DURHAM, NORTH CAROLINA, U.S.A. 30.7.63

A major value in Ascher and Hockett's excellent and stimulating paper is the placing of language firmly and integratedly within the complex of man's biological traits, an indispensable job if we are ever to have a genuinely holistic human biology; and never, in my opinion, has this been better accomplished than here. But precisely because this study carefully attends to the *context* of other biological traits of man, it invites comment on these other matters as well.

The first human revolution should perhaps be called the "Hunting Revolution," for it is in relation specifically to hunting that prehumans first became human. The authors properly stress the point; but on the one hand hunting must be even further emphasized, and on the other strongly qualified. It is useful to summarize the authors' argument, because much of it constitutes what perhaps most modern anthropologists now believe; my own comments represent critiques, differing emphases, and additions to this summary.

Because of climatic change, from whatever cause, grove-to-grove migration over open savannas became necessary to ancestral prehumans in seeking food, in accordance with "Romer's Rule" to preserve their basic tree-living adaptation; on such enforced treks, "hominoid" bipedality was adaptive, the better to see predators in savanna grasses, but more importantly because bipedality facilitated nonce weapon-carrying in prehensile primate hands, at the moment unoccupied either with brachiation or quadrupedal walking; savanna trek-behavior became further adaptive the more especially since stronger, more successful and earlier grove occupants (who thus remained conservative) tended to enforce a continued savanna habitat on the "hominoid failures" who were man's ancestors; from defensive use, these carried weapons were gradually turned to offensive use in hunting, and the onetime mainly vegetarian Miocene waifs consequently evolved from objects of predation to primarily hunting and meat-eating human predators; and meanwhile; if the hand had not freed the mouth from food-grasping and fighting, developed speech would have been impossible, and speech is a foundation of our human state; numerous related anatomical changes accompanied in 2-way causality these new functional adaptations.

1) Possibly *fire* might be more stressed in relation to jaw changes so portentous for speech—fire for food-preparation to lessen demands on jaws, fire for frightening off savanna predators, and fire for thus reducing defensive demands on fanged jaws. Probably *tools* might be stressed more in this context too, for Washburn is convincing in his argument that decrease in the size of the anterior teeth probably came *after* man was a maker of tools, which are thus implicated in 2-way jaw changes involving

speech; also, "larger brains [like-wise deemed necessary for human speech] were the result of the new selective pressures coming in with the use of tools" (Washburn 1959:25)—although this argument must be enlarged to include speech itself, as the authors show, as well as tools, in considering the factors affecting selective pressures toward larger brains.

2) Since chimpanzees kill birds and even young antelopes, must proto-human prey necessarily have been the postulated *"very* slow game"? Wherein would lie any prehuman/human distinction? Not in the fact of meat-eating, and surely not in the pursuit of *"very* slow game," an unnecessary and erroneous assumption, since ape-hunted prey is somewhat agile. And why could not the solitary man obtain such food if an ape could? I think that the distinction lies rather (a) in the *size* of the prey characteristically pursued, and even its speed (for a solitary ape could probably capture any meat food it eats), and (b) in a consequently needed protohuman habit of *group cooperation in hunting,* based on an earlier largely defensive primate gregariousness usefully retained by savanna hominids. Some apes use clubs and throw missiles (Kortlandt 1962:133, 138) and an ape can at times eat meat and still remain an ape. But with (a) protohuman weapons used against (b) larger and more dangerous or swifter game animals, in (c) concerted group hunting, our hominoid experiences conditions within which he both can and must become human.

3) The relative *size* of the hominid hunter and his prey is important; indeed, the matter of absolute size is repeatedly significant throughout primate evolution. The authors' mention of rodents reminds us that the wide success of this order in the Eocene may have influenced the displacement of the initially small early primates from the lower shrub strata to the upper 3 strata of the forest canopy (Barth, cited by Napier 1960:60), and with adaptive consequences: a small lemuroid or tarsioid, say, could fall a short distance with little damage, but for heavier primates *higher* in the trees improved prehensility would have selective advantage—and no excursus, this, from our main topic, since prehensility is later critically important in another way for our bipedal weapon-carrying savanna hunters who developed speech. Again, up to a point, greater body size was evidently useful in the change from a furtive, quasi-solitary, nocturnal early primate—the nocturnal habitus, incidentally, which perhaps initially gave the primate line its eye-primacy—to a day-active animal, especially as it also became gregarious (Montagu 1944). Another point about size: in 1773 the English naturalist Gilbert White noted that night-hunting owls had to have large eyes, and large eyes tend to require large heads. If the big-eyed early nocturnal primates establish the eye-primacy and large heads of this order, we must note that human eyes are still large, not merely in proportion to the body but absolutely (L. J. & M. Milne 1962:245). Probably eye-requirements should also be tossed into the complex organic equation as a factor in the relatively large skull size of primates, as well as brain size, and initially in prehuman primates perhaps eyes even more than brains. (Since it is the day-active birds and primates that have color vision,

it is probably the change from nocturnal to diurnal activity that brought color vision also to primates). Again, probably greater size in anthropoid apes relative to monkeys, but including in the argument large terrestrial baboons, is functionally related to their semi-terrestrial habitat, and hence our "hominoid" ancestor must have been a fair-sized primate. But again within limits: perhaps the gorilla can be more massive, largely for self-protection, than the necessarily more mobile protohuman hunter because the gorilla has *not* adapted to hunting larger game animals. Evidently our savanna-waif happened to be agile enough to become a hunter, but he was not big enough or otherwise equipped to go it alone, and hence in his new adaptation he remained (Romer's Rule) a *social animal* that developed speech. His accidental size is important here: if the hominoid somehow could have become a lone hunter and had ditched his primate gregarious-ness, he would surely never have developed speech and would probably be no more loquacious than a nest-pilfering, solitary orangutan.

4) Hunting has its bearing also on relative size in human sexual dimor-phism. Among mammals only the carnivores, including man, are food-sharers (Spuhler 1959:7), and compact animal protein high in calories is a good basis for group food-sharing only in *prey of sufficient size*. Would not such larger prey make demands not only for sufficient agility and size in the individual hunter, but also for social cooperation in hunting? Fruit-picking needs no special sexual dimorphism; but in our male hunting-hominid, would not relatively larger bones and muscles, greater vital ca-pacity, and even subcutaneous fat-nakedness (for diffusion of metabolic heat from the rapid spurts of energy required in hunting) be also selective factors in such a context—but not applicable to the female? Moreover, since our authors postulate hairiness in the ancestral proto-anthropoid an-cestor, would not hunting for the same reason (metabolic heat-diffusion) perhaps be selective for the glabrousness of human races relative to other tropical primates? In any case, food-sharing in hunters *reinforces* primate gregariousness and facilitates greater male interdependency. Not only this: hunting larger and more formidable meat prey itself *requires* and *gives selective advantage* to a closer primate gregariousness. And, as I shall argue a bit later, both this greater cooperation in a hunting context and dilemmas of sexuality and aggression arising in band life are perhaps the necessary preconditions for the change from a closed phatic to an open complexly-semantic communication-system (see also La Barre 1960:166–70, 207).

5) Meanwhile, in female sexual dimorphism, tree-living already fostered the single birth in higher primates, constant maternal carrying of the infant, increased maternal care of fewer young, longer nurture, and a closer interindividual mother-child relationship. If, as the authors well argue, the continuing advantages of a still larger brain in a hominid symbol-using animal select even for a neotenous and dependent child whose brain keeps on growing after birth, then the human mother is clearly specialized dimorphously in a wider pelvis to cope with the

(insufficiently) maximal skull size, in the human neonate mostly accounted for by brain, and also for the increased care (longer lactation) for the unfinished neotenous young. What I wish to insist upon is that these massive female sexual dimorphisms as well as an extravagantly long neotenous dependency in the child—all ultimately in the service of language and of culture—can hardly have taken place except in relation to a male sexual dimorphism adapted to hunting and hence food-sharing.

6) The authors' point that the alimentary and the sexual interest in the human female are now both "frontal" (gluteus maximum and, I would add, pelvic rotation in bipedality) *and reinforces adult male—infant assimilation,* is a happy one. This greatly aids explanation of an otherwise vexing problem of male humanization and fatherhood. What does " 'paternally' interested in infants" mean in explaining human paternity? It is a mere verbalism, naming the phenomenon to explain itself, unless we adduce the authors' other arguments and connect them up here. What are the anatomy and the biological mechanisms of social fatherhood?—this is a critical problem of man's humanization! The answers are not yet all in; but I believe that the authors have themselves supplied an important anatomically grounded insight here.

7) The change in possible coital position from the crouching primate breech-presentation to the prone-male supine-female human situation doubtless explains such virtually universal macrocosmic projections of human sexuality as the skyfather/earth-mother myths—a different coital geometry would have produced a very different cosmology in another animal! But human sexual dimorphism, based on the respective specializations of male meat-bringer and female producer and impresario of the huge-brained offspring needed for language and human culture, has a far more important bearing on specifically human biology. It is notable that in insects, birds, and many other animals, it is commonly the female who is master of the sexual situation—whence the necessity of animal "courtship," the spider female's free meal once she has obtained the male's genes for her offspring, the role of sexual selection in color in birds, etc. However, given the greater male strength in human dimorphism, the solitary human female is vulnerable to any sexual encounter. Can we not see in this situation the roots of male dominance, sexual possessiveness, "family" protectiveness toward the female too, and a necessity for some sort of rules and relative exclusiveness in sexuality?—for hunting males need social cooperation, which uncodified sexuality would tend to disrupt. The very predicaments of social living require complexer communication than that available in "closed" phatic grunts, if this new hominid band-, family-, and food-ecology is going to persist! The savanna-waif is booted once more (Romer's Rule) toward humanity.

8) Human "frontal" sexuality has if anything increased the significance of diffuse "play"-sexuality and symbolic body gesture already plentiful in prehuman social primates. If a large brain is needed not only for symbol-using language *but also for cortical control and inhibition* of instinctual

impulses—because of that indispensable protohuman food-ecology, the problems of band life, sexuality, etc.—we can see still further selective usefulness in the large brain. Conflicts within the group between adult and immature males are disruptive of the socializing process; but resolution of the problems rests on cortical dominance *and* delayed sexual maturity *and* family- or group-exogamy—which last may have an important bearing on the change from "closed" to "open" communication systems which the linguist should attend to. Specifically, human sexuality, with family-exogamy replacing primate band-schizmogenesis, is part of the total universe within which human speech arises. Meanwhile, the cortex is involved with selection pressures incident to the new hominid group-ecology in all these several mentioned ways, not only in the interests of language.

9) Food-ecology is indeed significant and indispensable to an understanding of protohuman "linguistic" process. Infra-human primates can each pick their own fruit in the trees, and gregariousness be useful mainly for mutual protection when coupled with a simple "closed" call-system, whereas a more complex and swiftly changing, dangerous and contingent kind of food-getting like hunting by our savanna-carnivores doubtless selectively favors an "opening" and further linguistic processing of the system to cope with the more complex group-situation. But I think perhaps the authors have a linguistic propensity to argue a premature dialecticizing of the call system. It is true that Maine and Pennsylvania crows have call-"dialects" that are unintelligible to French crows of the same species, and the same is true of American and French herring-gulls (L. J. & M. Milne 1962:46); likewise it is now well known that there are bee dance species-"dialects." But the former case deals with largely instinctual closed systems, and the second with differing species. There is no immediate selective advantage to be seen in the dialecticizing of protohuman communication at this point, when such call-"dialects" are merely functional alternatives at this basic and thoroughly pre-Whorfian stage. There are several reasons for a conservative view: (a) the conjunctive use of communication must have had selective primacy over the disjunctive uses of communication in these protohuman times of (b) sparse population, and (c) ecological pressures toward cooperation in what may have been somewhat semi-fluid groups that (d) because of the incest-taboo and other exogamic pressures may have had a churning-up of band personnel far more constant and massive than primate band-schizmogenesis. Further, (e) even in apes, insofar as a call is a territorial one, it must of necessity be intelligible in inter-band communication, and there are probably many other such situations, too, e.g., in out-of-band mating. And finally, (f) if we are to give due weight to the problem of "overloading" with ambiguities in an exiguous system of blended and erstwhile "closed" calls (which the authors convincingly argue), then premature dialecticizing anywhere near this level would only introduce a further difficulty in communication. Indeed, (g) I think that because of the discernible common traits of all human languages (openness, duality etc.), we must agree with the authors that "the

crucial developments must have taken place once, then spread," that blending and opening are pretty fundamental speech-processes, that "true diversity is found in more superficial aspects of language . . . rather than genetics," and that only with complete freedom from the instinctual given by openness and duality, can we have massive linguistic drift.

10) One minor "linguistic" problem troubles me. It is a curious fact that although the human ear is most sensitive to sound at a frequency around 3000 cycles per second, that is, minimal amplitudes can be heard at this frequency—whence the "piercing" quality even from far-off of a high-pitched scream from a woman or a child—nevertheless, the energy in the speaking voice, no matter whether it is that of a man, a woman, or a child, is mainly in frequencies below 1000 c.p.s. (L. J. & M. Milne 1962:40, 42–43). Ordinary talk simply does not exploit the frequencies we are most sensitive to, as if communication were not *that* important or as if we left that channel open, reserved for emergencies like high-pitched screams. I would hazard a guess that primate tree-calls are high-pitched and quite close to the optimal wave-lengths of the species' hearing. But in humans there is a problem. What protohuman Federal Communications Commission decreed a frequency band separation between "closed" and "open" system communication? Whence the massive flatting of speech-frequencies in man? Or did speech not arise out of "closed" primate call-systems after all, but rather from the lower frequencies of feckless play-chatter, where speech has remained ever since?

By FRANK B. LIVINGSTONE
ANN ARBOR, MICH., U.S.A. 14.7.63

In recent years there has been a remarkable outburst of interest in the problems connected with the origin of the hominids. These problems have great intrinsic interest for all of us but appear to have been somewhat neglected for many years. Perhaps new evidence, such as the many recent finds of the Australopithecines, has been responsible for some of this increased interest in hominid origins, but I think it is also due in part to a change in our theoretical outlook. We have begun to realize that fact do not speak for themselves but are always interpreted in a theoretical framework, and that, as much as we might wish it, we will never discover enough facts to reveal to us the total way of life of our transitional ancestors. Thus, the development of an adequate explanation of the origin of the hominids and their peculiar capacities will result as much from the sifting of theoretical speculations as from the uncovering of new facts. Ascher and Hockett's paper is a good example of this new wave of theoretical speculation. I agree with much of the reasoning, and the application of "Romer's Rule" to the problems of the reconstruction of hominid history seems to me to be a novel contribution which has much to commend it. The linguistic reconstruction I found interesting although beyond me at times, so that my comments will be with regard to the biological arguments. Although I agree with the general lines of the reconstruction, my comments will be critical.

First of all, I think the reconstruction of the proto-hominoids is a fiction which is due to the present imperfect classification of the primates. I think the consensus is now beginning to be that the gibbons have really little in common with the great apes and man. So their inclusion in the proto-hominoids tends to bias this reconstruction and reconstruct a non-existent animal. Most of the gibbon's similarities to the apes can be explained by parallelism—although this vague concept leaves much to be desired—and the common ancestor of the great apes and the gibbon would be way back in time, include many other animals, and perhaps look something like the monkey lemurs of today. In other words, the gibbon and great apes are not an adaptive radiation resulting from brachiation, but 2 different groups which adapted to brachiation.

Although I am not sure how one employs the comparative method of historical reconstruction, which the authors emphasize, I do not think it is particularly accurate or useful. Animals are adapted to specific ecological niches and are in turn in the process of adapting more completely to these niches. Thus, to reconstruct a proto-animal by averaging the physical characters or adaptations of its descendants results in an animal which is not particularly adapted to any niche.

To reconstruct the proto-hominoids—by which I would like to mean the animals who underwent the human revolution—I think it would be better to reconstruct from the hominids and the great apes of Africa, the gorilla and the chimpanzee.

Recent biochemical evidence indicates, as does comparative anatomy, that these 2 apes are very strikingly similar to man, so much so that if the Linnean system is to reflect common ancestry, these animals should have some group to themselves. We have run out of groups between the Hominoidea and the Hominidae, so that we need a new group, a sub-super family.

I think it is important to consider in ecological terms the way of life of man's ancestor prior to the human revolution. It has been the general opinion that this ancestor was an "unspecialized, generalized ape," which was rather unadapted to any way of life and just waiting around for its turn to evolve. Hence the search for generalized features on the fossils we now possess, the rejection of any fossils which appear to be adapted to the ape way of life, and the relegation of the pongid-hominid split to the Miocene or even Oligocene. But these animals were apes and were adapted to the ape way of life almost as much as any modern representative of the great apes. Simian shelves and other features may be recent adaptations of the great apes, but an animal with a simian shelf is not immediately ruled out as a human ancestor because it is too specialized. Such ideas are left-overs from orthogenetic, typological thinking which is implicitly anti-evolutionary. For this reason, I do not think the human fossil record prior to the human revolution is particularly sparse. It is the same fossil record as that of the African apes, and with the many Proconsuls, Kenyapithecus, and perhaps some of the Indian finds, it is rather abundant. Only the search for something that was not an ape makes it sparse. Although tropical rain forest is not optimal for fossilization, these apes were probably the most dense large animal in the tropical forest which covered most of the Miocene peneplain of Africa. This surface is still an obvious feature of the African landscape today, and it has only been since the Miocene that mountain building and rifting have both elevated and carved up the surface of Africa and created the many vegetational zones which are there at present.

This great diversification of environment also most likely separated many ape populations from the forest, and this separation was necessary for the development of the human ecological niche, although not sufficient. An animal species which is divided into populations between which gene flow occurs—and it does occur with contact—would not speciate the way Ascher and Hockett imply when they state that the losers who were kicked out of the trees became man. As long as the apes could fight for the old niche they would, even to the point of committing populational suicide: this has happened many times in both animal and human populations. Such a proto-hominid population had to be separated completely and forced to change their way of living, and for one population that was enough. The old Maxim "Necessity is the mother of invention" is quite applicable to obtain the human and the later neolithic revolutions.

Ascher and Hockett also implicate food-carrying and tool-using for protection against predators as the 2 major factors which led to bipedalism and the hominid ecological niche. Undoubtedly food carrying was important to the first hominids particularly if they were hunters of large game and the females and young did not participate in the hunt. But to implicate food carrying as the most important factor necessitates a stage of primarily scavenging for the proto-hominids which I do not think necessary. I also think the evidence at Olduvai has been misinterpreted to make these populations hunters of small game. There are immature pigs of a species as big as a rhinoceros at Olduvai in addition to antelope, but the hunters would have to cope with mother pig in order to capture the immature ones. This line of reasoning also makes me think that too much emphasis has been placed on predators as a controlling factor. The amount of time the average animal spends coping with predators is infinitesimal, but the time spent hunting for food is almost the animal's entire waking hours. Of course, in terms of natural selection, one mishap with a predator is much more likely to affect one's survival, but I still think predators are overemphasized. An animal does not change its way of life or basic mode of locomotion because of a predator, but only adapts to the predators of its particular ecological niche. This overemphasis of predators is in part due to the peculiar views of Western Culture about the tropics, the Tarzan mentality. It is much more reasonable that weapons of offense would result in habitual tool-using, tool-carrying, and then tool-making.

One final point: the human species is a very polytypic one compared to other species, so that human racial diversity does not appear to be slight from one point of view. It might be slight from another but this is not due to closeness of common ancestry as Ascher and Hockett imply.

By G. G. SIMPSON

CAMBRIDGE, MASS., U.S.A. 10.7.63

I probably should not comment on this paper because almost all of it is so far outside my field that it would be presumptuous of me either to endorse or to criticize.

There is some brickmaking without straw, but in general I find the article fascinating and convincing. The bits that do impinge on my field usually seem sound.

The applications of "Romer's rule" here made are probably reasonable, but I doubt whether the rule has the generality given it when it is first introduced. I also dislike such eponymous terms, but that is a personal preference.

The authors seem to take it for granted that much—all?—of hominid evolution was confined to East Africa until a "diaspora" (misplaced humor?) well along in the Pleistocene. I think that highly improbable, and the exiguous evidence can just as well be read in the opposite way. (For example, the most hominid-like Tertiary specimen known is from India.)

Footnote 8. I think I agree with the intention, but I do not find the expression of it clear. Of course life is subject to all the same laws as inorganic matter, but it is a flat contradiction in terms to say that life is *part* of the inorganic world. I further agree that culture is a biological phenomenon not different in principle from other behavioral adaptations. However, there *is* a difference between anatomical-physiological and behavioral-cultural (societal) adaptation, and we do need a way to make the distinction. There is also a real and important distinction involved in (not identical with) that between natural and artificial selection. Natural selection always and solely favors relative efficiency in reproduction. Artificial selection may and usually does favor other and frequently conflicting goals (and here they *are* goals). The 2 are not identical, and the pairing of concepts (I do not care about the terms) should not be abolished.

Footnote 6. I have suggested that the ambiguity and false implications can be cleared up by calling "utter extinction without issue" simply *termination*.

Footnote 8. *Propliopithecus* is still dubious, but there is little doubt that *Pliopithecus* (with synonym *Limnopithecus*), some forms of which are at least as old as *Proconsul*, was well along toward becoming a gibbon. For this and other reasons I think that the proto-hominoids (in these authors' sense) must have been considerably older than *Proconsul*. The splitting off of the Hominidae, however, could have been later. That probably did not occur within the proto-hominoid complex but from a *proto-Pan* (i.e. ancestral chimp-gorilla) stem *after* separation of the gibbon and orang lines.

REPLY

By CHARLES F. HOCKETT *and* ROBERT ASCHER

We are delighted with the comments that we have had the opportunity to see (those from Livingstone, Simpson, and La Barre). Far from quarreling with our presentation, these commentators supply highly useful clarifications, warnings, and amplifications. For this reason, the remarks that follow are few and brief.

(1) Both Livingstone and Simpson raise the issue of the taxonomic and phylogenetic status of the gibbons. Since we wanted to use, as part of our evidence, the relatively well described communicative behavior of the gibbons, we chose to attempt to reconstruct the lifeways of the latest common ancestors of all of the contemporary species usually classed as hominoids. We are quite willing to consider the alternative assumption that the hominids and the African great apes share a later separate common ancestry, and to apply the comparative method just within that more restricted group. In fact, the reader should detect some hedging.

However, we do not believe we should accept casual taxonomy. Simpson erects a proto chimp-gorilla; Livingstone wants a sub-super family for the gorillas and chimps. Biochemical evidence, according to Livingstone, indicates that gorillas are "strikingly similar to man." But in a recent paper we find that ". . . as far as the A-B-O blood groups are concerned, among the apes, gorillas are the most different from man, and most similar to monkeys, since the A-B-O groups for gorillas are more readily determined from their secretions than from their blood" (Wiener and Moor-Jankowski 1963:68). Our aim in giving this quotation is not to argue that Simpson and Livingstone are wrong, but merely to indicate that, though a major revision in anthropoid taxonomy may be in the offing, it has not yet arrived. When and if it has been achieved, the evolutionary account put forward in our paper will obviously have to be revised to accord with it.

(2) Livingstone expressed doubts about the comparative method. Such doubts are appropriate—surely there is no clear justification for reconstruction via averaging, which is avowedly what we did for certain aspects of our portrayal of proto-hominoid lifeways. Yet, unless a reliable comparative method can be achieved, we shall be in a very bad way not only for the investigation of human origins but for many other problems in zoological evolution. We refer the reader—and Livingstone—to fn. 3.

(3) Simpson challenges our emphasis on East Africa as the site of various early crucial developments. In this connection, attention should be called also to a recent article by Elwyn L. Simons (1963), who argues for a much wider geographical spread of a much smaller number of species of hominoids and hominids throughout the Miocene and Pliocene.

Until new archeological and paleontological discoveries require a change—if they do—we hold to our East African hypothesis. The argument is not fully explicit in our paper, and can usefully be summarized here.

(a) A series of crucial innovations took place among our ancestors, each building on those that had preceded it. (b) Each of these innovations about this in our paper, must have occurred in some relatively confined geographical area, among populations to which the preceding innovations had spread. (c) Each innovation would then spread to some, but not necessarily to all, allied subspecies and populations, thus coming to cover a wider or narrower geographical area. (d) Some of these innovations are of the sort that are not likely to have taken place independently in two or more places or times. (e) Many of the populations affected by some of the earlier innovations were dead ends, untouched by subsequent ones, and not ancestral to ourselves.

The preceding five assertions say nothing about absolute geography. If we now add the scanty evidence of paleoclimatology, of the known fossils, and of archeology (Clark 1963), we are led to East Africa as the most likely site for a number of the earliest innovations. It should be remembered that one of our chief points is the considerable antiquity of the crucial innovations that turned pre-men into men. The Human Revolution was *completed,* in our view, long before the date of the earliest hominid fossils known from anywhere in the world except Africa.

"East Africa" is, of course, a term of indefinite coverage, particularly when one remembers the geological and climatological changes that occur over lengths of time measured in millions of years. Conceivably, every one of the crucial innovations of the Human Revolution began on a spot that some would prefer to call peripheral to East Africa, rather than part of it. But *each innovation spread into East Africa,* and this claim cannot be made for any other geographical region inhabited at the relevant times by kindred hominoids—until, of course, population and gene movements *after* the completion of the Revolution. Such, at least, is our hypothesis, which we trust will be attacked and challenged from every possible angle.

At this point we should like to add a brief comment about the Weidenreich-Coon hypothesis, currently the target of so much discussion. Stripped of disagreements about terminology (such as, for example, the appropriateness or inappropriateness of using two different labels, *"Homo erectus"* and *"Homo sapiens,"* for temporally successive segments of an uninterrupted phylogenetic continuum), the argument becomes one of parallelism versus common origin. We have already expressed our skepticism about any proposal that, say, openness of vocal-auditory communication may have developed independently at two or more different times or places. But this and the other innovations of the Human Revolution indeed set a stage on which certain subsequent developments might take place in partial independence, and at different rates, among different populations. Some of these are touched on in the last section of our article.

(4) Livingstone and La Barre comment on predation. Livingstone believes we have misinterpreted the evidence from Olduvai in making the

populations there hunters of small game. Having had no first hand contact with the Olduvai evidence, we rely on the reports of others. Desmond Clark (1963) in a recent interpretative article summarizes the faunal and artifactual remains from the Zinjanthropus floor. Clark apparently supports the small game assertion. Perhaps we can agree to suspend discourse on this interpretation of the Olduvai material until more descriptive and, in particular, quantitative data are in print.

La Barre's comments on the *relative* speed and size of the hunter and hunted in pre-Zinjanthropus times, and the relationship of this to sexual dimorphism, suggest novel approaches to interpretation. These approaches, in our opinion, should not be overlooked when the Zinjanthropus and earlier materials are pondered.

(5) La Barre wishes we had stressed the importance of fire. Right now there is no archeological evidence for fire earlier than Choukoutien. However, the population at Choukoutien shows reduction in the size of the molar crowns as compared with the earlier East African populations, and Brace (1962:345–346) has argued that the change may be traced to changes in food preparation. If the rate of evolution of the relevant anatomical system is slow, and if the mastication of cooked food was a factor in molar grinding surface reduction, then fire may predate Choukoutien. Fire may have capped the Human Revolution after all, as La Barre's comments suggest, but we must await the evidence of the shovel.

(6) La Barre questions our ascription of dialect differentiation to very early stages, on the grounds that it would have no survival value. We believe the issue is somewhat different. As soon as mechanisms tending towards dialect differentiation had arisen, dialect differentiation took place except insofar as it was curbed by *antisurvival* properties. Openness was certainly such a mechanism, though we agree (and it is so stated in the paper) that duality, which came later, is a much more potent one.

COMMENTS

By GEORGE A. AGOGINO
PORTALES, NEW MEX., U.S.A. 16 XII 63

The authors have compiled a solid narrative account of human evolution from hominoids to hominids, in less than a dozen pages of useful information. However, the most skilled scientific writer cannot condense a subject of this scope into such a restricted space without distortion through generalization or the favoring of a particular theory without discussion of others. The Hockett-Ascher manuscript leans heavily on the theory that the proto-hominoids were arboreal in spite of considerable evidence that some of man's ancestors became terrestrial during the Oligocene period before the emergence of the great primates (Hooton 1946:105). This, of course, is difficult to determine beyond dispute since the remains of most fossil apes are restricted to jaws, teeth, and skull fragments (Montagu 1951:105).

If the proto-hominoids did indeed evolve to a terrestrial habitat before obtaining large size, they must have been supported by an already somewhat evolved, complex brain, for a small generalized primate would need intelligence to fight a hostile world at ground level. It is probable that the hominoid-hominid upright position was developed while still arboreal, for the brachiation common to all living anthropoids allows for movement through the trees in an upright position. Perhaps he did not walk upright immediately after leaving the trees; but, when his hands became full of tools, weapons, and food, he could walk upright because his body had already learned to withstand the physical demands of pumping blood against gravity, etc., while still swinging, with brachiation, in the trees.

It is possible, perhaps even probable, that our earliest ancestors, the proto-hominoids, had already developed their size (Weinert 1932), upright position and advanced primate brain to some degree before leaving the trees for a terrestrial environment.

If our primate ancestor descended to the ground while small, it would be reasonable for man to show a close relationship to the smaller primates today. In the same manner, he should not show the close similarity he exhibits to the African great apes. The late Earnest Hooton (1946:131–32) lists the following arguments to defend the possibility of a giant terrestrial proto-hominoid theory. All show man's close similarity to the present great apes and stress the possibility that their large size was obtained while still in the trees.

1) Suggestions of lumbar curve in great apes; reduction of number of lumbar segments and increased tendency to incorporate lumbar vertebrae in sacrum in great apes and man.

2) Lateral expansion of iliac blades foreshadowed in great apes; consolidation of sacrum.

3) Human resemblance to great apes in short relative leg length in embryonic period and at birth, and divergence from gibbon proportions at this time.

4) Shift of axis of foot from third digit to between great toe and second digit in man and great apes supposed to be attributable to large increase of foot size in giant brachiators.

5) Suspension of viscera in body cavities by type of mesenteries supposedly developed in gibbons and other apes as result of upright posture; flattening of the chest and back as in brachiators.

6) Great relative length of fore limb in which man approaches the giant apes and vastly exceeds the lower primates (except the brachiating spider monkey); lack of any of the muscular or bony specializations found in typically quadrupedal mammals; frequent occurrence in man of one or more extra heads of the biceps, as is regular in gibbon but uncommon or absent in great apes.

7) Power of rotation of thumb, approximated only in great apes.

8) Inheritance of Dryopithecus (generalized great pattern) of molar tooth form in man.

9) Detailed resemblances of brain pattern between man and great apes.

10) Results of psychological tests showing closest approximation to human intelligence in great apes.

I find fault with the authors' use of a gibbon-like proto-hominoid for describing all proto-hominoid action. The gibbons, as Livingstone points out in his review, have little in common with the great apes or man, except through parallelism. In addition, it is my belief that the gibbon builds no nest at all. In mentioning this gibbon-like proto-hominoid, the authors credit the animal with territories, "specific arboreal sites in which they build their nests." If the modern gibbon simply rests against a tree trunk and hooks his curved fingers over an overhanging branch for safety, why should we credit his proto-ancestor with a more constructive habitat? The authors also credit the proto-hominoids with using their mouths for handling and holding objects, a form of "lip service" that was dropped once he emancipated his hands for the same purpose. If we look about today at our pipe, cigarette, and cigar smoking public we pause to wonder if the mouth had been entirely abandoned as a carrying device.

I agree with reviewer Livingstone that the "linguistic reconstruction [was] interesting although beyond me . . ." Credit must be given to the authors for a bold attempt to reconstruct a linguistic structure in an area of human development that seems so far removed from the area normally covered by linguistics. In spite of these severe limitations, the reconstruction was on the whole realistic and worthwhile.

The authors appear to be correct in pointing out that the development of communication shows many discernible common traits that suggest that "the critical developments must have taken place once, then spread." However, nothing can be inferred at this time as to whether the spread was through migration of the human animal, carrying his linguistic ideas with him as he populated the earth, or through diffusion of linguistic thought, where the ideas of language were accepted or rejected by peoples already living over most of the Old World. One suggests bringing an established communication system into previously uninhabited regions of the world, the other a borrowing of preferred linguistic patterns by peoples already living over most of the world's surface.

In conclusion it must be said that the Hockett-Ascher article attempts to cover too much with too much speculation, in too condensed a manner. In spite of these limitations, their work shows a boldness and freshness of thought that must be considered most valuable. In my opinion one good new idea per article makes any manuscript valuable. In this respect the Hockett-Ascher paper certainly proves its worth.

By RAY L. BIRDWHISTELL
NARBETH, PENNA., U.S.A. 12 XII 63

This literate presentation of prehistorical reconstruction, theoretical speculation, and science fantasy deserves critical (in the most positive sense of the word) comment. However, such comment, particularly if it offers competitive reconstructions, should be based upon data, and that data remains equally unavailable to the critic and to the authors. To me, the central value of this article is that it makes manifest the shortage of the data so necessary for an adequate historical reconstruction of the bio-social evolution of man.

1) We need to know a great deal about comparative physiology. In particular, we need to know a great deal more about *human* biology. The hiatus between anthropological sophistication about osteology and genetics and about the remainder of man's physiological and biological behavior leaves a canyon in which theories can be launched to float on the winds of ignorance. We know so little about even such fundamentals as the necessary conditions for human pregnancy, about male and female sexual cyclicity, about the relationship between human courtship minima and successful mating, that retrograde prediction in this area is impossible. We know even less, if possible, about the relationships between food supply, ingestion, and nourishment as related to humans. Recent bio-environmental studies have made us face our ignorance about man's adaptive range in relation to weather, but we are hardly in any position to speak with confidence about the *possible* environmental range of man, much less the hominids or the hominoids. Our knowledge of soft parts of human growth is at best sparse. And we have only suggestive data concerning the relationship between growth and differential learning potential; obviously these are matters of consequence to the evaluation of the lives of our ancestors.

There is no need to continue to list *basic* (in the sense of their being fundamental to the biological base of pre-man's minimal thresholds of adaptation) areas of ignorance which, while they should not make us postpone attempts at reconstruction, should at least give us pause lest we fall again into the 19th century armchair. Anthropology must be based on biology. Blood, bones and chromosomes do not combine into a viable or describable organism.

2) Ethology has provided us with exciting insights into the complexities of nonhuman social organization. It has given us an escape hatch from the trap offered by the consideration of insect societies as though they were ancestral to human societies. But we lack a comparative sociology which will make it possible to generalize at all reliably on proto-human social possibilities. Baboons, chimps, gorillas, and gibbons *as presently known* provide only suggestions about non-human anthropoids. At best, these have been only preliminarily studied. But there is no assurance that, even when we know their sociology and social psychology, we will have a model for reconstructing the social life of either our common or differentiating ancestors. The Hockett and Ascher reconstructions manifestly demonstrate the need for comparative data on the sociology and social psychology of non-human groupings. Furthermore, it is not merely quibbling when I ask the authors, "how do they know," when they dismiss such a complex problem as jealousy by saying that male proto-hominoids would be "without

any jealousy *when they themselves were sexually satisfied.*" This, like the authors' casual usage of "family bond" in the preceding sentence is indicative of an almost cavalier confidence about the complex nature of concepts scarcely comprehended for even our best studied contemporary societies.

The suggestions in 2 become more cogent to the central theme of the paper when it is recognized that there is probably an absolute relationship between the *orders* of messages that need to be communicated in a society and the communicational system of that society. If we can conceive of the hominids and the proto-hominoids as minimally problematic, it is not difficult to assign them an exceedingly simple structure for governing interaction. The more we know about non-human societies, the less "simple" do they seem. I find Hockett and Ascher's social reconstructions dubiously and shakily skeletal in the face of growing information about wolves, deer, sheep, and even ducks and geese. More than that, I do not see that such reconstructions are necessary to the propositions stated in the article about the possible course of the development of language. However, they are probably necessary to a linguist-centered interpretation of human communication.

3) The authors are well aware that we have never cracked the code of a non-human communication system. And this includes gibbons. Further, they do stress the fact that animals do not merely signal out of some genetic base. They are explicit in their recognition that animals have a communication system. And, perhaps, the central point to the entire discussion is their lucid presentation of the duality of patterning present in every known human speech system. However, for me, it is a far cry from the recognitions that all human languages have duality and the fact that we have never detected it in undeciphered codes, to the proof that duality is peculiarly human.

Furthermore, it is perfectly possible that the communication system can be *open* even though the single modality, vocalic activity, is *closed*. I cannot speak of animal communication for the data is too sparse, but it is perfectly clear that human body motion (and perhaps other modalities, as well) operate precisely to combine apparently mutually distinguishing messages. It is *possible* that through multimodal communication, *certain* animals achieve openness.

That gibbons call from the food instead of returning to report to their fellows is scarcely sufficient evidence to conclude that the gibbons (and, by extension, all other non-humans) cannot express displacement. I realize that in their discussion, the authors are speaking of the development of language. However, it is all too easy to extend this to communication as well. That "displacement," "openness," and "duality" are characteristics of every human language, does not preclude the possibility that these functions were and are present in nonhuman communicational practices.

4) Finally—and again this may seem a small point, but it may ultimately be essential to the comprehension of the evolutionary pathway—despite their recognition of the Devore and Washburn reports, the authors

make a point of hominid "chatter." It is my suspicion, based on 15 years of careful and systematic observation of human interaction in a variety of contexts and upon extensive interview of field workers, that human beings talk a much smaller percentage of their interactional time than highly verbal intellectuals normally believe possible. My friends among the ethologists and zoologists tell me that except for those species which use some kind of sonar for space orientation, animals and birds are generally quiet, too. Other modalities are operative in inaudible situations. We need to know what situations require language.

In summary, let me say that everything I know as a student of communication leaves me sympathetic with the Hockett-Ascher emphasis on the acquisition of language as essential to the development of man as we know him. However, I think that, in the absence of vast areas of data, the declarative sentence form utilized in the reconstructions, however modified by disclaimers of tentativeness, is premature.

By ALAN LYLE BRYAN
EDMONTON, ALBERTA, CANADA. 16 XII 63

Hockett and Ascher's valuable synthesis of the many factors which led to the appearance of man with true language is a superb example of what may be called the hypothetical inductive method. Because I have become convinced that their argument is essentially correct, although details of certain of the many working hypotheses incorporated in the general explanatory theory must be expected to change as critical analyses of pertinent evidence accrues, my comments will be restricted to Hockett and Ascher's brief reference to my paper (Bryan 1963). Hockett's (1963*b*) pertinent comment to my paper arrived after I had composed and posted my reply, and a later addendum including my reply to Hockett was never published because of an unavoidable mixup in trans-Atlantic communication. Perhaps it is just as well, for Hockett and Ascher's paper is a more complete analysis of the failings of my approach which stressed the morphological factors necessary for the development of human speech and excluded discussion of the essential linguistic factors. When I wrote my paper I was attempting to show that the hominid speech tract was at least as essential as cortical development for the production of human speech sounds. I see no reason for abandoning this position, but it is now clear to me that certain purely linguistic factors, which have nothing directly to do with morphology, were the really essential prerequisites for the development of human language. Clearly man is the only living species with true language because he was the only one to discover the principle of duality of patterning, which allowed him to identify minute acoustic details as morphemes. Development of this linguistic feature had nothing to do directly with the ability to produce human speech sounds; logically, the ability to identify an unlimited number of morphemes could have been developed given any method of producing a limited number of distinguishable sounds (Hockett and Ascher suggest anal explosives; an adequate sound repertoire lacking any anatomical basis has been developed into "drum languages" by some cultures).

After absolving myself of my sin of omission, I would like to object to being classified with those who have attempted to infer articulate speech from anatomical details. I drew the inference that certain Australopithecines had language only from the presence of artifacts belonging to a cultural tradition which were found in association with the bones (Bryan 1963:297). The fact that Australopithecines were erect bipedal walkers, which thereby allowed the pertinent parts of their phonatory apparatus to become positioned so that human speech sounds as we know them could be produced, was discussed later (p. 300). Hockett and Ascher, of course, draw the same conclusion but point out that it was not logically necessary that this particular method of sound production be developed in order to allow discovery of the principle of duality of patterning. They also make the point that a certain minimal degree of cortical development, which was already present among the pre-hominids with a pre-language, was the other morphological precondition for the discovery of duality of patterning.

In conclusion, it seems to me that our positions are little different. Hockett and Asher have explained why man's speech and culture is significantly different from that of other hominoids, both living and fossil. I still strongly advocate an experimental approach to the problem with the avowed objective of establishing a technique for communication with another species. Furthermore, I eagerly await the results of studies by observers who are able to record all noises and associated actions produced by groups of primates (especially chimpanzees and gorillas) living in their native habitats. The rudiments of symbolic behavior as well as culture and pre-language, which are postulated for fossil hominoids by Hockett and Asher, may be directly observable among certain living hominoids.

By J. DESMOND CLARK
BERKELEY, CALIF., U.S.A. 12 XII 63

This is an interesting and stimulating paper and provides a useful model against which the fossil evidence can be more critically examined. While one cannot but admire the maximum use the authors make of the biological and behavioural data, greater use might with advantage have been made of the geological and archaeological evidence.

The authors rightly stress the importance of the East African region as one of the crucial areas in which the "human revolution" took place, but there is every reason to suppose, as fossils such as *Ramapithecus* indicate, that this was not the only part of the Old World where changes of this kind were taking place during the later Tertiary. East Africa happens to be the region where beds of this age are especially well preserved and where the most intensive fieldwork has been carried out, but if and when other localities in the tropics and sub-tropics—the Upper Siwalik Beds, for example—are investigated with equal thoroughness, a similar evolutionary pattern will most probably be found.

It seems to me that for our Miocene hominoid ancestors, the dangers of treeless savannah and of crossing open country have perhaps been exaggerated. Treeless savannah in the tropics is not necessarily less well supplied with water and food sources than woodland savannah or the forest itself. Indeed, in Rhodesia vervet monkeys are regular foragers in open grassland not always immediately adjacent to woodland; and they stand upright at regular intervals in order to see over the top of the grass. The danger from large predators in the savannah is not nearly as great as has been suggested. The most efficient and probably the most numerous predator in the African savannah is the lion, which is dangerous only when hunting; at other times the game shows little concern at the proximity of lions. Where man is concerned, lions would have been dangerous when, through injury or age, they had become inefficient hunters of fast game. But the leopard was likely to have been a more dangerous enemy in the forest than was the lion in the savannah, where it is probable that symbiotic relationships between lions and early hominid hunting groups were as important then as they are today with some hunting peoples. With Livingstone, therefore, I doubt whether the earliest tools were for defence.

The deterioration of the environment and the disrupting influences of the major earth movements at the end of the Tertiary, for which there is good geological evidence, must have made food-getting the most important of all the factors that led to erect walking and tool using among the pre-hominids of the dry savannah. Certainly the evidence of the earliest known stone tools suggests that they were artifacts used to make easier the acquiring and consumption of food, including hides which are a regular item of diet among certain northern Bushman groups and probably among many other hunting/collecting peoples besides. The Olduvai Bed I floors show that tools and the remains of meals are found together at the home base, and surely it is the establishment of this regular base to which food was carried back that would have permitted the young to be reared in comparative security as well as making easier the transmission of learned behaviour. If the need for weapons was one of the factors contributing to tool-using, these were surely weapons of offence primarily for hunting purposes, rather than of defence—the worked and natural stones or naturally sharp or club-like lengths of wood brought back to the living site.

The extremely simple stone tools on the living floors in the middle and lower parts of Bed I at Olduvai, as well as the nature of the living floors themselves, do not readily support the suggestion that the Australopithecines possessed open language. One would have expected to have found a much more elaborate material culture and a greater variation in the pattern of this culture had they been able to communicate on this level. One of the most significant characteristics of Lower and Middle Pleistocene culture is its monotonous sameness and the very slow and gradual rate of its development. However, such a revolutionary innovation as that of open language, when it came, was probably communicated from band to band with reasonable rapidity since fundamental inventions and improvements in technology were certainly quick in spreading—at least as quick, that is, as the title of Hockett and Asher's paper suggests! "Speciation" of culture in Africa did not take place until the beginning of the Upper Pleistocene.

I do not quite understand why the authors suggest that a large brain should be biologically too expensive. The extra long neck of the giraffe can hardly be said to have been an impediment to its survival! If language and culture selected for bigger brains, culture was, in the first instance, induced by environment, and it was biological adaptation that made culture both possible and necessary. As I see it, culture, language, brain size, and the evolution of the hand are so inter-related that it is impossible to say that one came before the other.

I would agree with Livingstone's comment that "we shall never discover enough facts to reveal to us the total way of life of our transitional ancestors." I would, however, emphasise that this is no reason why we should not attempt to make that record as accurate as possible. Hypothetical reconstructions such as this paper provides would be immeasurably more valuable if we had more facts. Our pre-hominid ancestors are preserved only as fossils, and the more fossil evidence that becomes available the more completely shall we be able to reconstruct their evolution, appearance, and behavior. At present the only region for which we have anything approaching a solid corpus of fact is East Africa, and much of this remains unpublished. The same is the case at the early hominid level. Although we have a lot of cultural material, we have only the Olduvai living floors on which to construct the evidence of behaviour. If theoretical reconstructions are to have any solid basis in fact, it is imperative that we have more properly organised field investigations and in other regions as well as in East Africa in order to provide more facts. Facts, as Livingstone says, must be interpreted in a theoretical framework, but that framework must have its basis in fact and not only in hypothesis and circumstantial evidence. Studies of artifacts alone are not enough, just as laboratory studies of primates can never be substitutes for investigation of behaviour in the natural habitat. What we need are more precisely excavated living floors, for, if we are ever going to obtain much factual evidence of the behaviour of the early hominids (and of the prehominids also, for that matter), this is going to come from a study of the assemblages and relationships of the artifacts, food remains, and other evidence at the living places as well as from the fossils themselves.

For me, this paper has been a most stimulating essay which, at the same time, serves to emphasise the vital need for more facts—which means more fieldwork throughout tropical and sub-tropical regions of the Old World and reasonably rapid publication of the results. The more numerous the facts, the less theoretical and speculative will be the framework.

By CARLETON S. COON
WEST GLOUCESTER, MASS., U.S.A. 4 XII 63

In my opinion this paper by Hockett and Ascher, the comments by La Barre, Simpson, and Livingstone, and the authors' gracious replies, represent a turning point in our thinking about the origins of language and culture, and I congratulate all hands, including the editor, for its appearance. My own reaction is that the authors' ideas are brilliant, creative, and essentially sound, as are some of the comments, while objections to the article involving terminology, the inclusion of the gibbons with the great apes and men, and the location of our most ancient ancestral home are equally valid and of no great consequence to the theories presented. I agree with the authors about the present evidence for slow versus fast game in the Australopithecine deposits and have nothing to add except that, in reference to footnote 29, Alakaluf, which I have heard, and Ona, which I have not, seem, to this non-linguist, to contain clicks.

By EARL W. COUNT
CLINTON, N.Y., U.S.A. 12 XII 63

At some stage in its pursuit of the details of human evolution, anthropology is obliged to attempt syntheses from the evidence and to develop configurative hypotheses. Hockett and Ascher seek the roots of human socio-culture in the biosocial matrix of the nonhuman primates (hereinafter, "alloprimates"), which is where these roots should be sought. If I must disagree with some of their propositions, it is to compliment them on their responsible boldness. I am sure, moreover, that we understand each other's frustration: they have attempted a book in the paragraphs of an article; and the comments are based on this writer's own research.

A. Some details may be disposed of preliminarily.

1) More than once the authors assert that the biggest and strongest males normally dominated in proto-hominoid society. Among vertebrates this frequently appears to be the case; nonetheless, the fact that aggressively decisive action on the part of physically lesser individuals often decides dominance, indicates a basic psychological factor. Furthermore even at the alloprimate level, two or more individuals may "gang up on" a bully. What we have learned about alloprimate sociality is restricted to but a few species or genera; we are not yet in position to assert so narrow a stereotypy for putative proto-hominoid social structuring.

2) The authors speak of man's "bigger and more convoluted brain, with a particularly sharp increase in the forebrain." Their meaning here must be guessed at. Undoubtedly, the first phrase refers to the cerebral hemisphere; but "forebrain" is a technical term for the anteriormost segment of the embryonic brain—long before there are any cerebral hemispheres. The authors presumably mean the frontal lobes of the cerebral hemi-

spheres; but this would make their statement erroneous. The notion that man's frontal lobes are disproportionately large (with supposed implications for thought processes) seems to come from the impressiveness of his forehead expanse. Actually, the frontal lobes of monkeys bear about the same proportion to total cerebral hemispheres as they do in man. The discrepancy here between man and monkey (and it is not large) rests with the parietal or parietotemporal region—noteworthily, a region very much concerned in the symbolopoeic process. It is likewise to be noted that the primates stand first among the mammalian orders in the brain-to-body-size relationship, man is preeminent among the primates, yet in exponential terms man's brain is but slightly greater than the ape's. (Two more binary fissions of the brain cells would advance the chimpanzee's brain to human size; but from zygote to definitive chimpanzee brain requires some hundreds of mitotic generations.)

B. The rest of this comment will discuss speech function ("phasia"), to which the authors so felicitously give prominence in the phylogenesis of man's biosocial morphology. Essentially, they derive phasia from alloprimate calls; they propound a kind of psycholinguistic theory by which a closed system is opened up; and they use an idiom related to the punch cards of computer machines; they state that the mechanism is the only known one which can start this transformation.

1) Their permutation of an AB (CD) + (EF) GH = ABGH undoubtedly is intended as an elucidative suggestion, not as a serious formula. Due allowance for this is made; furthermore, I am in no position to argue its linguistic applications with a proven linguist. But the phenomenon we are discussing is one of neuropsychology in biosocial context, a long-drawn-out process of past event. The question therefore is, has this formulation any "reverse-predictive" value?

It suggests to me the haplologies familiar to any linguist. And the authors suggest that the pre-language loosening of a closed system resulted from emotive conflict when a prehominid met an irreconcilable dual situation (their example is food-yet-danger). This strikes me as a far too narrow base for incipient pre-language; some of my reasons follow:

The problem is attacked at the wrong end. The origin of phasia must be sought first in the brain mechanisms that operate before vocalization is effected.

A great deal of pertinent information already exists on the evolution of nervous control from the simplest nervous circuit to the complexities of the mammalian central nervous systems. It is relevant here that differential refinement in neuromuscular complexes is a phylogenetic phenomenon at least as old as the mammalian class itself; and, as C. L. Prosser has said, in discussing stereotypy and plasticity, "Integration which provides for variability of response and ultimately for modifiability of behavior resides in small-fiber systems" (Prosser 1959:41). The evolution of phasia, I suggest, has continued this trend; and its account is to be sought for, with far greater promise, in neuropsychology.

2) The central fact about phasia is symbolopoesis (here I agree with the authors' footnote *in re* the operational ineptness of a distinction between "sign" and "symbol"); and this is a matter of brain regions other than those implicated in vocalization. But because we anthropologists have declined the earlier challenge of Broca to pursue the problem of phasia as a part of the evolution of brain mechanisms, we have continued to confine our considerations to vocalization—where the finished product rolls off the assembly-line. Very well then; let us consider this phase.

Calls represent distance-communications. Most communications among gregarious animals are proximate. Mammalian orders use their facial ("mimetic") muscles in proximate situations, and in primates these muscles are extraordinarily differentiated and refined. Their innervation is from the VII cranial nerve (the Facialis). Vocalic mechanism is innervated from another complex—parts of the V-VII-IX-X-XI-XII (oral-lingual-glottal). The cortical representations (in the inferior region of the pre-central gyrus) overlap considerably but they are not identical. Both mimesis and vocalization are equally represented in the two hemispheres; speech formulation is not. Peculiarly, only in man does electro-stimulation of precentral cortex elicit cries; presumably, the threshold of elicitation is lower in man than in apes. And only in human infants does there occur a period of non-phasic lalia—a (preadaptive) maturational process.

I am suggesting that phasia reflects, on its motor side, some *coalescence* of *two* communication-systems: vocalic and mimetic. They are already associated in other mammals—as indicated by the snarls, etc., of carnivores —to say nothing of other orders. (The authors themselves had to note that when baboons are interracting very intensively in close propinquity, they are silent.)

What we would like to know is not how a literal formula may be permuted to obtain an open system out of a closed one, but what organic processes have been occurring.

C. Commendably, the authors stress the fact that too frequently the interpretations of structural adaptation are but *post facto* rationalizations. Undeniably, our oral-nasal shape serves us happily for our speech. But this says nothing at all about the adequacy or inadequacy of the oral-nasal architecture of an alloprimate for a genuine speech performance—granted first the brain capable of organizing it, although on some rudimentary level. For all we know, all Autralopithecines may have been "talkers" after their fashion.

And yet, it seems to me that the authors fall into the current and widespread tendency to account for such positive and highly complex syntheses as phasia out of environmental factors (which remain unidentified) which somehow exert "selective pressures." I am bothered by circularity of this reasoning and the tautology of its expression, wherever encountered. To say that speech has high survival value since its exploiters have survived and put it to good use, really explains nothing at all; it is redundant—we know no more after it has been said than we did before; and (to me) it suggests no operational clues. Selective pressure, after all has been said in its favor, can act only upon something that exists; it cannot bring it into existence. A logical inversion here causes us to stumble into some pretty bare Lamarkianism—a most ironical impasse—as indeed the authors seem to have done with "hundreds of generations of chattering, first in a call system and then in pre-language, increases the innervation of the vocal tract and enriches the cortical representation of that region."

The neurological sciences have been developing profound insights into the architecture of phasia; they permit one to say that man speaks because his brain has elaborated cybernetic systems beyond what his ape cousins have done. But after a century of Darwin we are still as much in the dark as we have ever been as to what actually has taken place.

By ROBERT CRESSWELL
PARIS, FRANCE. 13 XII 63

This extremely interesting paper seems to me to combine the interdisciplinary summing up of a given question, which is the hallmark of CA, with the tightly reasoned and well documented theorizing anthropology needs. The reaction to the spate of sweeping generalizations and broad theories of the latter half of the 19th century has lasted long enough, and the time is indeed ripe to build up a conceptual framework into which we can fit the growing volume of facts and thus prepare the ground-work for future investigations. The remarks which follow therefore are not to be taken as detracting from the essential value of this article.

1) I would suggest that there is an underlying confusion in what is meant by comparative method, for, epistemologically speaking, there are not one but several comparative methods. Synchronic comparison of physical structure can, by successive generalizations, situate an animal group, for instance, in a proper taxonomic relation to other animal groups. Synchronic comparison of lifeways, by abstracting common denominators, might allow us to induce trends and tendencies in human behavior, if not "social laws." However, the diachronic extension of conclusions arrived at by this method, this averaging out of traits which Livingstone questions, only results in the reduction of the number of traits of the common ancestor at best, and in circular reasoning at worst. The comparative method of linguistics is something quite different. Reconstructing the proto-Germanic word for fish (Hockett 1958:487), for instance, does not impoverish the proto-Germanic vocabulary, for there is a one-to-one relationship in spite of the derivation of one word from 5. Finally, use of the comparative method risks neglecting convergent or parallel evolution. After all, why should the tool-using or call behavior of the chimpanzees as reported by Goodall (1963) not be in part the result of an independent evolution of several million years duration?

2) There are several reasons for the dichotomy of "biological" and "cultural" factors as used by anthropologists, one of the most potent being that

structural analysis of a human society would only be confused if this dichotomy were not taken into account. What should be extirpated, as the authors suggest, is the idea of contrast or opposition between the two members of the pairing, for they are interlocked in reality in a system of action and reaction. Just as "social organization" and "technology" cannot be separated in reality but are useful methodological concepts, so "nature" and "culture" brought these systems together. Lévi-Strauss (1949) effectively argues this point and adds that culture is neither juxtaposed to nor superposed on nature, but effects a synthesis with it.

The foregoing remarks fall in the category of destructive criticism, and are therefore negative as far as the discussion of this paper is concerned, even though I do feel that the central argument of this article is seriously damaged by criticism of the comparative method adduced as the second type of evidence. I should like to conclude this comment with something more positive.

3) I think more stress should be placed on technology. First of all, it has been shown that the transformation of the human foot preceded the liberation from purely locomotor functions of the anterior limb, and that this in turn made possible the development of the brain. (The same author has also shown that it is the freeing of the hand and its subsequent use for digging, capturing, tearing, etc., with the resulting reduction in the size of the canines and displacement of the facial muscles, concomitant with the reduction of the neck muscles that also resulted from the vertical posture, which are primarily responsible for the recession of the lower part of the face [Leroi-Gourhan 1955]. A really prognathous *Zinjanthropus* would be outrageous from a purely mechanical point of view.) The creation of a technological field of operations was the precursor of intelligence, as it were, making possible the use and carrying of objects and, ultimately, tools. Furthermore, since tiny ameliorations of tools accumulating over a period of several hundred thousand years result in forms which are beyond the individual intellectual capacities of the user and/or maker to invent (Leroi-Gourhan 1963), technology is as much a contributor as language to that cultural environment which, acting on and being affected by the new biological and ecological environments, was so powerful a factor in "humanization." Unless, of course, the authors believe that the human revolution was completed not only long before the first appearance of hominid fossils elsewhere than in East Africa, but also before the first appearance of tools in this area, which position might give rise to questions about the use of the word "human." In this connection, the authors do not make very explicit why they postulate that development of openness paved the way for tool manufacture.

4) Finally, I would like to suggest that rising up to look out over the savanna grasses had its origin in the possession by the proto-hominoid of that trait so characteristic and so widespread as to seem profoundly rooted in our instincts—simple curiosity.

By A. RICHARD DIEBOLD, JR.
CAMBRIDGE, MASS., U.S.A. 16 XII 63

I confess that my reactions to an earlier *viva voce* presentation of this study were unfavorable; I would like to state the reasons for those reactions and indicate how Hockett and Ascher's final printed version has allayed some of my initial reservations but reinforced others. Since there will be no space for conclusions or summary, I would like to assert right away my conviction that the study is a worthwhile contribution; in this respect it contrasts noticeably with an unsophisticated predecessor (Bryan 1963). The negative comments below refer to some very real flaws in Hockett and Ascher's paper, but they are intended to be constructively critical, and the knowledgeable reader can surely offer an equal number of positive ones: not the least would include citing the very able typological discussion of call systems and the distinctions between them and language (contained in the sections "Opening of the call system" and "The inception of duality"). More important is the paper's representational value for an important current trend in the behavioral sciences, one which is becoming increasingly receptive to consideration of the constitutional bases of human behavior and which is reflected in anthropology by its practitioners' dissuasion from an anti-reductionist view of the "superorganic" (exemplary studies include Count 1958, and the papers in Spuhler 1959 and Washburn 1961). It is with regard to its trend-setting role that I have reservations about the paper.

The discussion of evolutionary theory (and the varieties of historical inference possible in using it to interpret the paleontological record) is exceptional. But the "method" of comparison used to reconstruct the ancestral ethogram of the proto-hominoids, *relative to certain methods and new knowledge which were available to the authors,* is frighteningly capricious.

First of all, Hockett and Ascher do not succinctly state the aims of "the" comparative method they discuss and so miss the more fundamental analogy between comparative procedures in psycho-biology and in historical linguistics, namely the discovery of distinctive homologies: "the term 'comparative' in technical linguistic use has referred, not to comparison at large, comparison for comparison's sake (i.e. typological comparison), but to a process whereby original features can be separated from recent ones and where the aim of classification is subordinated to the aim of reconstruction" (Hoenigswald 1963:2; see also Greenberg 1959 for further elaboration). It is in this respect that the linguistic comparative method is analogous to the methods which are used by ethologists like Lorenz, Tinbergen, and others, to reconstruct "proto-behaviors". (The reader is here advised to note carefully in the bibliography the titles of the important references which follow, since they well document the ethologist's concern with comparative method: Hinde and Tinbergen 1958; Lorenz 1960; Baerends 1958.)

The ethological methods I refer to come chiefly from the intensive work being carried out by zoologists and psychologists, who, to be sure, have concentrated on the stereotyped behaviors (such as "taxes," "reflexes," "instincts") of lower animals (for a competent recent review of methods and problems, see Hess 1962). Constructing a phylogeny of innate behavioral attributes (such as "fixed action patterns"), established by rigorous ethological comparative procedures, is a plausible undertaking for the hominoids, especially now that intensified study of primate behavior is filling in some of the empirical gaps which earlier frustrated comparison. Just such a venture is currently engaging the attention of many investigators interested in primatology, such as R. J. Andrew and A. Bishop of Yale University (see, e.g., the papers in Buettner-Janusch 1962, and Andrew 1963). Also possible is the more ambitious task of studying the phylogeny of capacities for complex acquired behavior as manifest particularly in symbolically mediated insight learning; especially relevant here is the work of H. F. Harlow and others (e.g. Harlow 1962; Harlow and Zimmermann 1959). The anthropologist-reader properly apprised of these developments can only be astonished by their cavalier treatment in Hockett and Ascher's study; the psychologist might reasonably seize upon this flaw of omission as justification for dismissing the import of other defensible statements, such as those interpreting the paleontological record, or the exposition of the communications design of hominoid calls.

Hockett pointed out in an earlier study (Hockett 1960) that language evolution in the sense here considered has been a taboo topic since the turn of the century, when rampant speculation caused its obloquy. The speculation was in part a product of large gaps in knowledge. What has reinstated the topic as legitimate is *not* further discoveries in the paleontological and archeological records, although these reinforce our interest. Legitimacy has been regained partly by rethinking about communication theory (to which Hockett has been an outstanding contributor); partly the question has been reopened by advances in ethology (and in primatology in particular) as discussed above. But more important has been the increasing recourse to neurophysiology taken by psychologists, in which a departure from behaviorist concentration on simple, easily observed stimulus-input and response-output sequences is evident in some investigators' interest in the neurophysiological basis for speech. The possibilities which Chomsky (1959) and Lenneberg (1960*a*, 1960*b*), among others, envision for a neurophysiological approach to language were anticipated or subsequently realized by, among others, D. O. Hebb and W. Penfield. Both Hebb (e.g., Hebb 1949) and Penfield (e.g., Penfield and Roberts 1959) have explored the causal bases of behavioral integration (particularly as manifest in complex human language skills and cognitive processes), by investigating its relationship to the neurology of the central nervous system. Much is now known about the specific afferent paths leading from the receptors to the cortex, and similarly about the efferents leading to the motor areas used in speech. Although much is now also known about the localization of specific functions in the cerebral cortex, it is true that there remain areas of relative ignorance, e.g., the problems of storage and linkage between the sensory projection and motor areas. Nevertheless, comparative neurophysiology tells us that the great development of the cerebral cortex in man, in its association areas and in the thalamic nuclei, is unique among the primates, an extreme end-point in a long evolutionary history of encephalization. While Hockett and Ascher might object to my substituting a cerebral Rubicon for the older discredited skeletal diagnostics, it seems that it is just such a qualitative difference in the course of human evolution, to judge from the title of their study, that one would expect them to seek.

By THEODOSIUS DOBZHANSKY
NEW YORK CITY. 5 XII 63

Together with Simpson, I question one, as it seems to me, unessential assumption in Hockett and Ascher's discerning and enlightening analysis. I doubt the generality of what they call "Romer's rule," and I wonder if it is in fact a rule at all. It is almost a tautology that the survival value of a favorable evolutionary innovation is conservative in that it renders possible the survival, or even an expansion, of the group in which it has occurred. Whether or not it also renders possible the maintenance of the "traditional" way of life depends on circumstances. It may do so if a living species or population responds to an environmental change by a genetic innovation (or simply a genetic alteration) which compensates for the changed magnitude or sign of an environmental pressure. Thus, an increasingly colder, or warmer, climate may require metabolic changes, but may let the organism continue in its ecological niche otherwise undisturbed. Suppose, however, that a genetic change makes an animal able to exploit a new source of food, at first in addition to and eventually instead of the food on which it had formerly subsisted. Even the initial consequences of this change may well permit or force the animal to alter its way of life. It may now invade territories where it could not live before, or it may spend more time on the ground than in the trees (or vice versa), or it may adopt a more nocturnal or a more diurnal habit. The adaptations of weeds and of commensals and pests associated with man and his activities, to say nothing of the domesticated forms, furnish what seem to me abundant examples of changes in the ways of life. It is sometimes even difficult to figure out how the organism could have existed at all before it became associated with man. I concede, however, that it is often impossible to be sure which features of the changed ways of life were the immediate and which the secondary consequences of the genetic changes that have taken place to make possible the association with and the dependence on man.

By R. DALE GIVENS
RICHMOND, KY., U.S.A. 12 XII 63

The Hockett and Ascher paper, although at times somewhat unclear, is a major contribution in focusing attention on the role of language in the development of the hominoids and proto-hominoids. Not only is the article highly stimulating, but it is also suggestive of further speculation and research. The comments by La Barre, Livingstone, and Simpson are well taken and worthy of more detailed attention than was given to them in the reply by Hockett and Ascher.

In general, I am in agreement with the comments of the above trio, especially Livingstone, and so have little to add. I would like to call attention to the following, however:

1) It seems highly unusual to classify *Proconsul* as a dryopithecine even though he was undoubtedly closely related to this group.

2) I cannot agree with the statement, "but *Proconsul* was clearly an *early* hominoid, and at the moment he is the best fossil evidence available for the date and provenience we seek." I do not see why it is necessary to locate this "proto-hominoid" in Africa, even if the earliest fossil hominids and the earliest tool complexes are located there. Further, even as slight as the evidence is at present, I would consider *Ramapithecus* a much better candidate than *Proconsul,* whose significance is, if anything, highly overrated.

3) There would seem to be no necessity for assuming large interlocking canines as a characteristic of the "proto-hominoid," considering the great variation found in this feature among the dryopithecines.

By GORDEN W. HEWES
BOULDER, COLO., U.S.A. 9 XII 63

This excellent synthesis of current conceptions of hominization bristles with implications for more research, including stepped-up wild primate watching and experiments in natural open environments where subsistence variables can be radically manipulated. Inexpensive radio devices developed for remote-control training of hunting dogs could be used to keep experimental bands of chimpanzees within an observer's range, or to modify the behavior of particular individuals.

Hockett and Ascher's statement that "hominids . . . with their mouths rendered thus relatively idle except when they were eating," simply "chattered," seems a little simplistic. It also seems unnecessary to see something like "foresight" in the carrying of objects, as if this involved a conscious plan for future action; unwillingness to let go of an object of high positive valence need not involve a high degree of purposeful behavior. I agree with the authors that predator avoidance has played an important rôle in the evolution of primate behavior, including the troop-guarding and lookout function of the adult males. Even gorillas are bothered to some extent by leopards (Schaller 1963:302–04), and smaller primates cannot afford to relax their vigilance. For an early savannah-dwelling proto-hominid, canid predators of the Cape Hunting Dog (*Lycaon pictus*) variety may have been quite serious enemies.

Hockett and Ascher discuss carrying at some length, impelling me to add notes which supplement my own treatment of this topic (Hewes 1961). In a film made at the Cayo Santiago primate colony, rhesus monkeys can be seen running bipedally with armloads of monkey chow (biscuits) to places where they could eat unmolested by their fellows. Schaller (1963:82–83) noted a little bipedal locomotion in the mountain gorilla, observing that the dense undergrowth often forced quadrupedal locomotion on himself. Kortlandt (1962:133) photographed a chimpanzee walking bipedally, carrying several pawpaws, and comments (p. 134) that "apparently they walked bipedally in order to have their hands free—for example, to carry or eat fruit . . ." Under natural conditions, when the chimpanzees were not running to avoid danger, bipedal walking accounted for from 10 to 15% of observed locomotion (in terms of distances covered). Goodall (1963:293) photographed a chimpanzee walking bipedally from her tent, his hands loaded with bananas, and she adds that chimpanzees were observed "loading their arms with choice wild fruits, then walking erect for several yards to a spot of shade before sitting down to eat." Although she saw chimpanzees carry a tool—a twig for extracting termites from termite-hills—as far as half a mile, bipedal walking was not involved (p. 308). The suggestion by Hockett and Ascher that clothing may have orginated out of the use of carrying aids such as string girdles, straps, or hides used as carrying sacks, is original and provocative, as is La Barre's idea that human relative hairlessness may be connected with the need to dissipate body heat very rapidly after bursts of hunting effort. My own observation of captive macaques suggests a strong tendency to avoid warm sunlight, even in cold weather. Schaller's gorillas were seen sun-bathing (1963:294–95), but they were living, after all, in a cool, damp, high mountain forest. The selective pressure of heat and light on a proto-hominid scavenging or hunting in open savannah country must have been considerable.

Hockett and Ascher might have devoted some attention to grooming, not only because of its training rôle for fine manual operations utilizable in tool-manipulation, but also for its importance in social bonding. Sade's report of persistent high-frequency grooming between mothers and offspring, and between siblings into adult life, among rhesus monkeys, suggests the rudiments of the human recognition of parent, child, and sibling relationships throughout life (Sade 1963; cf. Count 1958:1075).

By ILSE LEHISTE
COLUMBUS, OHIO, U.S.A. 11 XII 63

The article is fascinating in many respects. The distinction between a call system and a language is well made, and the arguments connected with the "opening of the call system" certainly sound more plausible than many of the numerous earlier theories. Of course, starting from a call system as a given fact simply pushes the question about the ultimate origins of speech and language farther back into pre-history. As far as I could determine, the authors seem to take *phonation* for granted. I am not acquainted with the phonetics of gibbon calls, but they are profoundly important and, where opportunities for observation of diverse solutions are present, may make important contributions to tradition.

2) To the speculations on the importance of face-to-face coitus should be added the suggestions of Ford and Beach (1951) that there is an increase in the individualization of sex relationships due to the greater involvement of face, eyes, and mouth.

3) To the discussions of the Oedipus complex, I should like to add the importance of the development of a longer period of non-reproductivity —apes do not phonate the way humans do. It would be interesting to hear an opinion on the origin of phonation within the framework of the theory advanced by the authors.

At the beginning of the section entitled "The inception of duality," the authors discuss the distance between the glottis and the velum, stating that a physiological change increasing that distance increases the ability of the individual to perform articulatory motions of the kind involved in human language. I wonder whether there is really any direct connection between the distance of the velum from the glottis, and the ability of the individual to perform articulatory motions. After all, articulatory motions are performed primarily by the tongue and the lips. The velum participates in the opening and closing of the nasal tract, but is not an active articulator in a way comparable to the lips and the tongue. The glottis takes no part in the articulation of other sounds except the glottal stops, and as far as those are concerned, it makes no difference where the glottis is located. In what sense does then the increased distance between the velum and the glottis contribute toward the development of language? And while we are in the realm of articulatory hypotheses, it would be interesting indeed if the authors could also propose a theory for the purpose and function of the epiglottis.

By MARGARET MEAD
NEW YORK CITY. 19 XII 63

My comments will be made on the basis of intensive analysis of the behavior of living primitive peoples and theoretical exploration of possible evolutionary explanations of such phenomena as the Oedipus complex, primary process thinking, and the processes of character formation.

1) I believe that the Hockett-Ascher formulation should make more allowance for the effects of diffusion, both through imitation of the behavior of other bands and the incorporation of individual members of other bands, with different dialects and situationally or traditionally different behavior. They allow for gene flow between bands, but not for the consequences in teaching and learning arising from adoption, intermarriage, conquest, slavery, etc. (Mead 1964). Recent evidence on the development of situationally diversified behavior, such as the material on Japanese monkeys (Imanishi 1960; Itani 1958), and the behavior of rat colonies of identical stock when placed under a food ceiling (Strecker and Emlen 1953; Southwick 1955), or contrastingly stratified in age-sex membership (Calhoun 1962), suggests that situational innovations, even in mammals such as rats, may be profoundly influential until menarche and post menopausally in the female, with correlative changes in the male, with the potentialities thus provided for a longer period of learning and consequently a greater exploitation of brain capacity (Mead 1961; 1963c). In this connection the lowering of the age of puberty in Western populations, currently attributed to changes in conditions of nurture (Tanner 1955) may provide a new evolutionary hazard at a period in history when the complexity of modern knowledge calls rather for lengthening the period of learning before involvement in sexual activity and parenthood. For testing the relationship between the shortening of the reproductive period and learning, we need a more vigorous exploration of fossils, living primates, and comparative human materials on the occurrence and structure of the hymen, the age of menarche, the evolutionary history of the menopause, and male involutionary processes (Mead 1949; 1963a).

It may also be hypothesized that behavioral tendencies, now identified as the Oedipus complex, can be best attributed to a period of conflict between older and younger males, which coincided with the young males' attainment of sexual maturity and a diminution in the older males' strength, during a period of evolution when the young male and the older male were considerably more on a par in physical strength. The occurrence of Oedipal conflicts centering upon a single pair of parents is a function of social organization (Malinowski 1927; Mead 1963b).

In addition to the discussion of the origin of language and other forms of communication (Eiseley 1955), we have to account for those types of human thinking which are involved in dreams, ritual and artistic behavior, and symptom formation which involve mechanisms of the Freudian *primary process,* the Lowenfeld *proto system* (Mead 1952), and *paleologic* (Arieti 1956) which are as universal as the processes of language formation and change to which Hockett and Ascher refer. The need to maintain various sorts of balance between these different kinds of thinking and the resulting productivity in human imagination and creativity may explain the survival of the Oedipal conflict. The processes of repression and defense, in which the developing child becomes involved in the culturally imposed resolutions of Oedipal feelings, are also implicated importantly in the type of character formation necessary to human group cooperation and individual creativity (Mead and Schwartz 1960; T. H. and J. S. Huxley 1947; Waddington 1961). Parallel with the development of these mechanisms we need to seek for origins of the development of the human cosmic sense, of universal attempts to systematize experience, which may be specifically related to the evolution of the cortex (Hoagland 1963; n.d.).

By ASHLEY MONTAGU

PRINCETON, N.J., U.S.A. 9 XII 63

Hockett and Ascher's fine and stimulating paper is of especial interest to me because I have in press a volume of the same title (1964). Since I have covered much of the same ground as the authors I am delighted to find that we are so much in agreement. My comments, therefore, are restricted to a few points.

1) Gibbons and siamangs should not be ligatured with the great apes as sharing a common ancestry with man. All the evidence is against this.

2) The terms "natural" and "artificial" refer to very real differences. I think it was Oscar Wilde, that distinguished anthropologist, who first pointed out that the artificial is the highest form of the natural; and that is perhaps quite so, but the difference still remains: The natural is in the realm of the biological, the artificial is, surely, in the realm of culture?

3) It is very expressive to speak of being "pushed out," but it wasn't the fact. Surely it would be better to say that instead of abandoning the trees, the trees abandoned man?

4) Do the authors doubt "extinction through successive evolution"? I hope not.

5) Why would relations with adjacent bands have been hostile?

6) Any male past puberty cannot, as the authors state, nor can any female between menarche and menopause, produce a new human being in a matter of seconds. In the first place, it usually takes a spermatozoon a little longer than that to find the ovum, and in the second place, neither males at puberty nor females at menarche are capable of conception at all, because of the immaturity of the pubertal sperm in the one case and the anovulatory cycles of the female in the other (See Montagu 1957). What the authors should have written for the word "menarche" is "nubility," the period when the female becomes capable of successful reproduction.

7) The discovery of Australopithecine "lissoirs" at 3 different sites strongly suggests that the Australopithecines may have prepared skins for clothing, and incidentally, may also have used them as mats, covers, and for other purposes, such as the making of thongs, as pointed out by Dart.

8) As for hairlessness in man being produced by the wearing of clothes, may I point out that our charming distant relative, the rhinocerus, is hairless, and to my knowledge, at least, has never been accused of wearing

clothes. But like man, he does have a lot of sweat glands. I rather suspect that man's hairlessness came about as a result of his hunting way of life. A mechanism for the avoidance of overheating would then have been very necessary. Loss of hair with increased sweating capacity would have been the answer, and, I guess, it was. Incidentally, forest-dwelling animals have either no sweat glands at all or relatively few—another evidence of man's evolution upon the savanna.

9) Finally, the less said about the so-called Oedipus complex the better.

By HANS G. MUKAROVSY
VIENNA, AUSTRIA. 12 XII 63

The basic principles which have guided the authors of this paper must first be examined. They assert that their procedure is "very much like the comparative method in historical linguistics," and, finally, that they have provided us with "a plausible evolutionary sequence."

In fact, using the comparative method presupposes historical evidence or some equivalent of it, which must permit the application of its results in other independent test cases. It is up to biologists to see how far these conditions have been fulfilled. But, in contrast, there is also something which the comparative method does not permit: comparing the evidence gained from sources classed as non-related, in order to fit it into some sort of evolutionary sequence, be it plausible or not. This kind of procedure is considered unscientific in linguistics, and it also turned out to be misleading in early comparative studies in ethnology.

Resemblances of languages held to be non-related are thus considered to be either borrowings, or cases of chance convergence; but as soon as it is proved that 2 language stocks—e.g., Indo-European and Hamito-Semitic —are ultimately related on a higher level, all evidence pertaining to a single language belonging to either family will become relevant for all other languages of both stocks, unless this particular case is excluded by additional criteria. If no such criterion can be found, there are no means to determine how far back, within the greater unity, the emergence of this particular linguistic phenomenon is to be sought, once the exclusive character of the relationship established on a lower level is lost.

Now comparative biology operates on the basic assumption of an overall relationship, establishing sub-groups and their filiation by observing evolutionary changes, which may have affected the sound-producing and wave-receiving organs, as well as the brain-capacities, of living beings. But what does that mean with regard to the respective particular communication system in use? There is no necessary implication!

Strictly applying the comparative method, on the evidence offered, amounts roughly to this: human language is singular and can therefore be compared to nothing. Acoustic communication systems termed "prelanguages" exist among primates, other mammals, and birds, to cite but the most obvious of such systems. Therefore, as birds are phylogenetically considered to be the oldest species, we may consider that such pre-language originated with them, until further evidence to the contrary appears. But to learn this, I need not read CURRENT ANTHROPOLOGY; most of the people of the world know that birds talk.

From the notion of an overall relationship, we may further infer that all beings probably have communication systems of their own, although most of them have so far been hidden from our sight. But, returning to the communication systems of the birds, there is no evidence that it has improved since its origination; from what I have learned about gibbons from this paper, I am rather inclined to think the contrary—that there might once have existed more capable, "better" birds in earlier days than exist now. Nor, in a variety of particular cases, would decay in communication possibilities have necessarily resulted in the extinction of a particular species.

The above inferences were all simply transposed from material derived by the comparative method in linguistics, which is—as the authors admit —far from being perfect. But do they expect to attain valid results by the imperfect application of an imperfect method?

As to the transition from pre-language to language, we are told still another story, quite different from the rest. The emergence of language out of the hu-huh! ow! type of call system is a familiar idea among the speculations on the origin of language, although it smells of 19th century "emotionalism." Play-chatter, as La Barre suggests in his comment, is at least as good a case to start from.

What the authors would have needed is probably a general theory of communication systems. And even good writing cannot make up for methodological insufficiency.

By JOHN PFEIFFER
NEW HOPE, PENNA., U.S.A. 6 XII 63

The upgrading of the Australopithecines proceeds apace. As recently as 5 or 6 years ago the notion that they might possibly have been tool-makers and not merely tool-users was considered speculative, a bit on the daring side. Also, there was still a certain reluctance to concede that they had archieved the full benefits of bipedalism, one suggestion being that they could run but could not yet walk efficiently. Largely because of evidence obtained by the Leakeys at Olduvai, these and other reservations do not apply as strongly as they once did.

Now the next step has been taken, and it is a most significant step. There cannot be universal agreement on how far language had evolved among the Australopithecines, or on the nature of the evolutionary stages. Indeed, the concept of blending as a stage in the "opening of the call system" is considered unnecessary by Andrew (1963). But, as Hockett and Ascher point out, the basic point is that if the Australopithecines had achieved language, as well as upright posture and bipedal gait and tool-making, we can hardly think of them as "ape-man" or "near-men." If they are therefore men, they presumably belong to the genus *Homo*.

In any case, the latest step in the upgrading process has the effect of re-emphasizing the importance of continued and more intensive research on nonhuman primates for fresh insights into human evolution. It certainly heightens the already mounting interest in the possibility of finding fossil remains of the Australopithecines' immediate predecessors. (The lack of such remains represents what is perhaps one of the most serious gaps in our knowledge.) On the observational and experimental side, it calls for increasingly detailed studies of vocalization and other forms of communication among monkeys and apes.

This paper also suggests that certain psychiatric observations may have special meaning as far as a deeper understanding of the origins of human behavior is concerned. In general the coming of language provides an opportunity to develop a richer variety of mental illnesses; the authors draw attention to another potential source of conflict in the shift from the dorsal to the frontal approach in copulation, and its possible relationship to the ultimate appearance of the Oedipus complex. Furthermore, it may be that we exhibit a kind of "fossil" behavior under stress, behavior which is perhaps related to stereotypes and displays evolved among our nonhuman ancestors. In this connection disorders such as bruxism or tooth-gnashing, a neurotic condition especially intractable to psychoanalysis, may be of some relevence.

I think Hockett and Ascher deserve a vote of thanks for a paper which throws new light on one of Wittgenstein's subtlest and most penetrating remarks: "To imagine a language means to imagine a form of life" (1953:8).

By BERNARD POTTIER
STRASBOURG, BAS-RHIN, FRANCE. 10 XII 63

This is a well-reasoned article on the problem of the origin of language, and the authors' development of the theory concerning the successive stages of linguistic evolution satisfies the more exacting logical mind. But the existence of duality of patterning, characteristic of all human languages, is not a proof of a single birth "which has taken place once," for often in two or more different places various parallel creations may be observed independently. This problem is one that linguistics alone cannot properly solve.

By ADOLPH H. SCHULTZ
ZÜRICH, SWITZERLAND. 12 XII 63

This attempt to give a narrative account of the earliest and most decisive steps in human evolution—quite unnecessarily called revolution—will be most stimulating to the many anthropologists who have also naturally, often speculated about this fascinating problem, but have never dared to publish their idle thoughts. Since this inhibition has recently gone out of fashion, I gladly contribute some brief comments on the parts of this very readable story which are closest to my own interests.

In the enumeration of proto-hominoid characteristics, some unconvincing assertions have been included. For instance, that the size of gibbons "has decreased as an adaptation to brachiation" is contrary to palaeontological evidence and ignores the fact that the large orangs are also very capable brachiators. That the proto-hominoids had "large interlocking canines and could chew only up and down" is far from proved, and even with long canines the motions of the mandible are not limited to one plane with food between the grinding (and not merely crushing) molars. The old notion that "on the ground they could stand in a *semi*-upright posture" is literally untenable, since they would have promptly fallen on their faces; even infants do stand *fully* erect, though only for short periods. The authors assume very reasonably that the proto-hominoids had probably developed little sexual dimorphism, but the commentator La Barre believes that with sex-limited hunting among hominids, selection must have favored large males and may have produced other secondary sex differences, adding that "fruit-picking needs no special sexual dimorphism." On the other hand, the best recent hunters (of even large game) are the small Bambutis and Bushmen with very moderate sex differences, while the greatest of all sex differences exist in the fruit-picking orangs and gorillas, though there are no such noteworthy differences in the small gibbons.

That the proto-hominoid population practiced only dorsal copulation seems inconceivable in view of the fact that *all* recent man-like apes have been observed to behave in this respect with remarkable versatility, including "the invention of the frontal approach" (see Schaller 1963 for gorilla, and Schultz 1954, quoting additional relevant literature, for the other hominoids). This frontal approach (more appropriately termed "ventral position"), therefore, can hardly have been due to the erect posture and its accompanying "awkward expansion of the gluteus maximus," but is merely an expression of the extraordinary intraspecific variability of all apes in regard not only to their morphology, but also to their behavior. The authors' and La Barre's far-reaching comments on the profound consequences of the supposedly new "coital geometry" of hominids are hypotheses resting solely upon highly improbable speculation.

In the very plausible discussion of the important role of manual carrying for promoting bipedal walking, it might have been emphasized also that the weak and helpless infants of all hominoids, in contrast to the far more mature newborns of monkeys, can only cling to the hair of their mothers with very inadequate strength and security, and hence require the support of a maternal hand for many weeks until they are able to ride on the hairier back of the mother.

In speaking of the increasing complexity of a pre-language during early hominid evolution, the authors have fortunately mentioned the vital importance of cortical representation and have not merely dwelled on the commonly overrated minor topographic changes in the speech apparatus.

In the article itself, Hockett and Ascher have wisely followed the well-founded theory of a common origin for *all* hominoids, with an early divergence of the hominid branch. In their reply to the first comments, they had to listen to—but fortunately they did not succumb to—the siren songs, popular among modern specialists who itch to revamp primate systematics exclusively according to their latest biochemical or cytogenetic or even odontological findings, with utter disregard of the enormous mass of comparative anatomical and embryological evidence which has accumulated during a century. In Livingstone's version of this new trend, he states that "the consensus is now beginning to be that the gibbons have really little in common with the great apes and man," and he recommends rashly to reconstruct the proto-hominoids from the hominoids and the great apes of Africa alone. The writer feels confident that such a "beginning consensus" will not be the final one for reasons far too numerous to be mentioned here, but some of which he has recently published elsewhere (Schultz 1963*a* and *b*).

By HENRY LEE SMITH, JR.
BUFFALO, N.Y., U.S.A. 23 XII 63

Until only very recently linguists have been convinced that it is fruitless to speculate about the origin of language, and only one linguist in recent times, Otto Jespersen, saw any progress or advance toward greater efficiency in linguistic structures as they changed through time, and this only in the case of the Indo-European family. Biological evolution and the "evolution" of language have been generally and quite properly and necessarily separated. By the same token, cultural evolution and biological evolution, as we see them from our vantage point in time, differ not just in degree but in kind. Suffice it to say, as Hockett and Ascher do, that man's possession of true language has amounted to a revolution which makes man far more than "just the highest animal," since he is, by virtue of language, the possessor of a unique adaptive mechanism—culture.

In the light of the above, obviously I am taking exception to the statement in footnote 5. I do not believe that "anthropologists still fall constantly into the error of contrasting the 'cultural' and the 'biological . . . ,'" though I heartily agree that, "in the discussion of man's place in nature there is no place [and no *necessity*] for mentalism or vitalism." Of course, man is "subject to all the laws of physics and biology," and, of course, human culture is a series of structured systems set up to answer the universal problems of human existence—biological, psychological, *and*, if you will, spiritual. Man does not live, nor has he ever lived, by "bread alone," and any seeming simple reductionism cannot begin to answer the really pertinent questions about man as a unique creation, from *every* point of view.

The remarks above are in no way intended to denigrate the real importance of this brilliant and provocative article. To my knowledge it represents the first careful, systematic, and *informed* attempt to reapproach one of the most important questions anthropology has to concern itself with. The excellent applications of the authors' interpretation of "Romer's Rule" is a contribution of the highest order, and, as a linguist, I can only say that Hockett's ingenious speculations as to how true language *could* have emerged from a closed primate system of calls is fascinating and almost entirely convincing. Like Trager and some other linguists, I believe that true language is characterized by *triality* of patterning rather than the more simple and traditional *duality,* but this in no way vitiates Hockett's admirable account, assuming that it was from the call system that true language developed. (See the last few sentences of La Barre's comments.)

Again, as a linguist, I am in full accord with the inference that the emergence of true language needed to happen only once, however "sudden" or not so sudden the steps in the development may have been. The statement, "In at least one case, there was a brilliantly successful 'mutation': pre-morphemes began to be listened to and identified not in terms of their acoustic gestalts but in terms of smaller features of sound that occurred in them in varying arrangements," seems to *imply* (though not state definitely) that what has been called the "invention" of language occurred only once or *needed* to have occurred only once. This inference seems to be reiterated and emphasized later when we read:

"The crucial developments must have taken place once and then spread. The innovations could have been recent or ancient, except for an additional fact: in every language the phonological raw materials are used with remarkable efficiency (see footnote 27). This speaks of great antiquity, since we cannot imagine that such efficiency was an instant result of the appearance of the first trace of duality."

Finally, the authors are to be commended particularly for their statements as to how the possession of language and culture contributed to the further evolution of the size and complexity of the brain and of the development of "the essentially perpendicular human physiognomy." "For our ancestors of a million years ago the survival value of bigger brains is obvious only if they had *already* achieved the essence of language and culture." I am more than a little concerned with just what the authors mean by *essence* here, since I think they are saying throughout that language is *true* language or it is *not* true language, and are *implying* (at least) that without true culture is an impossibility.

Be that as it may, I find admirable their remarks bearing on the effect that the "habit of talking, in a true language that uses the kinds of articulatory motions that are now universal" had on "the genetically monitored evolutionary changes in what we now call the 'organs of speech.'" To me this argument is the exact opposite of circularity, granted their assumption that true language has been in man's possession for the necessarily long period of a million years. I find particularly attractive the suggestion that "organs of speech" now emerges, as no mere "metaphor but a biologically correct description."

In conclusion, I think this extremely valuable paper has gone a long way to bring the expertise, interests, and experiences of the human biologist, the paleoanthropologist, and the cultural anthropologist together so as to formulate a whole series of truly relevant questions in the very perplexing areas of human evolution in *every* sense of the word. The authors have shown us *positively* that we need no longer—or can no longer—duck these questions and that it ill behooves the specialist in one or the other of many areas of anthropology to propound solutions to problems that can only be tackled by pooling the knowledge and findings of many areas of inquiry.

By JAMES L. SWAUGER
PITTSBURG, PENNA., U.S.A. 11 XII 63

The comments of La Barre, Livingstone, and Simpson, particularly those of La Barre and Simpson, took the wind out of my sails, except for a minor point or two.

Exciting, provocative, the paper is without internal discrepancies. Other possibilities and probabilities can be marshaled to explain facts presented, but those of Hockett and Ascher are intelligent conjecture within an acceptable framework.

I am not fond of the wording of such a statement as "hundreds of generations of chattering . . . increases the innervation of the vocal tract . . . ," although I understand the meaning. It is more precise to state that superior vocal tract innervation in some animals, occurring as normal variation within a group, permitted more chattering—perhaps more meaningful chattering—by those so equipped, that this proved of survival value, and in time all the biological descendants of the group were superior to their ancestors in this respect due to selection, whether one call it "natural" or "social." It is but a matter of words, but exactness is a virtue.

It has yet to be demonstrated that cooking of food has anything to do with reduction in size of teeth and jaws. Large teeth and jaws are as efficient in eating cooked food as small ones. Shape of teeth and jaws has to do with the character of food eaten, size does not.

By GEORGE L. TRAGER
BUFFALO, N.Y., U.S.A. 9 XII 63

I agree with the conclusion that with language there took place a *revolution* in human development. And for this reason I think that the discussion, in evolutionary terms, of the possible ways that language arose, is fruitless and beside the point. Language is not, in my opinion, an evolutionary development. It is an *invention*—the *first* cultural invention. All the rest of culture followed, automatically, as it were. This statement means, of course, that I reject evolution as a *cultural* mechanism. Culture proceeds and changes by sudden spurts—inventions.

It also follows that the nature or basic structure of language must have been, from the start, what it is today. This structure I hold to involve a trinity, rather than a duality (see Trager 1963): there is sound—the material or components of which language is made—its "diacritics"; there is shape—the grammatical structures (morphemic and syntactic) into which the sound is arranged—the "substance" of language; and there is sense —the meaning (that is, linguistic or structural meaning) which arises from the arrangement of the elements of shape—the "relations" of the parts of the substance. ("Referential" or "metalinguistic" meaning is something that involves the relation of language as a whole to the rest of culture. It is not a matter of the structure of language as such, but of the relation of linguistic structure, in detail, to other cultural structures.) Hockett's failure to separate shape and sense is a defect in his analysis. The first language must have had this kind of structure, and all languages since (presumably developed from it) have had it. This is why I hold that language was an invention. Inventions have an essential structure that does not occur "in nature." The first wheel—much later than language, of course—was in essence like every wheel since; and there are no wheels in nature. (The uses to which wheels have been put—from pull-toys, as among the Aztecs, to the tape-reels in computers—are analogous to the "metalinguistic," developmental, uses of language.)

How the first language was invented (and I agree this must have happened only "once"—a term that can stand some explication in this context) is not known, and is perhaps unknowable. But looking for the *how* in present-day primate behavior is beside the point. The living primates do not make inventions. Nor do any other creatures that we know of, except man. I suggest, however, that possibly domesticated animals, especially pets, may give us some clues.

As an anthropologist, I must seek a *cultural* basis for culture, not a biological one.

The paper is interestingly and plausibly written, and will no doubt be cited often and will be called important. Despite denial of teleological intentions, it is, nonetheless, teleological in its rigidly evolutionistic approach. The superorganic (= cultural?) is ruled out so thoroughly that we end up with reductionism and biology. And the avowed speculation needs only a little personalization to read like science fiction.

By EUGENE VERSTRAELEN

CEBU CITY, PHILIPPINES. 13 XII 63

I am not competent to comment so the following remarks are meant only to elicit answers and clarifications.

This paper lacks one point which I consider essential. The patterning of the phonological components are extensively treated, but not so the patterning of the meaningful elements. Nevertheless I think that in this very respect there is a critical momentum in the development towards man.

In the patterning of the meaningful units, one comes across the so-called morphemes. A number of these morphemes symbolize concepts which may be and generally are different in different languages; the logicians speak about the different "intensions" and "extensions." The development of these morphemes is perhaps sufficiently clarified in the paper. But language is more than a system for generating only disparate symbols with their different meanings. As far as I know, all natural languages can generate matrices in which these morphemes are incorporated and by which their meanings are combined in a meaningful combination. And, if I am not mistaken, these matrices correspond to the operations of logic: there may be some detailed differences in the functions of the matrices of the different languages, but they are always subsumed in one of the operations of logic; e.g., all languages can generate a formal matrix of predication (which may consist of a distinct order of special morphemes, eventually with additional markers and intonation, etc.) which corresponds to a statement having the meaning of a proposition in logic. In a predication, a matrix of a complementation may be incorporated; this matrix corresponds to the relation in logic. It is, of course, not the subject matter proper of linguistics to study the statements in so far as they represent propositions with their truth-values; the linguist is mainly interested in the system (language) by which statements—meaning either true or false propositions—can be generated. But to understand the human revolution, I think it is essential to explain the development of language into a system which can generate the above-mentioned matrices.

By ROGER W. WESCOTT
NEW YORK CITY, 11 XII 63

For zoological as well as linguistic purposes, the most useful definition I know of the terms "signal" and "symbol" is that of philosopher Charles Morris (1946): a signal is an intentional sign, and a symbol is an arbitrary signal—that is, an arbitrary, intentional sign. In these terms, Ascher and Hockett are more than justified in rejecting mere symbolization as a distinctively and exclusively human activity, since both fish and insects, not to mention birds and mammals, produce and respond to symbols. What is most unique in human communicative behavior is rather symbolic *layering,* or the phoneme-morpheme hierarchy which the authors term "duality of patterning."

Arguments over the priority of biology or linguistics in regard to evolutionary theory seem to me as invidious as most other hen-or-egg debates. Phylogenetically, we usually reach a point of origin at which hen and egg are indistinguishable. As regards evolution, the philosopher Leibnitz (1890) adumbrated parallel hypotheses on the development of both species and languages over half a century before either Lamarck or Jones. During the following century, linguists refined their developmental theories earlier than biologists, but biologists effected a more radical revision of the general climate of scientific opinion.

The authors, like many of their predecessors, are of course quite justified in holding that there is a causal concatenation between Miocene desiccation, bipedalism, the freeing of the hands for tool-use, and the freeing of the mouth for elaborate vocal communication. But, as Haldane puts it, in the realm of organic behavior, causality is more often a net than a chain: not only must we allow for feed-back effects but also for parallel or simultaneous evolutionary developments within populations (1943). And here there is room, I think, for Cappanari's neuro-physiological thesis that, because of the proximity of lingual to digital control areas in the brain, acquisition of delicate finger control occurred concomitantly with the development of equivalent tongue control (1962). The tongue thus became "the finger of the mouth," an organ pre-adapted to the use of that phatic tool which eventually differentiated, by a dichotomous process analogous to gastrulation, into language.

The authors' insistence on what they call "physicalism" and "exogeny" in zoological and anthropological discourse seems to me just as arbitrary as its antithesis, dogmatic "vitalism" or "superorganicism." Here I prefer Russell's "neutral monism," according to which mind and matter are equally aspects of a single underlying reality. More precisely, I follow Huxley, White, and others in seeing *energy* as the undifferentiated "stuff" from which both the physical and the cultural are derivations.

On the other hand, I agree with Simpson that the distinction between natural and artificial selection is both objective and useful, inasmuch as the latter involves deliberate manipulation of the reproductive behavior of one organic group by another. By the same token, I dissent from the authors' view that such institutions as marriage and burial are "natural" outgrowths of human foetalism and longevity. Here too I see an "artificiality" of behavior too gross to be reductionistically explained away, even though we may have eventually to depend on psychoanalysts rather than on ethologists for enlightenment on the difficult subject of taboo—a trait which seems, if anything, to be more distinctively human even than language.

The authors' emphasis on the importance to our species of ventral coitus is surely justified. If anything, I would stress it even more than they, pointing out that it further accelerates the foetalization process already manifest in man's relative hairlessness, hypercephalization, and behavioral plasticity. More precisely, it seems not only that the adult male becomes, in face-to-face copulation, a surrogate suckling to the adult female by virtue of his position; but also that, tertiarily at least, the adult female becomes a surrogate suckling to the adult male by virtue of her behavior, which is that of soliciting and receiving a life-giving liquid from an adult bodily protuberance.

The authors' emphasis on the importance of verbal play in the development of language is equally commendable. To it, I would only add a reminder that such play, which presupposes the prior existence of words and hence of language itself in a minimal sense, must have been preceded by a a longer period of phatic play or babbling. And phatic play, in turn presupposes a more general kind of oral play, involving sucking and mouthing. Oral play, finally, could be held to be only one type of still more general play, which might be called orificial, since it could involve any of the readily libidinizable body orifices—including the anus, to which the authors themselves refer, seriously and with good warrant, as a potential speech-center.

Unfortunately, the authors' assertion that language is a pan-Pleistocene phenomenon of about 1,000,000 years' antiquity is ambiguous, since they do not make it clear whether they prefer the traditional view that hominids have existed for no more than 1,000,000 years or Leakey's view that they have existed for over 2,000,000 years. If the former, they are clearly agreeing with Trager (1959) that language and man are co-terminous. If the latter, they seem to be saying that bipedalism rather than language defines the diachronic boundaries of the hominid family.

My own very tentative inclination, based partly on Swadesh's finding that all known languages converge on a monogenetic vanishing point about 40,000 years ago (1960), is rather to believe that language in the full sense does not antedate Neanderthal man. If asked what kind of vocal repertory the Australopithecines had, I would guess that it was simply an expanded version of the general hominoid repertory; and if asked the same question about the Pithecanthropines, that it was still a phatic (or paralinguistic) system enriched by phonesthemes or functionally equivalent imitative referentials; but that the phoneme-morpheme dichotomy was an invention of Upper Paleolithic Europe.

REPLY

By CHARLES F. HOCKETT *and* ROBERT ASCHER

We do not reply below to: (a) criticisms based on misunderstandings, unless we feel that we did not express ourselves clearly enough in the paper; (b) expressions of disagreement unaccompanied by supporting evidence; (c) expressions of disagreement with such support, if our own opinions are essentially unaltered and were adequately expressed in the paper; (d) proposals that it would be nice if we had more evidence of one sort or another—though we agree with all such proposals; (e) discursive passages, however interesting, that have little bearing on our paper; or (f) praise.

(1) We withdraw our ascription of large interlocking canines to the proto-hominoids. Schultz and Givens challenge this point, and Givens cites great variability in this respect among the dryopithecines.

(2) We withdraw the suggestion challenged by Schultz on several

counts, that the reduction in size from proto-hominoid to gibbon was an adaptation to brachiation.

(3) Our assertion that proto-hominoid males were "without jealousy when they themselves were sexually satisfied" is contested by Birdwhistell on the ground that the evidence is inadequate. We agree. We say, instead, that if in fact the proto-hominoids were thus free of jealousy, the development of jealousy in our own ancestry is understandable in terms set forth in our paper.

(4) Evidence cited by Hewes makes it likely that hand carrying may actually have characterized the proto-hominoids, instead of being a later development. Since our timetable on this point was highly indefinite, we do not believe our main narrative need be altered.

(5) Our hypothesis (greatly elaborated by some commentators) about the behavioral consequences of the frontal approach in copulation is challenged by observations cited by Schultz, and must at least be greatly modified, if not completely discarded. We are not yet quite ready for outright rejection; we want to study the relevant ethological reports, and perhaps wait for further observations of nonhuman primate sexual behavior.

(6) Hewes cites grooming behavior as another general primate inheritance of the carrying of infants to the proto-hominoids to which attention should be paid as we try to unravel human evolution. We welcome the addition.

(7) Schultz reinforces our ascription of the carrying of infants to the proto-hominoids, by pointing up the general weakness of newborn hominoids compared with newborn monkeys. The added evidence is very important.

(8) Clark remarks that "treeless savannah in the tropics is not necessarily less well supplied with water and food sources than woodland savannah or the forest itself." Some of our discussion suggests the contrary. Modification (we think minor) is clearly called for.

(9) Livingston and Clark both question our proposal that the earliest tools were for defense, and argue quite reasonably that they were for food-getting and offense. We think we have in this regard a conflict of plausibilities, somewhat like the contending claims for priority, left unresolved in our paper, of food-carrying and weapon-carrying.

(10) La Barre proposes, and Montagu and Hewes take up, the notion that human hairlessness may have resulted from the requirements of dissipation of body heat after the strenuous exertions of hunting in tropical savannahs. This is a brilliant notion, and we happily abandon our timid guess that clothing might have played a part in the development of hairlessness.

(11) Montagu corrects our reference to menarche as the age after which a female can conceive; we accept his emendation to "nubility."

(12) Count exposes our misuse of the term "forebrain"; the phrase, "with a particularly sharp increase in the forebrain," should simply be deleted from the sentence in which we wrote it (Chronology, sixth paragraph).

(13) Mead wonders if we should not have allowed for diffusion as well as gene flow from band to band in early hominoid and hominid times. Indeed we should have; the omission was accidental, not intentional. Agogino hints at the same point, and Clark says ". . . such a revolutionary innovation as that of open language, when it came, was probably communicated from band to band with reasonable rapidity since fundamental inventions and improvements in technology were certainly quick in spreading." Now this last suggestion is quite another matter. The development of openness was surely not so blatantly obvious that it could spread from one band to another via some sort of stimulus diffusion. We doubt, as a matter of fact, that a community would be capable of acquiring something via stimulus diffusion of any very elaborate sort until *after* it had at least open pre-language, if not language. We picture the development of openness as a much more gradual thing, involving many contributory steps and stages, both genetic and traditional, which blur together into a single "sudden" event only because it all took place so long ago.

(14) Finally, we are distressed that our formulation of "Romer's Rule" should elicit the criticism of two of the deservedly most prestigious biologists in the world today, Simpson and Dobzhansky. Let us clarify. Romer's Rule is not a law of biology; it is a principle for straight thinking. Evolutionary hypotheses are historical, not experimental. They concern not what *would* or *will* happen under such-and-such circumstances, but what *did* happen, where and when, and with what interconnecting lines of causality. Romer's Rule forces us to distinguish between causes and consequences, and can be of heuristic value when we look for causes. We cannot believe that Dobzhansky means quite what he says in his remark that a species "responds to an environmental change by a genetic innovation (or simply a genetic alteration) which compensates for the changed magnitude or manifestation of an environmental pressure." Such a response is not always possible; there is, after all, such a thing as extinction. When the response is possible, it is because the gene pool (or the repertory of traditional lifeways) already contains the wherewithal for the new adaptation. When it does, why does it? Not, certainly, because of some mystical or teleological "preadaptation"—none of us would propose that. Sometimes, at least— suggests Romer's Rule—because of earlier more subtle selective factors of a conservative sort.

There are further insights in the comments. We are tempted to discuss more of them, but elect not to do so because we want to ponder them.

References Cited

ALTMANN, STUART A. 1962 "Social behavior of anthropoid primates: Analysis of recent concepts," in *Roots of Behavior*. Edited by E. L. Bliss, pp. 277–85. New York: Harper and Brothers.
ANDREW, R. J. 1963 The origin and evolution of the calls and facial expressions of the primates. *Behavior* 20:1–109. [ARD, JP]

ARIETI, SILVANO 1956   Some basic problems common to anthropology and modern psychiatry. *American Anthropologist* 58:26–39.   [MM]

BAERENDS, G. P. 1958   Comparative methods and the concept of homology in the study of behavior. *Archives néerlandaises de zoologie* 13:401–17.
                                                                                      [ARD]

BARTHOLOMEW, GEORGE A., JR., and JOSEPH B. BIRDSELL. 1953   Ecology and the protohominids. *American Anthropologist* 55:481–98.

BINGHAM, H. C. 1932   *Gorillas in a native habitat*. Carnegie Institute of Washington Publ. No. 426.

BLOOMFIELD, LEONARD. 1933   *Language*. New York: Henry Holt and Company.
——— 1936   Language or ideas? *Language* 12:89–95.

BOLWIG, N. A. 1959   A study of nests built by mountain gorilla and chimpanzee. *South African Journal of Science* 55:286–91.

BRACE, C. LORING. 1962   "Cultural factors in the evolution of human dentition," in *Culture and the Evolution of Man*. Edited by M. F. Ashley Montagu, pp. 343–354. New York: Oxford University Press.

BRYAN, ALAN L. 1963   The essential morphological basis for human culture. *Current Anthropology* 4:297–306.

BUETTNER-JANUSCH, J., ed. 1962   The relatives of man: modern studies of the relation of the evolution of nonhuman primates to human evolution. *Annals of the New York Academy of Sciences* 102:181–514.   [ARD]

CALHOUN, JOHN B. 1962   The ecology of violence. Paper presented to the Annual Meeting of the American Association for the Advancement of Science, Philadelphia, Penna., Dec. 29.   [MM]

CAPPANARI, STEPHEN. 1962   The origin of speech. Paper presented to the Annual Meeting of the American Anthropological Association, Chicago.
                                                                                      [RWW]

CARPENTER, C. R. 1938   Netherlands Committee for International Nature Protection, Communication No. 12:1034.
——— 1940   A field study of the behavior and social relations of the gibbon. *Comparative Psychology Monographs* 16, No. 5.

CHANCE, M. R. A. 1961   "The nature and special features of the instinctive social bond of primates," in *Social Life of Early Man*. Edited by S. L. Washburn, pp. 17–33. Chicago: Aldine Publishing Company.

CHILDE, V. GORDON. 1936   *Man makes himself*. London: C. A. Watts & Co. (Reprinted 1951. New York: New American Library of World Literature).

CHOMSKY, N. 1959   Review of *Verbal behavior*, by B. F. Skinner. *Language* 35:26–58.   [ARD]

CLARK, J. DESMOND. 1963   The evolution of culture in Africa. *The American Naturalist* 97:15–28.

COON, CARLETON S. 1962   *The origin of races*. New York: Alfred A. Knopf.

COUNT, EARL W. 1958   The biological basis of human sociality. *American Anthropologist* 60:1049–85.

CRITCHLEY, MACDONALD. 1960   "The evolution of man's capacity for language," in *Evolution after Darwin, Volume II, The Evolution of Man: Man, Culture, and Society*. Edited by Sol Tax, pp. 289–308. Chicago: University of Chicago Press.

DOBZHANSKY, TH. 1956   *The biological basis of human freedom*. New York: Columbia University Press.
——— 1962   *Mankind evolving*. New York and London: Yale University Press.

DuBRUL, E. L. 1958   *Evolution of the speech apparatus*. Springfield: Charles C. Thomas.

EISELEY, LOREN. 1955 "Fossil man and human evolution," in *Yearbook of anthropology—1955,* pp. 61–78. New York: Wenner-Gren Foundation for Anthropological Research. [MM].

FERGUSON, CHARLES A. 1963 "Assumptions about nasals: A sample study in phonological universals," in *Universals of Language.* Edited by Joseph H. Greenberg, pp. 42–47. Cambridge, Mass.: The M.I.T. Press.

FORD, C. S., and F. A. BEACH. 1951 *Patterns of sexual behavior.* New York: Hoeber. [MM]

GOODALL, JANE, and HUGO VAN LAWICK. 1963 My life among wild chimpanzees. *National Geographic Magazine* 124:272–308. [RC, GWH]

GREENBERG, JOSEPH H. 1959 "Language and evolution," in *Evolution and Anthropology: A Centennial Appraisal.* Edited by B. J. Meggars, pp. 61–75. The Anthropological Society of Washington, Washington, D.C.

HALDANE, J. B. S. 1943 2d edition. Animal biology. New York and London: Oxford University Press. [RWW]

HARLOW, H. F. 1962 "The development of learning in the Rhesus monkey," in *Science in progress: 12th Series.* Edited by W. R. Brode, pp. 239–69. New Haven: Yale University Press. [ARD]

HARLOW, H. F., and R. R. ZIMMERMANN. 1959 Affectional responses in the infant monkey. *Science* 130:421–32. [ARD]

HEBB, D. O. 1949 *The organization of behavior: A neuropsychological theory.* New York: John Wiley & Sons, Inc. [ARD]

HEDIGER, HEINI. 1961 "The evolution of territorial behavior," in *Social Life of Early Man.* Edited by S. L. Washburn, pp. 34–37. Chicago: Aldine Publishing Company.

HESS, E. H. 1962 "Ethnology: an approach toward the complete analysis of behavior," in *New directions in psychology.* R. Brown, *et al.,* pp. 157–266. New York: Holt, Rinehart and Winston. [ARD]

HEWES, GORDON W. 1961 Food transport and the origin of Hominid bipedalism. *American Anthropologist* 63:687–710.

HINDE, R. A., and N. TINBERGEN. 1958 "The comparative study of species-specific behavior," in *Behavior and evolution.* Edited by A. Roe and G. E. Simpson, pp. 251–68. New Haven: Yale University Press. [ARD]

HOAGLAND, HUDSON. 1963 Toward a redefinition of culture. Proceedings of the Conference of the American Academy of Arts and Sciences, May 10–11. Not published. [MM]

———. n.d. personal communication. [MM]

HOCHBAUM, H. ALBERT. 1955 *Travels and traditions of waterfowl.* Minneapolis: University of Minnesota Press.

HOCKETT, CHARLES F. 1948 Biophysics, linguistics, and the unity of science. *American Scientist* 36:558–72.

——— 1956 Review. *Language* 32:46–49.

——— 1958 *A course in modern linguistics.* New York: The Macmillan Company.

——— 1959 "Animal 'languages' and human language," in *The Evolution of Man's Capacity for Culture.* Edited by J. N. Spuhler, pp. 32–39. Detroit: Wayne State University Press,

——— 1960a The origin of speech. *Scientific American* 203:88–96.

——— 1960b "Logical considerations in the study of animal communication," in *Animal Sounds and Communication.* Edited by W. E. Lanyon, and W. N. Tavolga, pp. 392–430. American Institute of Biological Sciences, Publ. No. 7. Washington, D.C.

——— 1963*a*   "The problem of universals in language," in *Universals of Language*. Edited by Joseph H. Greenberg, pp. 1–22. Cambridge, Mass.: The M.I.T. Press.

——— 1963*b*   Comment on "The essential morphological basis for human culture," by Alan Lyle Bryan. *Current Anthropology* 4:303–4.

HOENIGSWALD, H. M. 1963   The history of the comparative method. *Anthropological Linguistics* 5:1–11.   [ARD]

HOOTON, E. 1942   *Man's poor relations*. New York: Doubleday, Doran and Company, Inc.

——— 1946   *Up from the ape*. New York: Macmillan.   [GAA]

HUXLEY, THOMAS H. and JULIAN S. HUXLEY. 1947   *Touchstone for ethics*. New York: Harper.   [MM]

IMANISHI, KINJI. 1960   Social organization of subhuman primates in their natural habitat. *Current Anthropology* 1:393–407.   [MM]

ITANI, JUNICHIRO. 1958   On the acquisition and propagation of a new food habit in the natural group of the Japanese monkey at Takasaki-Yama. *Primates* 1:84–98.   [MM]

KELEMEN, G. 1948   The anatomical basis of phonation in the chimpanzee. *Journal of morphology* 82:229–46. (Reprinted in 1949, *Yearbook of Physical Anthropology*, 4:153–80).

KING, JOHN A. 1955   *Social behavior, social organization, and population dynamics in a black-tailed prairiedog town in the Black Hills of South Dakota*. University of Michigan Contributions from the Laboratory of Vertebrate Biology, No. 67.

KORTLANDT, ADRIAAN 1962   Chimpanzees in the wild. *Scientific American* 206:128–34, 137–38.   [WLB]

KROEBER, A. L. 1948   *Anthropology*. New York: Harcourt Brace and Company.

LaBARRE, WESTON. 1954   *The human animal*. Chicago: University of Chicago Press.

LANGER, SUSANNE K. 1942   *Philosophy in a new key*. Cambridge, Mass.: Harvard University Press. (Reprinted 1948. New York: The New American Library of World Literature).

LANYON, W. E. 1960   "The ontogeny of vocalization in birds," in *Animal Sounds and Communication*. Edited by W. E. Lanyon and W. N. Tavolga, pp. 321–47. American Institute of Biological Sciences, Publ. 7. Washington, D.C.

LEAKY, L. S. B. 1959   A new fossil skull from Olduvai. *Nature* 184:491–93.

LEAKEY, L. S. B., G. H. CURTIS, and J. F. EVERNDEN. 1962   Age of basalt underlying Bed I, Olduvai. *Nature* 194:610–12.

LeGROS CLARK, W. E. 1955   *The fossil evidence for human evolution*. Chicago: The University of Chicago Press.

LEIBNITZ, GOTTFRIED WILHELM VON. 1890   *Works*. Translated by G. M. Duncan. New Haven, Conn., U.S.A.: Tuttle, Morehouse and Taylor.   [RWW]

LENNEBERG, E. H. 1960*a*   "Language, evolution, and purposive behavior," in *Culture in history: Essays in honor of Paul Radin*. Edited by S. Diamond, pp. 869–93. New York: Columbia University Press.   [ARD]

——— 1960*b*   Review of *Speech and brain mechanisms,* by W. Penfield and L. Robert. *Language* 36:97–112.   [ARD]

LEROI-GOURHAN, ANDRÉ. 1955   *L'équilibre mécanique des cranes des vertebrés terrestres*. D.Sc. dissertation, University of Paris.   [RC]

——— 1963   "Les origines de la civilisation technique," in *Histoire générale des techniques, Tome I.* Published under the direction of Maurice Daumas. Paris: Presses Universitaires de France. [RC]

LÉVI-STRAUSS, CLAUDE. 1949 *Les structures élémentaires de la parenté.* Paris: Presses Universitaires de France. [RC]

LINDAUER, MARTIN. 1963 *Communication among Social Bees.* Cambridge: Harvard University Press.

LORENZ, K. Z. 1960 Prinzipien der vergleichenden Verhaltensforschung. *Fortschritte der Zoologie* 12:265–94. [ARD]

MALINOWSKI, BRONISLAW. 1927 *Sex and repression in savage society.* New York: Harcourt, Brace. Reprinted 1960. New York: World Publishing Company. [MM]

MEAD, MARGARET. 1949 *Male and female.* New York: Morrow. Reprinted 1955. New York: New American Library. [MM]

—— 1952 "Some relationships between social anthropology and psychiatry," in *Dynamic psychiatry.* Edited by Franz Alexander and Helen Ross, pp. 401–48. Chicago: University of Chicago Press. [MM]

—— 1961 "Cultural determinants of sexual behavior," in *Sex and internal secretions,* 3d. edition. Edited by William C. Young, pp. 1433–79. Baltimore: Williams and Wilkins. [MM]

—— 1963*a* "Some general considerations," in *Expression of the emotions in man.* Edited by Peter H. Knapp, pp. 318–27. New York: International Universities Press. [MM]

—— 1963*b* "Violence in the perspective of culture history," in *Violence and war with clinical studies.* Edited by Jules H. Masserman, pp. 92–106. New York, London: Grune and Stratton. [MM]

—— 1963*c* *Totem and taboo* reconsidered with respect. *Bulletin of the Menninger Clinic* 27:185–99. [MM]

—— 1964 *Continuities in cultural evolution. The Terry lectures.* New Haven, London: Yale University Press (in press). [MM]

MEAD, MARGARET, and THEODORE SCHWARTZ. 1960 "The cult as a condensed social process," in *Group processes, Transactions of the 5th Conference, 1958.* Edited by Bertram Schaffner, pp. 85–187. New York: Josiah Macy, Jr. Foundation. [MM]

MILNE, LORUS J. and MARJORIE. 1962 *The senses of animals and men.* New York: Atheneum. [WLB]

MONTAGU, M. F. ASHLEY 1944 On the relation between body size, waking activity, and the origin of social life in the primates. *American Anthropologist* 46:141–45. [WLB]

—— 1951 *An introduction to physical anthropology.* Springfield, Ill.: C. C. Thomas. [GAA]

—— 1957 *The reproductive development of the female.* New York: Julian Press. [AM]

—— 1964 *The human revolution.* Cleveland and New York: World Publishing Company (in press). [AM]

MORRIS, CHARLES. 1946 *Signs, language, and behavior.* Englewood Cliffs, N.J., U.S.A.: Prentice-Hall. [RWW]

NAPIER, JOHN. 1962 The evolution of the hand. *Scientific American* 207:56–62. [WLB]

NISSEN, H. W. 1931 A field study of the chimpanzee. *Comparative Psychology Monographs* 8, No. 1.

OAKLEY, KENNETH P. 1961 "On man's use of fire, with comments on tool-making and hunting," in *Social Life of Early Man*. Edited by S. L. Washburn, pp. 176–93. Chicago: Aldine Publishing Company.

———. 1962 Dating the emergence of man. *The Advancement of Science* 18:415–26.

PEDERSON, HOLGER. 1931 *Linguistic science in the nineteenth century*. Cambridge: Harvard University Press.

PENFIELD, W., and L. ROBERTS. 1959 *Speech and brain mechanisms*. Princeton: Princeton University Press.   [ARD]

PITTENGER, R. E., C. F. HOCKETT, and J. DANEHY. 1960 *The first five minutes: An example of microscopic interview analysis*. Ithaca: Paul Martineau.

PROSSER, C. L. 1959 "Comparative neuropsychology," in *Evolution of nervous control from primitive organisms to man*. Edited by B. B. Brodie and A. D. Bass. American Association for the Advancement of Science, Publication No. 52.   [EWC]

ROMER, A. S. 1958 "Phylogeny and behavior with special reference to vertebrate evolution," in *Behavior and Evolution*. Edited by Anne Roe and G. G. Simpson, pp. 48–75. New Haven: Yale University Press.

——— 1959 *The vertebrate story*. Chicago: University of Chicago Press.

SADE, DONALD. 1963 Grooming patterns and the family in a group of free ranging rhesus monkeys. Paper presented to the Annual Meeting of the American Anthropological Association, San Francisco, November 21.   [GWH]

SAHLINS, MARSHALL D. 1959 "The social life of monkeys, apes, and primitive man," in *The Evolution of Man's Capacity for Culture*. Edited by J. N. Spuhler, pp. 54–73. Detroit: Wayne State University Press.

SCHALLER, GEORGE B. 1963 *The mountain gorilla: ecology and behavior*. Chicago: University of Chicago Press.   [GWH, AHS]

SCHULTZ, ADOLPH H. 1954 Bemerkungen zur Variabilität und Systematik der Schimpansen. *Säugetierkundliche Mitteilungen* 2:159–63.   [AHS]

——— 1961 "Some factors influencing the social life of primates in general and early man in particular," in *Social Life of Early Man*. Edited by S. L. Washburn, pp. 58–90. Chicago: Aldine Publishing Company.

——— 1963a "Die rezenten Hominoidea," in *Ein Jahrhundert menschlicher Abstammungslehre*. Edited by G. Heberer, pp. 56–102. Stuttgart, Germany: Gustav Fischer Verlag (in press).   [AHS]

——— 1963b "Age changes, sex differences, and variability as factors in the classification of primates," in *Classification and Human Evolution*. Edited by S. L. Washburn, pp. 85–115. Chicago: Aldine Publishing Company.   [AHS]

SIMONS, ELWYN L. 1963 Some fallacies in the study of hominid phylogeny. *Science* 141:879–889.

SIMPSON, GEORGE G. 1945 The principles of classification and a classification of mammals. The American Museum of Natural History, Bulletin 85, New York.

——— 1949 *The meaning of evolution*. New Haven: Yale University Press. (Reprinted 1951. New York: The New American Library of World Literature).

——— 1958 "The study of evolution: Methods and present status of theory," in *Behavior and Evolution*. Edited by Anne Roe and G. G. Simpson, pp. 7–26. New Haven: Yale University Press.

SMITH, ELIOT. 1913 "The evolution of man," in *Smithsonian Report for 1912*, pp. 553–72. The Smithsonian Institution. Washington, D.C.

SOUTHWICK, CHARLES H. 1955 The population dynamics of confined house mice supplied with unlimited food. *Ecology* 36:212–25. [MM]

SPUHLER, J. N. 1959 "Somatic paths to culture," in *The Evolution of Man's Capacity for Culture.* Edited by J. N. Spuhler, pp. 1–13. Detroit: Wayne State University Press.

—— Ed. 1959 *The evolution of man's capacity for culture.* Detroit: Wayne State University Press. [ARD]

STRECKER, ROBERT L., and JOHN T. EMLEN, JR. 1953 Regulatory mechanisms in house-mouse populations: The effect of limited food supply on a confined population. *Ecology* 34:375–85. [MM]

SWADESH, MORRIS 1960 *Tras la huella lingüística de la prehistoria.* Suplementos del Seminario de Problemas Científicos y Filosóficos, Segunda Serie, No. 26. Mexico, D.F.: Universidad Nacional de México. [RWW]

TANNER, JAMES M. 1955 *Growth at adolescence.* Springfield, Ill.: Thomas. Reprinted 1962. [MM]

TRAGER, GEORGE L. 1958 Paralanguage: A first approximation. *Studies in Linguistics* 13:1–12.

—— 1959 "Language," in *Encyclopaedia Brittanica,* Vol. 13, pp. 695–702. Chicago: William Benton. [RWW]

—— 1963 *Linguistics is linguistics.* Studies in Linguistics, Occasional Papers, No. 10. [GLT]

VON FRISCH, KARL. 1950 *Bees, their vision, chemical senses, and language.* Ithaca: Cornell University Press.

WADDINGTON, C. H. 1961 *The ethical animal.* New York: Atheneum. [MM]

WASHBURN, S. L. 1959 "Speculation on the interrelations of the history of tools and biological evolution," in *The Evolution of Man's Capacity for Culture.* Edited by J. N. Spuhler, pp. 21–31. Detroit: Wayne State University Press.

—— 1960 Tools and human evolution. *Scientific American* 203:63–75.

—— Ed. 1961 *Social life of early man.* Chicago: Aldine Publishing Company. [ARD]

WASHBURN, S. L., and IRVEN DEVORE. 1961 "Social behavior of baboons and early man," in *Social Life of Early Man.* Edited by S. L. Washburn, pp. 91–105. Chicago: Aldine Publishing Company.

WHITE, LESLIE A. 1949 *The science of culture.* New York: Farrar, Straus & Co. (Reprinted 1958. New York: Grove Press).

—— 1959 "Summary review," in *The Evolution of Man's Capacity for Culture.* Edited by J. N. Spuhler, pp. 74–79. Detroit: Wayne State University Press.

WIENER, ALEXANDER S., and J. MOOR-JANKOWSKI. 1963 Blood groups in anthropoid apes and baboons. *Science* 142:67–68.

WIENER, NORBERT. 1948 *Cybernetics.* New York: The Technology Press and John Wiley & Sons.

WEINERT, HANS. 1932 *Ursprung der Menschheit.* Stuttgart, Germany: Ferdinand Enke Verlag. [GAA]

WITTGENSTEIN, LUDWIG. 1953 *Philosophical investigations.* New York: Macmillan. [JP]

Brains, Genes, Culture, Immaturity, and Gestation

M. F. ASHLEY MONTAGU

Man is not only a symbol user but also a symbol maker, and it is through the increasing complexity of his symbol making that he has achieved his present high technological development. With the creation and usage of organized systems of symbols man created a new dimension of experience which at the same time yielded him an increasing control over his environment. This new dimension of experience we call *human culture*. Man-made culture is the special kind of environment man creates the better to control as much of the general environment as he desires.

As the late Alfred Korzybski pointed out, plants capture one kind of energy, convert it into another, and store it up; plants may therefore be described as belonging to the chemistry-binding class of life. Animals, being characterized by the faculty and freedom to move about in space, may therefore be defined as the space-binding class of life. Since he has the capacity to summarize, digest, and utilize the work, achievements, and experiences of the past for the benefit of the present and the progress of the future, man may therefore be said to belong uniquely to the time-binding class of life.[1] This is an important series of distinctions, but man is much more than a time-binder —he is also a remarkable innovator. He is not merely a discoverer, one who finds out, but also one who thinks up, devises or mentally creates innovations which are original and novel. These mental innovations he converts into systems and into tangible realities. This he does principally through the use of symbols. As he creates new symbols, his symbols create him. The process of symbol usage is called *symboling,* and a thing or event which is dependent upon symboling is called a *symbolate*. Symbolates acting in interaction with one another are of the essence of culture. When we study the cultural world it is from the standpoint of the universe of symbolates operating in interaction with each other largely in an extraorganismic or extrasomatic context, whereas the same relationships between symbolates viewed from the standpoint of their functional relationships to the behavior of individuals and their motivations, in other words, in an organismal or somatic context, become psychological. Thus, the difference between the sciences devoted to the study of culture and psychology arises simply out of the difference in the focus of interest.

Ideas, attitudes, acts, and objects have as a common factor the process of symboling, and there are three kinds of symbolates: (1) ideas and attitudes, (2) overt acts, and (3) material objects. The meaning of symbolates, it is important to note, can only be understood by human beings who have learned to translate them. And this is precisely what each culture enables its members to do according to its own specifications. In this way every member of a particular culture is custom-made, tailored according to the pattern prevailing in that particular culture. Thus, culture has become man's principal means of adapting himself to the environment, and so, indeed, it was from the very beginning of man's early development. The difference in the culture of early man compared with that of later man lies principally in the difference in complexity which characterizes some of the more technologically advanced human cultures compared with those of early man. Culture, then, consists of the things and events dependent upon symboling which the individual learns as an organized system of behavior, ideas, beliefs, attitudes, sentiments, acts, customs, codes, institutions, forms of art, speech, tools, implements, utensils, ornaments, fetiches, charms, and the like.[2] Culture is a completely new zone of adaptation, a wholly new dimension into which man has moved, in which he creates and directs his own adaptation to the environment. The change over from tool using and occasional tool modification to tool making was the first of the steps which initiated the peculiarly human development of culture. The augmentation of plant gathering by the gathering of juvenile and slow-moving animals in the satisfaction of hunger represented a still further step in this cultural development. But it was not until the development of hunting, the actual chasing of game in co-operation with others, that the development of human culture and of the peculiarly human traits of man received its greatest stimulus.[3]

Hunting does not appear to have received its proper due as a factor in contributing to the cultural and physical evolution of man. This is all the more interesting because it is in this manner that man earned his living for almost the whole of history, only ceasing to do so in a few areas of the earth less than 10,000 years ago. Hunting always presents an enormous variety of challenges which call for all sorts of ingenious responses. Nothing puts so concentrated a pressure upon the hunter's imagination, resourcefulness, and inventiveness. Demands are made upon the faculties which lead to experiment, discovery, and invention—to the development of intelligence.

Intelligence is, of course, not only useful in the hunt, but is of highly generalized value. It is also the best defense against falling victim to other animals. With intelligence to draw upon, neither natural nor artificial weapons are necessary. It is probable, then, that it was hunting that served as the selective pressure that gave the greatest encouragement to the development of human intelligence, and to the corresponding decline in the efficacy of instinct. The consequences of this are what made man increasingly human—for man's development as a human being has paralleled the development of each of his peculiarly human traits, the most all-embracing of which is culture.

The human brain is as large as it is because a creature that must learn and perform the necessary cultural skills of man requires a brain large enough to accommodate all the necessary neural elements. There are a prodigious number of these. There are probably more than ten billion neurons in the cortex of the brain alone, more than double the number in any ape brain.

When one compares size of brain with ability to solve complex problems in different related species, the species with the larger brains are found to be more proficient than those with smaller brains. A purely quantitative increase in the number of neurons and therefore in the size of the brain enables the organism to respond to a much wider range and finer detail of stimuli than would otherwise be possible. The increase in the number of neurons means that the number of associative connections between them will increase in geometric progression. This means a great increase in functional capacities and skills. The emphasis is on the *functional capacities and skills,* and this needs to be underscored, for it is to these traits that the size of the brain is most closely related. As Gerard points out, the size of the motor area of the brain, which controls various muscles, is not related to the size of the muscle but to *the skill in using it.*[4] The motor area for the tongue in the human brain is much larger, for example, than the whole motor area for the leg in the chimpanzee.

The role of toolmaking and tool using in the growth and development of the brain is reflected in the great enlargement of the hand area of the motor cortex of the brain. Allowing about thirty years to a generation, there have been about 65,000 generations since the australopithecines. The brain has increased during that time about two and one-half times in size. Compared with similar changes in other animal groups this tempo of gowth reflects a very rapid selection rate.

The fossil evidence indicates that the rate of increase in the size of the brain in prehistoric man was quite rapid, culminating in a brain size of, on the average, 1550 cc. in Neanderthal man. This rate of growth suggests the action of strong selective pressures favoring genes for increased brain size. The average brain size of the human species since the day of Neanderthal man has stabilized itself at about 1400 cc., although in major groups such as the Mongoloids brain size remains at about 1500 cc. The increasing self-domestication of man has possibly had the same effect in reducing brain size, a phenomenon observable in domestic animals. Domestic animals, while retaining the body weight of their wild counterparts, undergo a reduction in brain weight of about 20 per cent.[5] Considering the virtually explosive rate of growth of the brain in man, it will be of interest to inquire into the nature of the pressures which placed so high a selective value on genes for brain size.

GENES, MENTAL ABILITY, AND CULTURE

Changes in frequencies of genes are usually brought about through natural selection in adaptation to environmental challenges. The adaptive value of mental abilities is, in and of itself, insufficient to account for the velocity of brain growth in prehistoric man. While natural selection adapts the population to environmental changes, man performs this adaptation for himself by means of his mental abilities, by which, among other things, he selects and controls the environment and alters it by cultural means to suit his purpose. By producing such alterations man correlatively produces the conditions which lead to those gene changes which are adapted to meet the challenges of the altered environment. Every new invention, every new discovery, had, as it were, a self-accelerating, an autocatalytic effect upon both the genetic and the cultural systems. It put a selective premium upon those who were able to take advantage of the new inventions and discoveries, and by both means facilitated further invention and discovery. Every cultural advance increased the selective advantage of those who were capable of utilizing it and of increasing the selective disadvantage of those who were incapable of using it. In this way the cultural pressures on the genetic evolution of man for increasing ability to adapt himself to the cultural environment have played a dominant role in the evolution of man. Without being aware of it man has produced the changing conditions of his own evolution,[6] and has been selecting himself increasingly in relation to the cultural zone of adaptation. It would seem clear, then, that in the evolution of man cultural and genetic changes have proceeded in an interactive positive feedback relation, that, as Caspari has put it, "genic changes have caused an increased ability for active adaptation by cultural means, and adaptation by cultural means has changed environmental conditions in such a way that different selective pressures have arisen, giving rise to further genetic changes in the population." [7] These two processes have interacted upon one another throughout the evolution of man, and continue to do so. Cultural evolution has not suppressed or supplanted genetic evolution, but interacts with the genetic system to produce both genetic and cultural change—but the adaptation, and the genetic changes, are now largely in relation to the cultural changes that man produces, for culture markedly affects the adaptive value of genes. Selective pressures have increasingly placed a premium upon genes for cultural competency. The characteristics of fitness now change from a genotype of fixed responses to a limited environment, to a genotype without fixed responses, but with the capacity to respond adaptively to a large range of environments.

Culture, then, represents a biological adaptation, based on genetic changes, but transmitted non-genetically, that is, through the socially interactive process of learning. Culture is man's social heredity. Within the limits set by the genes every *human* act of the organism is learned, acquired, through the action of the culture upon him. Though based on genetic factors which make it possible, culture is itself an extragenetic, a superorganic, system which functions in the service of man just as any tool does, to enlarge and extend the satisfaction of his needs.

IMMATURITY-DEPENDENCY

A creature that must learn as much as the human child in order to function adequately as a member of his society must undergo a long period of learning. Human beings are characterized by an extended learning period, which lasts far beyond childhood. It has been a matter of interest that the human infant is also characterized by a prolonged period of immaturity, far more prolonged than that of any other mammal, during which it cannot even move around for itself. What can be the significance of this protracted period of infant immaturity? Let us consider the facts.

The newborn elephant and the fallow deer are able to run with the herd shortly after they are born. By the age of six weeks, the infant seal has been taught by his mother to navigate his watery domain for himself. These animals all have long gestation periods, presumably because animals that give birth to small litters are unable to protect them as efficiently as predatory animals, and must, therefore, give birth to young who are in a fairly mature state. A long gestation period serves to allow for such maturation.

The elephant, with a gestation period of 515 to 670 days, gives birth to a single infant. In animals such as the fallow deer, which give birth to a litter of two or three, the gestation period is 230 days. In the seal, which produces only a single pup at a birth, the gestation period varies from 245 to 350 days. Predatory animals, by contrast, are very efficient in protecting their young, and have a short gestation period. The lion, for example, which generally produces a litter of three cubs, has a gestation period of 105 days. Man has a gestation period of 266½ days, which is distinctly in the class of long gestation periods. Since this is so, what can be the meaning, the purpose, of man's being born in so extremely immature a state?

Baby apes are also born in an immature condition, but remain in that state for a much shorter time than does the human infant. The gestation period in the gorilla is about 252 days, in the orangutan 273 days, and in the chimpanzee 231 days. Labor in the apes generally lasts not more than two hours, as compared with an average of fourteen hours for the firstborn and eight hours for the later-born in the human female—we shall return to the possible significance of this difference shortly. As in man, one infant is usually produced, but compared with that of man the development of the young ape is somewhat more rapid, so that the infant ape takes about one-third to two-thirds of the time the human infant does to develop such traits as lifting the head, rolling, worming along, sitting alone, standing, and walking. Ape mothers tenderly care for their young for several years, and it is not uncommon for breastfeeding to continue for three or more years. Man's immaturity in infancy, therefore, may be regarded as an extension of the basic hominoid infant immaturity characteristic of all man-like forms. Among anthropoids the care, feeding, and protection of the young fall exclusively to the females. The males act to protect the females and the young only when they are endangered.

While the length of the gestation period is virtually within the same range in anthropoids and in man, there is a marked difference in the growth of the fetus in the two groups. This is seen in the great acceleration in the growth of the human compared with the anthropoid fetus toward the end of the gestation period. This is most clearly observed in the growth of the human fetal brain, which by the time of birth has acquired a volume of about 375 cc. to 400 cc. Total body weight of the human newborn averages 7 pounds. In the chimpanzee total body weight of the newborn is, on the average, 4⅓ pounds (1800 grams), and the brain volume is about 200 cc. In the gorilla the total body weight of the newborn is about 4¾ pounds (1980 grams), and brain size at birth would appear to be not much more than that of the chimpanzee.[8]

The smaller size of the anthropoid newborn is to some extent probably correlated with the short duration of labor in the anthropoid female. However, in man the large body size, and especially the large size of the head at 266½ days of fetal age, necessitates the birth of the child at that time, for if it were not born then and it continued to grow at the rate at which it is organized to grow, it could not be born at all—with fatal consequences for the continuation of the human species.

As a result of the adoption of the erect posture the pelvis in both the human female and male has undergone major rearrangement in all its parts. Among these changes has been a narrowing of the pelvic outlet. During parturition, the pelvic outlet enlarges a little owing to the relaxation of the pelvic ligaments, enough to permit the head of the child, with a certain amount of compression, to pass through. In adaptation to this situation the skull bones of the human infant have grown so much less than those of the ape infant of the same gestation age, in relation to the membranes in which these bones develop, that a considerable amount of movement and overlapping is rendered possible in accommodation to the compressive forces that will act upon them during the process of birth. The human infant, then, is normally born when it is because as a result of the rapid growth of its brain during the last month of intra-uterine development its head attains the limit of size consonant with viable birth. The brain growth of the anthropoid infant presents no such problems, particularly in view of the mother's generous pelvic arrangements.

Not only does the prolonged period of behavioral immaturity of the human infant indicate that it is born in a most unready state, so also does its biochemical and physiological immaturity. For example, several of the enzyme systems which render later effective physiological functioning possible are undeveloped in the human infant. In this the human infant shares a trait not uncommon in many other mammals, except that in the human infant, unlike most other mammalian infants thus far investigated, most of these enzymes are not present at all. In guinea pigs and mice, for example, the liver enzymes develop during the first week of life, but require some eight weeks for full development. It appears that in all mammals some factor is present in the uterine environment which represses the formation of liver enzymes in the fetus.[9] In the human infant the liver enzymes do not appear to be fully developed until a good many months have passed.[10] Gastric enzymes are present which are fully capable of dealing with the ingested colostrum and milk from the maternal breast, but they cannot effectively metabolize foods normally consumed by older children.

UTEROGESTATION AND EXTEROGESTATION

All the evidence indicates that, while the duration of the gestation period in man differs by only a week or two from that of the apes, a large number of factors, all combining to lead to the much more prolonged development of the human infant, causes him to be born before his gestation period has been completed. One would think that a creature developing at the rate of the human fetus in the later stages of uterine development and during childhood should, developmentally, enjoy a much longer period of gestation within the womb. After all, every one of the developmental periods is greatly extended in duration in man as compared with that in apes (Table I); why not also

TABLE I

LENGTH OF GESTATION AND POSTNATAL GROWTH PERIODS AND LIFE SPAN IN APE AND MAN

Genus	Gestation (days)	Menarche (years)	Eruption of first and last permanent teeth (years)	Completion of general growth (years)	Life span (years)
Gibbon	210	8.5	?—8.5	9	30
Orangutan	273	?	3.0—9.8	11	30
Chimpanzee	231	8.8	2.9—10.2	11	35
Gorilla	252	9.0	3.0—10.5	11	35
Man	266½	13.5	6.2—20.5	20	75

the period of gestation? The reason, principally, is that the growth of the brain of the fetus is so rapid during the latter part of "gestation" and the mother's pelvis is so narrow, the fetus must be born no later than the time at which its head has reached the maximum size congruent with its passage through the birth canal. That is no mean accomplishment. Indeed, the passage through the four inches of the birth canal is the most hazardous journey a human being ever makes. The fact appears to be that the human fetus is born considerably before his gestation period has been completed. The rate of growth of the brain is proceeding at such a pace that it cannot continue within the womb, and must continue outside it. In other words, the survival of the fetus and the mother requires the termination of gestation within the womb (*uterogestation*) when the limit of head size compatible with birth has been reached, and long before maturation occurs.

Gestation, then, is not completed by the process of birth, but is only translated from gestation within the womb (*uterogestation*) to gestation outside the womb (*exterogestation*). The limit of exterogestation in the human infant may be set at the stage of development of effective locomotion on all fours, that is, when the infant begins to crawl about for himself. The average duration of exterogestation lasts exactly the same time as the period of uterogestation, namely, 266½ days. In this connection it is also of interest to note that while the mother continues to nurse her infant, pregnancy will not usually occur for at least 266½ days after the birth of the child. Nursing the child at the breast suppresses ovulation, and thus constitutes a natural method of child spacing. It also suppresses menstrual bleeding. Menstrual bleeding tends to be heavier and longer when a baby is not breastfed, and the mother's reserve energies tend, therefore, to be somewhat depleted. The premature cessation of breastfeeding would, then, result in distinct disadvantages, especially for a mother who already has other children to care for. Hence, breastfeeding not only confers advantages upon the baby but also upon the mother, and therefore upon the group. This is to mention only the physical advantages of breastfeeding. Even more important are the psychological advantages which are reciprocally conferred upon infant and mother in the nursing situation, especially in a species in which the mother is symbiotically designed to continue the gestation of her child outside the womb.

To learn what the child must learn in order to function as an adequate human being, he must, then, have a large warehouse, a large brain, in which to store the necessary information. It is a striking fact that by the time the human child has attained its third birthday it has virtually achieved the full size of the adult brain. Brain volume of the human three-year-old is 960 cc., while the brain volume of the human adult, attained at the age of twenty, is 1200 cc.; that is to say, after the end of its third year the human brain will add only another 240 cc. to attain its full size, and that 240 cc. will accumulate by small accretions over the next seventeen years. In other words, at the end of three years of age the human child has achieved 90 per cent of its brain growth. Significantly, the infant brain more than doubles in volume by the end of its first year to about 750 cc., or 60 per cent of its adult size. Almost two-thirds of the total growth of the brain is achieved by the end of the first year. It will take another two years to add almost another third to the volume attained at the end of the third year. (Table II.) In its first year, therefore, the infant's brain grows more than it will ever again in any one year.

TABLE II

GROWTH IN BRAIN, AND CRANIAL CAPACITY, BOTH SEXES

Age	Weight (gm.)	Volume (c.c.)	Cranial Capacity (c.c.)
Birth	350	330	350
3 months	526	500	600
6 months	654	600	775
9 months	750	675	925
1 year	825	750	1,000
2 years	1,010	900	1,100
3 years	1,115	960	1,225
4 years	1,180	1,000	1,300
6 years	1,250	1,060	1,350
9 years	1,307	1,100	1,400
12 years	1,338	1,150	1,450
15 years	1,358	1,150	1,450
18 years	1,371	1,175	1,475
20 years	1,378	1,200	1,500

Source: *Growth and Development of the Child*, Part II, White House Conference. New York, Century Co., 1933, p. 110.

It is important that most of the brain growth be accomplished during the first year, when the infant has so much to learn and do, for the first year of life requires a great deal of seemingly unobtrusive packing for a journey that will endure the rest of the wayfarer's life. To perform this packing successfully he must have a brain much larger than 375 to 400 cc., but quite clearly he cannot wait till he has grown a brain of 750 cc. before being born. Hence, he must be born with the maximum-sized brain possible, and do the rest of his brain growing after birth. Since the human fetus must be born when its brain has reached the limit of size compatible with its admission and extrusion through the birth canal, such maturation or further development as other mammals complete before birth the human mammal will have to complete after birth. In other words, the gestation period will have to be extended beyond birth.

The human infant is almost, if not quite, as immature at birth as the little marsupial which, born in an extremely immature state, finds its way into its mother's pouch, there to undergo its exterogestation until it is sufficiently matured. The human infant remains immature much longer than the infant kangaroo or opossum, but whereas the marsupial infant enjoys the protection of its mother's pouch during its period of immaturity, the human infant is afforded no such advantage. However, the human infant constitutes part of a symbiotic unit; the mother, having given it shelter and sustenance within the womb, is fully equipped to continue to do so outside the womb, at least as efficiently as the marsupial mother is for her young. The biological unity, the symbiotic relationship, maintained by mother and conceptus throughout pregnancy does not cease at birth; indeed, it is naturally designed to become even more intensively functional and interoperative after birth than during uterogestation.

To put the preceding discussion of infant brain volume in proper perspective, it should be observed that, while an adult cranial capacity of 1400 cc. was not achieved by man until a stage of his development later than the australopithecine, the forms of man that immediately followed the australopithecines undoubtedly had larger brains than they. The pithecanthropines of Java and China had an adult cranial capacity of about 950 cc. In any event, the narrowing of the pelvis in the small post-australopithecines, whoever they were, and in the australopithecines themselves, together with the increasing size of the brain in the late fetus, would have presented much the same problems as those that we know to prevail in modern forms of man. A two-year-old pithecanthropine, *Homo erectus robustus* from the Lower Pleistocene of Modjokerto in East Java, indicates that the infant pithecanthropine already had a comparatively large brain in relation to adult brain size. Whatever the brain volume of early infant man may have been, the preceding discussion is believed to apply in general to the conditions that prevailed in early man. It should be remembered that both body size and weight in early man were less than they grew to be in later forms of man, and that therefore it is always the size of the brain in relation to body size (and weight) which must be borne in mind in comparing brain sizes of early man with those of later, larger forms of man.

References

1. Alfred Korzybski, *Manhood of Humanity*. 2nd ed. Lakeville, Conn., Institute of General Semantics, 1950.
2. Leslie White, *The Science of Culure*. New York, Farrar, Straus & Co., 1949; Leslie White, *The Evolution of Culture*. New York, McGraw-Hill Book Co., 1959.

3. Ashley Montagu, *The Human Revolution*. New York, Bantam Books, 1967.
4. Ralph W. Gerard, "Brains and Behavior." In J. N. Spuhler (ed.) *The Evolution of Man's Capaciy for Culture.* Detroit, Wayne University Press, 1959, pp. 14–20.
5. W. Herre, "Einfluss der Umwelt über das Saugetiergehirn." *Deutsche Medizinische Wochenschrift,* vol. 83, 1958, pp. 1568–74. Bernhard Rensch, "The Evolution of Brain Achievements." In Th. Dobzhansky, M. K. Hecht, Wm. C. Steere (eds.), *Evolutionary Biology,* vol. 1, New York, Appleton-Century-Crofts, 1967, pp. 26–68.
6. C. D. Darlington, "The Genetics of Society." In A. J. Gregor (ed.), *A Symposium on Race.* Honolulu, University of Hawaii Press, 1963, pp. 1–36.
7. E. Caspari, "Selective Forces in the Evolution of Man." *American Naturalist,* vol. 97, 1963, pp. 5–14, and the present volume pp. 159–69.
8. George B. Schaller, *The Mountain Gorilla.* Chicago, University of Chicago Press, 1963.
9. W. R. Jondorf, R. P. Maichel, and B. B. Brodie, "Inability of Newborn Mice and Guinea Pigs to Metabolize Drugs." *Biochemical Pharmacology,* vol. 1, 1958, pp. 352–4.
10. Clement Smith, *The Physiology of the Newborn Infant.* 3rd ed. Springfield, Illinois, Charles C Thomas, 1960.

The Biological Basis of Human Sociality

EARL W. COUNT

THESES

1. An animal's organizational morphology must include not only its anatomy and physiology, but its characteristic "way of living." Hereafter this life-mode is termed its "biogram."

2. The psychic activity of animals, either individually or in the aggregate, is the expression of the entire neurophysiological process; it is therefore coextensive with centripetal and centrifugal neural currents together. Behavior is the symptomatics of these neurophysiological processes, on the centrifugal or effectory side.

3. If there is a morphology of the nervous system, there must be a morphology of behavior. Hence the biogram is a configuration.

4. The taxonomy of vertebrates should cover the gamut of their morphology from anatomy to behavior; this follows as a conclusion from the three preceding statements. We may therefore speak of a "vertebrate," a "mammalian" biogram, and so forth.

5. Since the vertebrate nervous system has undergone evolutionary elaborations, from the most primitive Classes to the Families and Genera of the warm-blooded Classes, it is expectable that the biogram has correspondingly been elaborated, but without being destroyed or otherwise radically modified.

6. Man's biogram is consistent with his taxonomic position. Culture is man's peculiarly elaborate way of expressing the vertebrate biogram. Until this truth has been established, man's place in nature, first determined in the 19th century on the basis of comparative anatomy, remains incompletely visualized.

7. A major task of anthropology is to account for the emergence of

NOTE: This study was undertaken in 1951 under the kindly prodding of Professor Kroeber. Its existence is herewith gratefully attributed to him, but he is in no wise responsible for any of its statements. The lines of evidence come from numerous sciences: zoology, ethology, psychology, psychoanalysis, neurology, sociology, anthropology. The author disclaims being versed in all these; nevertheless, he believes that he has not misread their data. The essay abbreviates a much longer monograph, and therefore amounts to an abstract. It is hoped that the abruptness of many of the statements will be taken in this light.
From *American Anthropologist*, Vol. 60, 1958, pp. 1049–85. Reprinted by permission.

a culturized biogram out of a prehuman nonculturized biogram. In measure as this task progresses, cultural and biological anthropology effect the junction for their integration.

PROCEDURE

1. To obtain a perspective on the vertebrates, and also to appreciate more clearly what a "biogram" is, we shall glance at the biograms of some social insects.

2. Since the biogram is postulated as a correlate or a consequence of organic evolution, we shall review (minimally and selectively) pertinent features of vertebrate phylogeny.

3. Since behavior is a function of neurological mechanisms, and since these mechanisms produce differences in behavior according to what endocrine stimulations they are undergoing (hereafter we shall say that the mechanisms are under a certain endocrine "tonus"), we shall try to understand the bio-grammatic phenomena as neuroendocrinal consequences.

4. We shall be forced to reconsider the meaning of "innate," "instinctive," "conditioning," "learning," "training" from three standpoints: (1) how the vertebrate psyche matures during its ontogeny; (2) what neurophysiology has been discovering about psychic processes; and (3) how the vertebrate psyche has been elaborated as brain mechanisms have evolved.

5. We shall reconsider culture as an emergent out of these processes, once a given level of brain evolution has been reached in the Primate line. This is tantamount to saying that man has a culturized vertebrate (mammalian, Primate) biogram.[1]

INTRODUCTION

The waters of the earth contain many animal phyla, some of them more primitive than others, certain of them representing "stem" levels from which other and more evolved forms have sprung, yet each of them having a morphology so radically sui generis that each merits the cardinal distinction of phylum.

Terra firma has never gestated a phylum, and only two of the marine phyla have ever successfully exploited dry land: the Arthropoda and the Vertebrata.[2] Of the Arthropoda, the Class Insecta has evolved "socialized" biograms repeatedly and independently in various Orders; and their life-ways are clear-cut devices for exploiting the possibilities of atmospheric-terrestrial habitat.

Not so the vertebrates. Their socialized biogram had developed its essential scheme before they attempted invasion of the land; they have kept the stamp of this ancient situation, along with anatomical and physiological traits which recall their marine derivation; and they have fitted it to their terrestrialization.

BIOGRAMS OF THE SOCIAL INSECTS

The insects, as we have just noted, have evolved socialized biograms repeatedly and each time autogenously, so that there is no single "type." Still, as they all are quite unlike the vertebrate biogram, any one of them would serve our purpose. Colonial ants, bees, wasps are most familiar, and therefore readily usable. We shall limit ourselves to a minimum description.

A colony or society of bees begins when a female, fertilized at some previous time, starts to build a hive, lays eggs in its cells, and tends them while they complete a metamorphosis from larvae to adult workers. When they finally emerge, they are thoroughly—even anatomically—preadapted for performing the maintenance-tasks of the colony. When this happens, the "queen's" (a misnomer) behavioral syndrome which included cell-building and larva-feeding recedes, leaving nothing but egg-laying. The offspring at this time, all female, never carry their germ-cells to the point where they are viable.

Toward the end of the season, viable males and females emerge; none of them perform any of the vegetative duties of the colony. There ensues the "nuptial flight" and the death of the males. After a period of quiescence, each fertilized female literally lays a new colony.

Sociologic Comment. There is but one ancestress to a colony, and there are no further generations. Egg-producing and egg-tending—a parentalism which in noncolonial insects is embodied in the same individual—are apportioned to one egg-laying specialist and an enormous number of sterile egg-tenders. Not a suggestion of mating behavior obtrudes to interrupt, deflect, or otherwise modify the social metabolism.

The male sex is completely eliminated as a potential contributor to the social metabolism. When sex obtrudes at all, it indicates simultaneously a sort of "synapse" of generations and of societies.

Social role is genetically predetermined. The unfortunate term "caste" has been applied to "soldiers," "workers," and so forth, among those insect colonies which have gone even further than bees in dividing up the tasks of the colony.

A society of bees, ants, or wasps is an elaborate mechanism for insuring that eggs shall be produced and matured in greatest abundance. This is the one objective. The hive where the eggs are laid and tended is thus a hub from which the group extraverts for this one purpose, and to which it converges back for this purpose. It has been a highly successful biological scheme.

Speaking as higher vertebrates, we are struck by the impossibility of there ever being any transmission of experience from one generation/ society to another, because the societies do not overlap. Psychologically, there is a maximum of maturation of innate behavior-patterns in an individual's development, and a minimum of experiential learning. No individual trains another.

Kinship is meaningless. Biologically, the workers are sisters; socially, not a shred of mutual attitude attaches to that fact. The fertile males and females who mate to produce the next colony are biologically brothers and sisters, but they never meet and interreact as personalities: their common derivation from the same parents is utterly as though it were not. The individuals seem to remain strangers in all their contacts with each other, because they never mold each other's individualities.

Here is a biogram so utterly without any points in common with our own that our imaginations must exert a tour de force to understand it at all, but the description has served its purpose if we have been led to see a biogram as a configuration.

THE EVOLUTION OF THE VERTEBRATE BIOGRAM

In this section we shall treat the vertebrate biogram as we have a generalized Hymenopteran one in the preceding section. The latter we described flatly as it is; we did not concern ourselves with how it evolved. But the vertebrates we cannot treat in this way, since the entire course of their evolution from Cyclostome to Mammal includes an evolution of a socialized biogram that is coeval with the phylum; and its elaboration expresses the evolving power of the brain from fish to man.

Let us state a principle. Without the organic morphology that supports it, the vertebrate biogram is incomprehensible; conversely, organic morphology has but limited meaning until the biogram it subserves is understood. By corollary, for any given taxomonic category its biogram becomes one of its diagnostic features.

In attempting to describe the vertebrate biogram, we shall use the Cyclostomes (lampreys, hagfishes) as a base and introduce its modifications as we proceed to higher evolutionary forms.

The cardinal fact about the vertebrate biogram is that it is a drama with two alternating phases: a nonreproductive and a mating phase. The former lasts longer in the lowest vertebrates, but as we ascend the phylogenetic scale and the reproductive efforts become greater and more complex, the two phases change in relative length.

The mere fact of seasonal periodicity and rhythm, such that animals alternate between a phase of sexual activity and one of sexual quiescence, is very general also among invertebrates. It is the content of those phases—what is happening to and within those vertebrates—which is the substance of the vertebrate case; and to this we return later.

THE NONREPRODUCTIVE PHASE OF THE VERTEBRATE BIOGRAM

Many, if not all, Cyclostomes live congregatively in a feeding-territory, but I know of no studies on possible interreactions between individuals. We may call a group of like animals a society rather than an aggregation or a congregation when they not only interreact, but these interreactions are a strong force in holding them together and getting them to move in some kind of concert. In a society that lives gregariously, individuals keep a certain distance-balance between themselves, and this is again a matter of interreactivity. Are the Cyclostomes a society, or are they but a congregation? When in their mating-phase, Cyclostomes betray the kind of social awareness that also obtains among other vertebrates at such a time. This suggests that all we lack is a proper investigation to reveal that in the nonreproductive phase likewise they are no exception.

At any rate, shoals of fishes demonstrate that they are a society. An advancing school of herring reverses instantly when the leading rank alone has made sensory contact with a danger; the animals react to each other, not to the external stimulus. Students can often tell when a congregation of animals has become a social group, because the individuals have "got used to each other." On the bird level, flocking is familiar and often spectacular, as when the animals maneuver in rehearsal for emigration. Getting used to each other—"taking each other's rhythms"—takes time and practice. As far down the vertebrate phyletic line as we can trace any signs of sociality, the prime cohesive appears to be individual interstimulations.

Now, the energy patterns of no two individuals are alike; hence repeated interindividual contacts "shake down" into dominance-subordinance arrangements as individual physiology fluctuates; these arrangements are vulnerable to change. At any given moment, all individuals possess status-position held with respect to one or more other individuals. A group of individuals may thus form into social hierarchies. In this contrast to insect society we have, I believe, the key to vertebrate social configuration.

Sensitivity to one's fellows, however, is even-handed. It not only makes possible the synchronized movements of fishes and birds; it also induces mass-hysterias—the spreading excitement of the poultry-yard, the stampedes of cattle and of humans. Such molar behavior is well recognized in vertebrates, but it is far from adequately understood.

One reason for suspecting that even at the Cyclostome level the animal group is more than a congregation is that their mode of origin allows them ample opportunity to become what other vertebrates become under like circumstances: the young hatch almost simultaneously, join in an aggregate, and migrate together back to the feeding-grounds whence their parents came. Among higher vertebrates, individuals born and brought up in isolation never learn to act like the rest of their kind.[3] Such animals remain maladjusted and "socially retarded."

This implies a most important psychoneurological fact about the vertebrates—one which will come up again, but which must be mentioned here. The vertebrates possess innate neuropsychic mechanisms, which must be appropriately stimulated at the right point in maturation if they are to become properly activated; otherwise, the animal's maturation is permanently stunted and its personality is deformed.[4]

Among fishes (and Cyclostomes), the first mutual interstimulation is likely to occur between age-mates; for in very many genera the parents desert the nesting-spot immediately after laying and fertilizing eggs. This age-peer interstimulation is phylogenetically the oldest socializing process. Among the vertebrates which have developed parental care, the youngster is exposed to interreactions with a parent at least as early as with nest-mates. Among those mammals which produce only one offspring at a birth, interreaction with the parent precedes interreaction with age-peers. None the less, any human parent who has twins or triplets is fully aware of the socializing power of interreaction with one's age-peers, and every human parent knows what he has to contend with as soon as the single youngster begins to interreact with age-peers outside the family. The juvenile age-group occurs as a subsociety throughout the vertebrate gamut, from the fish level up.

THE REPRODUCTIVE PHASE OF THE VERTEBRATE BIOGRAM

The onset of the mating-phase, from the Cyclostomes to the warm-blooded vertebrates, is signalized by an activation of the pituitary gland which, although it may strike both sexes at about the same time, frequently occurs first in the males, and apparently never first in the females. It activates distinctive conduct. The males segregate from the females and migrate en masse to another territory. Among the Cyclostomes, the migration is upstream. Their attitude changes again on arrival; they no longer can tolerate each other's proximity; each stakes out a nesting-territory, expels any intruding male, and hollows out a nest. The females arrive somewhat later. The males fall to courting them, and then lead them to the nesting-site. Details vary with the genus; in some, the female may help finish the nest. Once the female has laid her eggs, she leaves; the male milts over them. In some genera, the parents then die.

As we rise above the Cyclostome level, the parental activities take on complexities. To the best of my knowledge, no vertebrates merely expel their germ cells without making any provision for their welfare. Where a parent prepares a nest, but forsakes the spot after depositing eggs and sperm, we shall speak of *nest parentalism* or *elementary parentalism*. In many species of fishes, amphibians, reptiles, and birds, the parent lingers during and after incubation, and actively tends the progeny. This clearly marks a further psychoneurological evolution. When a parent tends young, the young react to the parent, and we have a true sociopsychological ingredient in the total reproductive situation. This is *full parentalism,* or *familialism*. If both parents tend the young, we have *biparental familialism*. Training the young is *complete familialism* (whether done by one or both parents), and represents a yet further stage in the psychoneurological evolution. It is found only among birds and mammals.

Leaving aside those fishes, amphibians, and reptiles which bear the young alive (viviparity), among the rest of the lower vertebrates there are some genera in which it is the male who tends the young; in others, it is the female; in yet others, it is both. Among the fishes and the more primitive birds, parental care more frequently falls upon the male. The more highly evolved genera of birds show both parents tending the young. Species in which the female alone tends them are exceptional. From this it is evident that parentalism is not an integral feature of femaleness; rather it is the way in which adult vertebrates take care of the next generation. When, therefore, we find exclusively female parentalism, it calls for special explanation.

From all this we derive the following about the vertebrate mating-phase: the males initiate and conduct the reproductive cycle, as far as the cycle involves behavior and is not merely physiological (e.g., gestation). Wherever the male selects a nesting-site, courts the female, and keeps out intruders, the female is accepting a situation which the male has created for her.

The mating phase very commonly finds intrasex competitions—males competing for the females, females competing for the males. This reinforces the tendency to social hierarchialism, but both observation of natural events and laboratory experiment show that the two phenomena are not identical. They can be separated; the hierarchialism can be exercised even during the nonreproductive phase of the biogram. The hierarchialism is intrasexual, so that a hierarchy exists for each sex. More often than not, the male hierarchy tends to dominate the female hierarchy. Hierarchialism has been documented for all Classes from the Teleost ("bony") fishes to the mammals, except for the amphibians.

Looking at the two phases of the biogram together, we note that the physiology of the mating phase is more complex than that of the nonreproductive phase; and that to enact each phase, the society migrates to a different territory, either literally or in the psychological sense that the same territory alters meaning and is treated differently.

It is during the mating phase that individuality is heightened in such a way that there is isosexual intolerance and heterosexual attraction. Yet paradoxically, in those species where the individuals tend to disperse during the nonreproductive phase, they tend to congregate during the mating phase.

SEX IN THE VERTEBRATE BIOGRAM

All vertebrate individuals are sexually viable, and all are ambisexual (a term preferable to hermaphroditic). We shall discover that no other fact about the phylum has more important social consequences. It is enough by itself to make comparisons with insect biograms completely incommensurable.

The embryos of all vertebrates show very early a certain undifferentiated or "indifferent" tissue (an "anlage" or "primordium") which eventually produces either an ovary or a testis; in certain genera, in fact, both are produced in the same individual "normally"; in others —man, for instance—this is rare but not unheard of. In all cases, the accessory genital apparatus develops through patterned emphases and de-emphases of parts of the same set of structures common to both sexes in the earliest stages of the embryo. But even though the anatomy of the sexes is distinctive to the eye, each remains throughout life capable of secreting the hormones of both sexes; they also retain the capacity of producing the behavior patterns of both, even to the field of specific sexual actions; and these actions are very much involved with the hormonal secretions. In sum, the presence of both "sexes" pervades the entire organism of every individual; sex distinctiveness is a matter of patterned differential emphases. To be sure, these different emphases in the respective formulae of the two sexes produce, as quotients, spermatozoa and ova, respectively, and also uterine parity in the female mammal only. But this in no wise vitiates the principle just expounded. The facts have long been heavily documented and recognized, from anatomy to psychology.

Unlike the bees and the ants, all vertebrate individuals participate equally in the two phases of the biogram. During the mating phase, each sex is under the dominance of a different hormonal pattern, so that their activities are mutually complementary, no matter how the activity-pattern differs from one species to another. During the nonreproductive phase, the hormonal syndromes that are active in the mating phase subside, and sexual behavior disappears. But does this mean that during the phase of sexual quiescence, the social behavior of the individuals is identical, in the sense that the physical fact of their belonging to one sex or the other has no weight or effect upon the ordinary course of behavior?

The evidence conflicts, although perhaps, if we knew more, we should see it simply as paradoxical. Among the infants of at least the birds and the mammals, the sexes often give the impression of already being different in their behavior, at least "on the average" or "modally"; yet secretion of sex hormones has never been certainly detected. When the adults of vertebrates—from fish to mammal or bird—are observed for any length of time during their phase of sexual quiescence, there is a cumulative impression that the sexes have different behavioral textures. In many species, the males tend to dominate, but this may indicate an average higher metabolism or an average larger size. There are species of birds in which heterosexual pairs formed during the mating phase persist companionately during sexual quiescence, and here differences of behavior do identify with the sex of the animal. There may indeed be average quantitative differences of capacity, but the more striking fact is that the potential behavioral repertoires of the two sexes are identical. Even the behavioral repertoire associated directly with sex is lodged indifferently in the neurological mechanisms of both sexes; the hormones elicit them selectively. Except for behavior directly involved with anatomic specializations or initiated by the autonomic system (e.g., egg laying, parturition) the individual will spontaneously engage in the acts of the opposite sex when injected with the hormones of the heterosex. The female, for instance, can be induced to mount and to execute pelvic thrusts. The behavior of intersexual and homosexual individuals can be interpreted in the light of such facts.

Ambisexualism has consequences also during the phase of sexual activity. Nesting, egg-incubating, the brooding of young, are actions performed by the nonsexual anatomy of the animal; there is nothing about them that prevents motivation in either sex. Moreover, we encounter acts such as incubating and brooding which in one species are executed by the male, in another by the female, and can be experimentally elicited in the opposite sex; in still other species these acts are normally expressed by both sexes.[5]

In sum, in any species, such and such is the sex-differential emphasis upon anatomical features, such and such the accompanying differential of hormonal patterning which taps the common neurologic mechanism in this selective way, resulting in these particular assemblages of potential psychic symptoms which thus comprise species-specific behavioral syndromes.

THE EVOLUTION OF THE VERTEBRATE BIOGRAM,
WITH SPECIAL REFERENCE TO PARENTALISM

1. *The Poikilothermal[6] Vertebrates.* That the next part of the discussion may be clear, we offer a partial summary of the methods of reproduction in selected vertebrate categories:

Cyclostomes: Oviparity, with external fertilization.
Elasmobranchs: Internal fertilization (copulation), with oviparity and ovoviviparity.
Teleosts: External fertilization, with oviparity; internal fertilization with ovoviviparity.
Amphibia: Copulation, with oviparity and external fertilization; a variety of combinations not encountered elsewhere among vertebrates.
Reptiles: Internal fertilization, with either oviparity or viviparity.
Birds: Internal fertilization, with oviparity.
Mammals: Internal fertilization, with viviparity.

The original method of vertebrate reproduction undoubtedly was the simple one of extruding unfertilized eggs and spermatozoa into water, in some quiet spot where they were assured of mixing. But already at the Cyclostome level we find some ancillary behavioral patterns. At the Teleost level there is full parentalism. At every level, psychological and physiological patterns complement each other. The various amphibian patterns are transparently modifications of some ancestral fish patterns. On the other hand, ornithologists have been as entertained by the reproductive patterns of fish, as ichthyologists by the patterns of birds—though without committing themselves as to the strange parallels that occur.

Copulation—which is not necessarily the same thing as internal fertilization, as witness the frogs—simplifies the behavior otherwise attendant upon external fertilization. Internal fertilization turns the female into a portable nesting-site. In marine vertebrates this releases the species from having to spawn in shallow waters; it has enabled the extension of the feeding-range to deep waters. Copulation removes from the male the onus of choosing a nesting-site and ever tending fertilized eggs. Still, we cannot taxonomize the vertebrates in terms of this feature: it is so scattered over the phylum that we are led to surmise that it is a device potentially present in all vertebrate lines which only some of the lines have exploited. It is essential for terrestrial living; yet it is practiced by vertebrates which have never attempted the conquest of land.

Once a fertilized egg is free of the parent's body, there is nothing about it to determine that it must remain the care of one particular sex. Where fertilization is external, the male is the last to extrude; [7] so that theoretically nothing stands in the way of male parentalism; he can move directly to caring for the entire mass. As already pointed out, male parentalism occurs abundantly among fishes and birds, and to some extent among amphibians.

If a parent remains with the incubating young until they emerge, whether by hatching, simple extrusion, or parturition, a new set of parental actions ensues immediately without exception: these actions elicit from the young an innately-determined behavior which attaches them to the source of the elicitation. This occurs in every class from fishes to mammals and birds. Here is a psychological parent-offspring mutualism that justifies the appellation "familialism."

This illuminates the significance of the Amphibia in a way that, as far as I know, has never been noticed before. It is they who contrived to develop, for the entire line of land-vertebrates, anatomical and physiological devices for transferring the nonreproductive phase of the biogram to a terrestrial habitat; but they failed to do this for the mating phase. For a mating phase on land there must be internal fertilization in a portable egg-container; thereafter, the young may be incubated in situ until ready to move freely. Or else there must be a drought resistant envelope, which allows O_2/CO_2 exchange, that can be extruded and permitted to incubate. Obviously, such devices could not develop before land-dwelling in the nonreproductive phase had become a reality. When (after another few million years) the amphibian succeeded in transferring the reproductive phase onto land, it thereby turned into a reptile.

2. *The Nonreproductive Phase in the Amphibia and the Reptilia.* The gross movements of amphibians are slow, even though some particular mechanisms are swift (insect-catching by frogs). Urodeles remain more skillful in water than on land. Perhaps this accounts for a sluggish, if not totally absent, sociality on land during the nonreproductive phase.

Far too little is known about this phase in the reptiles. Lizards (Anolis) tend to be solitary and to preserve a sense of territory, although it is dulled as compared with that during the mating phase. Some reptiles gather to hibernate or to lie about; but this does not constitute a society (compare crocodiles lying congregated along a river-bank). For a society is constituted by inter-individual reactions which produce status and molar or concerted maneuverings, and on such matters we have few data.

3. *The Mating Phase in Amphibia and Reptilia.* With the onset of the mating phase, Urodeles and Anura migrate to their breeding-grounds and perform mating-rituals of an amazing variety, but uniform in essential principle. The movements of males and females contrast and are complementary. Male Anura take up stations, identify these stations with cries, and lure the females. Copulation techniques vary widely; some produce internal fertilization and others external. There is some nest-building and other devices for securing eggs in protected spots. Some frogs and toads protect their young after they hatch, and the young orient to their guardian. The males of some Brazilian frogs (Phyllobates and Dendrobates) transport their young in their mouths from their hatching-ground to the pond where they spend the nonreproductive phase of their lives. The habit of transporting the young in their mouths occurs also among a number of fish genera.

Gravid reptilian females dig nests and lay eggs in them. Some species abandon the eggs immediately, others hover near. Some snakes incubate their eggs by coiling themselves about them. Crocodilian mothers remain near the covered nest until the youngsters set up a piping within their shells. This stimulates the mother to dig them out hastily, and to conduct them to the water; the youngsters immediately orient to their mother.

Sea-living tortoises illustrate the degree to which habitat is tied up with behavior-pattern. Here are animals who have returned their nonreproductive phase to the sea, leaving the egg-laying business on the land. After the females have gone ashore to lay their eggs, the males congregate near the coast; when the females return to the water, they are courted and fertilized and the spermatozoa are stored until the next batch of eggs ripens at a much later time. It is obvious that behavior segments of the total drama have been shifted into new alignment with respect to each other, along with a shifting in the physiological events.

No extant reptiles display male parentalism, but we must remember that the extant amphibians and reptiles are mere remnants of once widespread and varied faunas of the upper Paleozoic and the Mesozoic respectively. It is not hard to understand this lack of male parentalism. Once internal fertilization has occurred, there is no sustaining stimulus to keep the male attendant until the female extrudes her eggs. From studies of other animals, sustaining stimuli are known to be necessary to hold behavior over any period.

4. *The Biogram of Birds: Nonreproductive Phase.* As with other vertebrate classes, less is known about this phase than about the mating phase. With the exception of raptorials, few genera appear to be solitary, suggesting that the stem-reptiles were gregarious. If we may trust the cages in the zoological gardens, there are dominance-subordinance and peck-orders, even when sex is inactive, just as there are among fishes. Among parakeets and mallard ducks (Masure and Allee 1943; Schelderup-Ebbe 1924) the females "dominate" during the nonreproductive phase but not during the mating phase. For instance, if the female parakeet tries to leave the incubating and brooding nest, the male drives her back on. (We recall that among fishes too, where the male is responsible for providing the embryos a chance to develop, it is he who carries the task through to and beyond hatching.) But in other bird species, the males dominate the females in the nonreproductive phase and cease to do so during the mating phase (Allee 1952).

Bird flocks definitely are societies even when not in the mating phase. Vultures about a carcass may be no more than a congregation, but a group that maneuvers with precision is responding very sensitively to interindividual stimuli. But whether there is any group leadership in such cases is not determined. When one individual is startled, the rest take flight without waiting to sense the source of danger. Apparently there is nothing more impressive than the peculiar "military drills" which great masses of penguins execute (Levick 1914). Penguins, incidentally, have a very full social life—they play, take excursion-rides together, palaver. In some bird genera, the liaisons formed during the mating phase continue on into the nonreproductive phase as semi- or quite permanent monogamous "marriages."

5. *The Biogram of Birds: The Mating Phase.* For this phase, the birds migrate—physically and geographically in many species, but always psychologically. Even where they remain on their ground throughout the year they treat it differently, and likewise behave differently toward their fellows.

Though there is a range of variation, the males generally migrate first, stake out their territories, drive off intruding isosexuals, often begin nestbuilding, court the females when they arrive, and invite them to the site. The more primitive genera (most Paleognathae) show male parentalism either exclusively or prevailingly; almost all the rest show biparentalism. A few show female parentalism alone, but even here there is indication that males are guardians of the flock. In biparentalism, the total task is often divided into two roles, but not in all cases nor always in the same way. In one the male may build the basic nest while the female lines it; in another, the male brings the materials and the female places them; again, the female incubates and broods, while the male mounts guard; yet again, the mates "spell" each other on the eggs. These are examples of the point, already noted, that the entire behavioral pattern is lodged in the neurological mechanism indifferently as to sex, and that it is differentially sensitive to elicitation by hormones. Mention was made earlier of ambisexualism in the vertebrates even with respect to sexual conduct. Taibel (*vide* Beach 1948:183) tells of tying down a turkey-cock on a clutch of eggs; when released, the animal—which otherwise never incubates—continued to set of its own accord. The behavior was evoked by nothing more than the stimulus of a contact with the eggs—the same stimulus that is involved when a hen incubates.

Females of some species indicate subordinance and invite copulation by a peculiar flattening of their bodies before their male mates; in other cases, by soliciting food from the male in the way a half-grown fledgling will do. I have never heard of a case where the male behaves this way toward his female, or of his ever being fed by her.

A youngster's first social contacts other than response to parental care are with his nest-mates; his next (and expanded) social contacts are with the young that have left other nests. When the young begin to show the flight-impulse, the parents stimulate them. This kind of stimulating falls under the definition of "training." In those species where this particular action occurs, it is a step in the program of emancipating the young from the parent. Of course, barnyard fowl do not emancipate their young by the techniques used among high-nesting birds.[8] It is not fully appreciated by some students of animal society (and certainly this is true of many a human parent) that to emancipate the young from the parental bond is a part of the parental behavior pattern quite as genuinely as parental care is, and that in many species it requires positive and definite acts.

Birds have been called "glorified reptiles." It is a matter of taste which word one cares to emphasize, for the reproductive physiology is far closer to the reptilian than the mammalian; on the other hand, the homoiothermal ("warm-blooded") metabolism of birds has given them a much more powerful brain and therefore a much richer life-mode than that of any reptile. Nevertheless all the embellishments continue to be constructed upon the base of a vertebrate biogram.

6. *The Mammalian Biogram.* The mammals originated many millions of years before the birds—for that matter, before our common "bony fishes" (Teleosts). They have declared as exclusively for viviparity [9] as the birds have for oviparity. For reasons already clear, fertilization is internal. In sharp contrast to the birds, parentalism is universally a female specialty; for the mammals generally the definition of family becomes that of mother-and-offspring. There is a uniquely intimate and complex gestation within a very specialized uterus, and with a corresponding endocrine drama. This one feature is enough to affect the entire biogram, though without destroying its essentially vertebrate character.

To classify a mammalian species as "solitary" or "gregarious" (as has been done by some mammalogists) has but limited usefulness, and can be misleading. Social attitudes often change when the mating phase becomes activated; male "hermits" and "bachelor clubs" (various deer, carnivores, pinnipeds) seek out female company and the sexes remain together for more or less prolonged periods. Social attitudes vary between sexes of the same species: bovine bulls, rams, billies do not live as herds, while cows, ewes, and nannies readily do. Wild dogs and male lions may or may not temporarily form into packs for hunting; most cats do not. Bison probably lived dispersed in small groups which united but for seasonal migration. Seals and some deer live as sex-moieties when not in rut—the adult males as "bachelor clubs," and the females with their young of both sexes. The females, that is, live as "grouped families." The young males eventually leave to join the bachelors. Monkeys live as bands, the size of the band depending upon the species.[10] Some bands develop "splinter groups," and there may be "hermit" males, single or paired (frustrates and/or deviants?). A chimpanzee band disperses widely during the day and reconvenes toward evening. Orangs seem to become more "solitary" as they age. Exceedingly few mammals live as monogamous pairs; possibly rhinoceroses do. Equid stallions and bull seals collect temporary harems during rut. Muskoxen, caribou, prairie-dogs, beaver, and monkeys live as bisexual social groups. Clearly, we cannot always characterize the sociableness of the entire species with one term.

Permanent bisexual herds behave differently from sex-moieties temporarily united. Among the former, with no exceptions that I know of, the males form a rampart for the entire herd against external threat; while among the latter (e.g., roe deer) the sexes separate in flight.

Mammals living as small groups develop pronounced dominance-subordinance relations and social hierarchies. That their behavior in this matter is more complex than it is among the birds is attributable to the difference in cerebral development. There are intrasex hierarchies and interindividual (paired) heterosexual ones; they change with age, physiological vigor, phases of the biogram, and other circumstances.

In this context we must consider the intrauterine gestation of the female and the mammalian definition of family: mother-with-offspring. There is no doubt that the mammalian oestrus cycle evolved from a reptilian reproductive equivalent, but it is more complex anatomically, physiologically, biochemically and neuropsychologically. Here we can but note that the luteinizing hormone, or a chemically related substance that presides during mamalian pregnancy and is present in other vertebrates, must be phylogenetically far more ancient than the mammals themselves. The role of the evolution of hormones in relation to the evolution of the vertebrate biogram offers a recognized but still unresolved problem for biology. We note additionally and immediately that the menstrual cycle of the Catarrhine primates (Old World monkeys, apes, humans) is but the mammalian oestrus cycle as expressed by the variant kind of uterus which is common to these primates.

Some mammalian females ovulate but once a year (ungulates, foxes); in others ovulation occurs several times a year. The determining factors are multiple. They are internal as well as external. Every organism has its own biological time-scale and time-pattern, which is not strictly commensurate with some telluric or sidereal scale. For instance, mice ovulate every five days after the age of 3 months, until they are old at 1 year of age; rabbits develop ova continuously but ovulate only under the excitement of copulation.

The gestation period follows impregnation, and the endocrine drama changes. The contrast between mammalian gestation and the incubation period of birds is enlightening. The interval between fertilization and egg-laying among birds is not long; it requires only the accumulation of egg-yolk and shell (for which fertilization is not necessary). But once the eggs are laid, the parents—either or both—actively incubate. Here the behavior pattern of the parents is elaborate, while the eggs are inert and unresponsive. From the standpoint of the embryo (not from that of the parent), this period is comparable to that of intrauterine gestation in the mammal, and hatching corresponds to birth. This is tantamount to saying that the period of incubation in the mammal has disappeared inside the mother's body so that the psychological segment of the process, so well developed in birds, is utterly lost in the mammals, and with it disappears male parentalism.

The embryogenesis of mammalian behavior thus starts within the maternal body. But whatever stimuli come to the embryo are mediated by the maternal physiology. What this may mean to the psychology of the postnatal mammal can only be guessed. At any rate, the brain of the mammal is extraordinarily large and powerful. It is reasonable to suppose that only in animals possessing intrauterine gestation instead of egg-laying could it have come into existence, since it is unlikely that enough yolk could ever have been stored up in an egg to carry a mammalian embryo through to hatching.

Vertebrate parentalism is a most remarkable process of complementation between physiological and psychological factors; and there is nothing that throws into greater relief the differences of biogram between our phylum and the various social insects than this aspect. The potentialities of the vertebrate process reach climactic expression in the mammals. Their ontogenesis is best understood as a graded emancipation of offspring from parent. Birth is the first step in this emancipation. Hitherto the offspring has been absolutely dependent physiologically upon the parent, and the "psychic environment" of an external world has been lacking. Now there is established a psychological factor in the parent-offspring relationship. Suckling is a mutual adaptation, a trophallaxis. It is both physiological and psychological; its exercise is a homeostatic phenomenon: there is a detensification in both mother and offspring. At the same time, maternal care eases the connection that must be established between the new sensing organism and the sensed environment. The next step in the emancipation is weaning, which detaches the young from its physiological dependence upon the mother, but not its psychological dependence, which undergoes further revision. Psychological dependence remains mutual, and this fact can hardly be overstressed if we wish to understand what happens at the human level. The final step detaches the offspring completely from the parent; socially and psychologically, they cease to be related. Mutatis mutandis, birds and mammals show striking parallels in this whole drama. Complete maturity involves a de-orientation by both parents and offspring. This may include definite emancipative acts.

To return to the early childhood of mammals—in proportion as the young start de-orienting from the mother, enter into social relationships with each other. As we have seen, this is phylogenetically the older sociopsychological process; but as parentalism evolves among vertebrates it becomes ontogenetically subsequent to the establishment of sociopsychological relations with a parent. Most conspicuously, these young-young interactions are expressed through "play." Both birds and mammals play; nor is play confined to the immature. We are still far from understanding what play is, although much is being discovered. It suggests a surplus of psychoneurologic energy beyond what is needed for mere survival.[11] Failure to participate in play with one's fellows produces or is symptomatic of an inadequacy in the individual (see note 3).

We return to the sex cycles of adults. A mare has one oestrus cycle in the year and gestates for 11 months. Thus, she may be pregnant again before her first lactation is over; one reproductive phase overlaps another; the ancient vertebrate nonreproductive phase is in limbo, but, let it be stressed, it remains latent. During pregnancy, the mare ceases to be erotic, and she is not exercising parental care upon young. She carries on activities present also in the non-reproductive phase. It is, so to speak, as though laminae of the two phases have become so displaced that they are arranged in echelon.

The reproductive configuration of mammals is essential to an understanding of the orientation of the sexes, particularly in apes and man. The mammalian male possesses but one reproductive orientation: toward his female as a sex partner. If he constitutes a rampart for the herd, it is primarily by extension of the territorialism which, in other vertebrates too, is an aspect of the self-identifying complex, and is not confined to the mating phase. Among some mammals, we have cases of the male who consorts monogamously with the female whose young he has sired (foxes, coyotes); and he takes an interest in them, not only acting as a rampart, but also by bringing them maimed prey to worry and kill. Solitary males temporarily "adopt" youngsters (monkeys, and perhaps bears). It appears that a male who consorts with a female until after she gives birth eventually comes to tolerate her unaccountable annexes as part of her "configuration" and even develops an active relationship with them. The instances are more familiar than they are understood scientifically, but they may ultimately provide the clue to human biparental familialism.

The mammalian female, the human not excepted, has a more elaborate sexual cycle and a double orientation: toward a male as a sex partner, and toward a brood as its parental fosterer. This double orientation has already been noted among birds, where it is more diagrammatic in that experiments with hormones and with brain insults have in some measure sorted out its constituents. It appears to be generally true that copulation and young-tending (e.g., suckling) are mutually inhibiting;[12] but they can run concurrently as latencies in mammals. It remains possible for a lactating mother to be erotic.

It does not seem far-fetched to see in this dual pattern the prerequisite for the human scheme of familialism—a scheme which developed tens of millions of years after the deployment of the mammalian lines in the very early Tertiary period.

7. *The Primate Biogram.* For simplicity's sake, we shall confine ourselves to the Catarrhines. As far as I know, they all live in groups (orangs are often supposed to be "hermits," but better acquaintance makes pseudo-exceptions of them) and possess the rapid sexual periodicity of the menstrual cycle.

I can think of no more weighty factor than the latter in the shaping of human sociality. In a Catarrhine community, the females in the aggregate are in all stages of the cycle and in all degrees of sexual receptivity. The matter is most complex and paradoxical. Although the female is sexually "out of the running" during pregnancy, there is never a time when some members of the band are not copulating or youngsters being born. At least among monkeys, an erotic female seems practically assured of sexual attention. (The frigid female and the permanent spinster seem to be cultural artifacts.) The nine-month pregnancy of man (and comparable length among apes) does not have the force it would carry in the equid society; for the primates originated in latitudes that lack the annual cycle of the temperate zones and do not have an annual rut. Adult primate individuals never have a period when their psychoneural mechanisms are without the tonic stimulus of the sex hormones. This fact lies at the base of Freud's major discoveries. Together with the high capacity of the primate brain for making associations that can produce endlessly complex motivations for actions, this makes for a versatile psyche. For instance, a female monkey who can be erotic and yet be caring for youngsters of different ages and therefore different needs has to have a varied behavioral repertoire "on tap."

Prolonged primate immaturity coupled with the rapid menstrual cycles practically guarantee that the family will contain youngsters of more than one age, so that the young learn behavioral adaptation to different age-levels concurrently.

The essential family remains mother-and-offspring. A chimpanzee father may take a playful interest in the offspring, inducing it to climb and romp; or he may discipline any obstreperous youngster. But it is the mother who fondles, cuddles, and coaxes out the incipient attempts to shuffle about under its own power. Male familialism in apes and monkeys is fractional, even when present, but males are ramparts for the entire herd against intruders.

The dominance-subordinance behaviors and the hierarchies have been studied in great detail.[13] They are complex and anything but static. In monkeys, the male hierarchy (within the limits of our observations) commonly outranks the female, but this would demand qualifications. Heterosexual gibbon pairs show no clear-cut sex dominance. Male chimpanzees dominate females more often than the reverse, but there are plentiful exceptions. Where the male dominates, the female frequently develops the technique of offering herself sexually, even when not particularly erotic, as a bribe for favors from her consort. (Technically, this is called "prostitution.") When the female is highly erotic, her male consort offers her favors or refrains from exercising dominance; and she takes liberties which she does not attempt when not in a sexy condition.

As youngsters begin to widen their foci of interest, they form transfamilial play-groups, and so commence to de-orient from their mothers. Among chimpanzees, they become large and boisterous gangs. Although chimpanzees of a certain minimum level of maturity cooperate to secure a goal that is of interest to each of them, there never is team play.

8. *Summary of the Vertebrate Biogram.*

1. The vertebrate biogram is diphasic. It is an integral facet of the vertebrate morphology, and so participates of necessity in the differential evolution of the phylum.

2. The biogram itself testifies to the existence of a configurative neurologic-psychologic mechanism which cannot be other than innate. Differences which are diagnostic of any given vertebrate kind must be accounted for as variations upon a common theme.

3. The diphasic nature testifies to a corresponding endocrine cycle: the configurative activity of a hormonal system where hormones are activated and deactivated, where one gland stimulates another, and there is reciprocation.

4. It is inescapably implied that these neurological and endocrinal

mechanisms are innate and genetic. Hormones activate neurological mechanisms and so supply them with a certain tonus. In the absence of the endocrine action, the neurological mechanism may remain latent and unexpressed.

5. The vertebrates are ineluctably ambisexual. This makes it possible for segments of conduct in a total syndrome to be expressed variously by one sex or the other, depending upon the genus in question, and also for both sexes to engage in the same activity within a given syndrome—even the reproductive syndrome.

6. The units of operation are individuals, and an individual, being an organism, is a biological determinate; its status is the resultant of psychological interreactions with its kind. The behavior of statuses may be treated as constituting the metabolism of a society. This feature sets off vertebrate biograms from those of insects.

7. Status unavoidably involves dominance-subordinance relationships in interindividual contacts; repeated contacts among individuals produce social hierarchialism. These occur in either phase, but they are more intense or more general during the mating phase.

8. To act out the two phases of their biogram, vertebrates either migrate to a different locale or change their attitude toward the territory they occupy continuously ("psychological migration"). Vertebrate interreactions are always contextual; territorialism becomes part of that context.

9. The mating phase produces heightened and more complex interindividual behavior: iso- and heterosexual behavior, with intrasexual intolerance and competition and patterns of intersexual complementary behavior.

10. More often than not, the males take the mating initiative, such as selecting the site of the reproductive drama and courting; but nest-building and all other accessory reproductive activities may be engaged in variously by either sex or by both. A basic determinant of the respective sex roles is the elemental biological method of extruding the germ cells. The reproductive syndrome develops nest-parentalism, full parentalism, bi- or uniparentalism, and complete parentalism. All but the last of these variations occur as far down as the fish level.

11. Part and parcel with status-definition is the maturative course which vertebrates must undergo. It is communal to begin with: interindividual contacts of age-peers train the young, who thus become socialized.

In addition to these general features of the vertebrate biogram, we note the following mammalian particulars:

12. Intrauterine gestation makes the mammalian family ineluctibly

one of mother-and-offspring; the male is often relegated to the role of rampart for the entire group, if it is gregarious.

13. This gestation requires a double orientation for the female and a single orientation for the male. The female orients toward a male as her sex-partner and toward offspring as the object of parentalism; she is intimately bound up with two phases of sex-hormonal activity. The male orients toward the female as his sex-partner, but has no special orientation toward the offspring. Where males show interest in the offspring of their female partners, the matter requires a less obvious explanation.

14. The primate menstrual periodicity is characterized by rapid turnover of the two biogrammatic phases, a nonsynchronization in the female population taken as a whole, births taking place throughout the year, all aspects of both biogrammatic phases taking place within the group at all times, the nervous mechanisms never free from sex-hormone tonuses. Coupled with this is an exceptionally powerful brain, in a Class already remarkable for this trait.

The "archaic" vertebrate brain—roughly, what in mammals is known as the brain-stem—is entirely adequate for administering the whole biogram. Addition of the neopallial cerebral hemispheres in the mammals introduces complexities within the behavioral syndromes which make up the biogrammatic configuration, but the addition in no wise destroys or vitiates the biogram.

HOW "INNATE" IS (HUMAN) BEHAVIOR?

It seems hardly possible to survey the biograms of the vertebrates without becoming impressed with the parallelisms that occur repeatedly between the Classes; and, knowing what we do about the neurophysiological constructions that pervade the phylum, it becomes equally difficult to suppose these parallelisms to be without a common genetic basis. But the bulk of investigation upon the psychology of man, to say nothing of other mammals, has been directed upon the learning processes. Coupled with this goes the fact that it has proven practically impossible to pin any specific behavioral item to Mendelian heredity, so that a rigid proof based on the presence of genes is not available for human behavioral patterns as it is for certain physical traits. However, experimental psychology is rapidly demonstrating conditions where rats, dogs, monkeys, and humans show similar regularities that are hard to appraise as due to something other than hereditary mammalian pattern. It is, I believe, already possible to present a very reasonable case for the supposition that man, with all his

capacity for self-conditioning, has not escaped from an innate vertebrate biogram; the evidence comes from ethology, psychology and
psychoanalysis, and neurology. A few of these matters shall be reviewed.

In any act or series of acts, the whole question of what is determined by innate neurological mechanisms and what is modification
or adaptation that reflects the experience of the individual, has been
advanced to a very sophisticated level by the ethologists, the best
known of whom are K. Lorenz and N. Tinbergen. Ethology is a European comparative psychology which, instead of jettisoning "instinct," has proceeded to analyze it. Unlike experimental psychology
in America, wherein the experimenter sets up a laboratory situation
and measures the subject's responses to a situation created by the experimenter, ethology seeks to keep the natural and normal situation
for the animal in order to discover factorially just what it is that the
animal would respond to selectively in its own environment. Most of
the investigations have been made on fishes and birds; it is presumed
none the less that the findings and the method have relevance to human behavior.[14]

Tinbergen (1951:6, 37) considers that "most" American psychologists have been investigating higher levels of conduct than the innate
and instinctive, and so have been in no position to identify those
foundations of behavior. Be this as it may, there are two principles
which are moral certainties. (1) There are no purely "instinctive"
acts and no purely "learned" or "conditioned" acts; only acts in
which one or other aspect is more observable. All acts are but
symptoms of psychoneural activity, compounded from a highly intricate network of biological processes. (2) "Conditioning" cannot
be effected unless there is something conditionable that is innate in
the first place. Moreover, there are important, deep-lying formations in
the psychoneurology of even the most "intelligent" organisms which
participate in the gross totality that is called an "act," yet which lie
beyond the control of those portions of the brain which are directly
amenable to conditioning influences. Shortly we shall find ourselves
forced to take up the matter of the brain as the organ of neuropsychic
processes; for the present we shall consider certain features of vertebrate social psychology as treated by the ethologists, since they promise an insight into the problem of the instinctive in man.

The members of a species have so much behavior in common, even
when they have never been exposed to a common conditioning situation or to each other, that a genetic inheritance has to be assumed in
the absence of any other satisfactory explanation. Yet this does not

mean that the behavior is rigid and invariant. No ethologist believes instinctive behavior to be unmodifiable; nor does he believe that it can be dissolved or remodeled without limit. In matured fishes and birds, there are potential patterns of behavior which "spill over" (our expression) if the proper stimulus occurs at the appropriate moment. The stimulus becomes a sort of cue—a key to an "Internal Releasing Mechanism" (IRM; Tinbergen 1951). When a male and a female engage in a courting ritual, the act of one becomes a stimulus evoking a response in the other, which response is in turn a stimulus to the next act of the first. To illustrate: [15] A male three-spined stickleback is guarding his virgin nest. A gravid female appears. Were she another male, the first male would react in a certain way; as it is, he reacts to specific traits about her and performs a zigzag dance. This induces her to respond with a peculiar courting behavior which stimulates the male to lead her toward the nest. His leading stimulates her to follow. If she follows, he continues to lead until he has shown her the entrance to the nest. When she sees the entrance, she immediately enters. As soon as she is in, the male begins to prod her gently and rhythmically. The female needs this prodding in order to reach the condition where she can extrude her eggs. As soon as they have appeared, the male drives her out and enters the nest in her stead. There the presence of the eggs stimulates him to milt. Tinbergen speaks of this as a serial lock-and-key arrangement. But only a member of one's own kind is endowed innately with the correct behavioral complementation. This is what causes failure in the occasional interspecific attempts at courting (Lorenz 1937).

However, segments of a total pattern may also take part in other complexes, and under appropriate circumstances they may be released by another stimulation; e.g., two fighting birds stop to preen; a female solicits her mate sexually by begging food from him like a fledgling. (Boys or men may express affection for each other by giving each other a pommeling.) Violent tragedy may produce a laughing-hysteria. These are "Übersprungsbewegungen"—"displacement activities" (Tinbergen 1951:115). Conversely, the tonus for an activity may be built up to such a pitch that it breaks into action without the final stimulus that normally unlocks it; e.g., a caged bird goes through a large part of the nest-building performance without materials or a partner. These are "Leerlaufverhandlungen"—"vacuum activities" (Lorenz 1937; Tinbergen 1951:67).

Tinbergen (1951:105, 174) cites a significant though little appreciated paper by W. Craig (1918) who pointed out that animals perform a number of behaviors that start as a broad search and narrow down progressively toward a final "consummatory" act; these search-ing behaviors Craig called "appetitive." At this point, it will be help-ful to use the term "syndrome." A number of acts are organized, un-der a certain neuroendocrine urging, into a characteristic patterned composite, and composites may be further compounded. Thus (bringing Tinbergen and Craig into alignment with the phrasing of this assay) site-seeking, nest-building, courting, are each syndromal composites of appetitive behaviors leading to consummatory actions. Yet each of these in turn becomes an effective setting for the next composite, and all of them summate as an overall reproductive syn-drome: together they are a Gestalt—a configuration—none of which "makes sense" except as a part of a totality. In many cases, the con-summatory act may pass out of the jurisdiction of the voluntary sys-tem into that of the autonomic; e.g., esophageal peristalsis after swal-lowing; compulsive excretion; sexual orgasm.

Unlike conditioned reflexes, innate behavior mechanisms of the kind we are discussing are not artificially synthesized by particular and unique external stimulations; rather, they are notable for their uniformity of response though subject to elicitation from a variety of stimuli. These mechanisms have an ontogenesis, precisely because they are part of the organism's morphology. When they reach some stage of ontogenesis, they become capable of elicitation for the first time by an appropriate stimulus. However, when thus elicited, they are not precisely discriminative, even though they are quite definite. Thus, a new-born colt seeks randomly for its mother's teat; the horse-breeder often finds that he can help matters with a little expert guidance. Yet once the connection has been made, skill develops that is never lost. None the less, some segments of innate behavior require repeated elic-itations before they become focally oriented. This sharpening of orien-tation Tinbergen (1951) calls the "taxis" aspect. Thus, fledglings do not attempt to fly nor humans to walk until a certain period in their maturation-timetable; they cannot even be persuaded to try. Once the period has set in, simulating may encourage the impulse to come forth. A Navaho boy is the equal of his white brother in walking, though in infancy long bound to his cradle-board. As for taxis—when nestling birds are extremely young, any slight jarring of the nest will cause their beaks to fly open, directed skyward. Later, they orient toward the arriving parent and finally they actively peck at the morsel in the parent's beak. Their action has become very specific; and their own cooperative share in the feeding-process has increased, with a corresponding relieving of the parent. Discriminative ability develops in infant mammals also. The extremely young respond to the approach of an individual without any favoring; later (again following their maturation-timetables) they accept the approach of the fosterer but are terrified by strangers. The "training" which birds apply to the innate behavior mechanisms of their offspring Lorenz terms "Dressur." In the early infancy of birds and mammals, when discrimination is still indifferent, a substitute stimulus may elicit the innate response; this condition may have such a strong valence-bond that, once the connection has been made, it is irrevocable and subsequent application of the normal stimulus is ineffectual. Thus, a newly-hatched chick will fasten upon the first animal who fosters it—duck, cat, human—who thereafter is its "parent." Lorenz (1937) terms this a "Prägung" —"imprinting." This innate mechanism, which reaches a stage of viability at a specified point in the individual life cycle, has this further quality: it does not continue indefinitely to be in readiness. If an appropriate stimulus does not elicit it at the proper time, the quality becomes permanently stunted or perverted. Here belong the "Kasper Hausers" among chicks, lambs, children.[16] An innate behavior mechanism matures programmatically, and the program itself is a species characteristic.[17]

Let us bring together a number of points. The vertebrate individual is at all times an extremely complex and dynamic organization whose potentials are poised or discharging or recuperating. The organisms own processes are its stimulations—interstimulations with feedbacks. Strictly speaking, the external environment furnishes no "stimuli" whatever—only energies which the organism itself translates into stimuli. The organism, we might say, is its own internal environment. This is significant no matter what the organism may be; at the human level it is fraught with peculiar and enormous significance in connection with the emergence of the symbolizing function—a point to which we shall return presently. An external "stimulus" is an event thrust into the stream of processes; the organism integrates the injection with what has been going on inside it prior to the event. The integration occurs distributively throughout the central nervous system. Involved in all this are hereditary organic mechanisms whose organization constitutes the instinctive portion of an activity; a programmatic maturing of the hereditary mechanisms which nevertheless require activating stimuli to assure their maturation; the harvest of experiences which constitutes the instinctive portion of an activity; a programmatic maturing of the hereditary mechanisms which nevertheless require activating stimuli to assure their maturation; the harvest of experiences which constitutes the psychic resources called memory—the harvesting itself being genetically determined (a monkey's memory capacity is not that of a dog); the messages of the occasion which, after being duly digested by the neuropsychic process, are compounded with memory-stuff and returned to the stream of response. A bit of all this is "consciously" perceived, but most of it is not. Consciousness, in any case, is only a matter of the moment. A human may realize what he is doing here and now, but he cannot be conscious of an entire appetitive syndrome of which his momentary act is a unit. An adolescent girl enjoys the company of age-peer boys and reacts to them, using as her artifactual implements the enculturative patterns she has experienced. She competes with other girls and enters a social hierarchialism. All the time she is quite aware of many of her specific acts and her techniques; but unless she has been given an education in the matter, she does not realize that all these performances are way-stations along an appetitive syndrome (in Craig's sense) stretching from menarche to consummatory act. As many a girl has found out, no matter what her culturized ritual may be, the consummatory act may descend suddenly and overpoweringly—she "cannot help herself." Of course she can't. She was a female vertebrate hundreds of millions of years before she became human.

BRAIN, PSYCHE, AND SYMBOL

We have already noted that all the vertebrate Classes which lack the cerebral hemispheres of the mammal nevertheless play through the entire drama of the vertebrate biogram; and that the addition of the mammalian cerebral hemispheres serves to enrich but not to destroy this pattern.[18]

We shall term this brain minus hemispheres the "archaic" brain; roughly it equates with the "brain-stem" of human anatomy (the cerebellar hemispheres are being disregarded); and we shall confine our attention to the two gross, anterior divisions of this archaic brain: the telencephalon and the diencephalon.

The first of these, the telencephalon, receives chemical stimuli from the environment and registers them as smell-tastes. In addition, the telencephalon associates with these smell-tastes other stimuli that are passed on to it from the diencephalon: visual stimuli, but more important still, visceral sensations that have "emotive" effect. Through the diencephalon pass the nervous tracts of vision, to register in the yet more posterior region of the "optic lobes." The diencephalon is perhaps the most complicated part of the entire brain. It also contains the "head end" of the autonomic tracts to and from the viscera; it is intimately connected with the pituitary—the "master gland" of the body; a certain portion of it is essential to consciousness; in the higher organisms, it "screens" nervous impulses and passes a part of them to the cerebral hemispheres for further "digestion"; in its reticular system it apparently is the final synthesizer of the total response to be made by the organism.[19]

The fishes move through a simple world of smell-taste-visceral sensations, "digested" and organized in but a rudimentary degree (see MacLean 1949). We err gravely, none the less, if we underestimate their biogrammatic capacities; as the details from the lives of sticklebacks and cichlids amply show (Tinbergen 1951). But as we pass through the successive levels of the amphibia and the reptilia, the associative regions of the telencephalon expand and finally elaborate the cerebral hemispheres of the mammalia. Contrary to some popular opinion, the cerebral hemispheres are a relatively simple and uniform tissue—certainly nothing comparable to the varietal structuring of the brain-stem. We might say, informally, that using what materials they receive from the brain-stem, they possess an enormous capability for fine-grained analyses, storage of experience, correlations between data, selectivity for responding; and they return a product to the diencephalon for final organization with autonomic impulses before the organism responds.

If Kubie is right, the symbolizing process has finally issued from the continued coordination between the "visceral brain" and the cerebral hemispheres, particularly the temporal lobe (the seat of memory), as the hemispheres have reached human calibre.

What has become increasingly evident in more recent work is the fact that this ancient brain—much of which lies in the depths of the temporal lobe, with its dreamy states of psychomotor epilepsy and its body-memories—had extensive relationships with both the neopallium and the hypothalamus [i.e., cerebral hemispheres and a portion of the diencephalon] . . . This part of the primitive forebrain lies in the basal-mesial portion of the temporal lobe with direct connections to the hypothalamus, becoming thereby a crossroads for both *internal* and *external* perceptions arising from the eye, the ear, the body wall, the apertures, the genitals, and viscera. These reach the temporal lobe via the diencephalon. Smell reaches it directly. Here, then, within the temporal lobe and its connections, is the crossroads where the "I" and the "non-I" pole of the symbol meet. It is impossible to overestimate the importance of the fact that the temporal lobe complex constitutes the mechanism for integrating the past and the present, the phylogenetically and ontogenetically old and new, and at the same time the external and internal environments of the central nervous system. It is through the temporal lobe and its connections that the "gut" component of memory enters into our psychological process, as the symbol acquires its dual poles of reference. Thus in the temporal lobe and its deeper primitive connections is the mechanism for the coördination and integration of all of the data which link us to the world of experience, both extero- and interoceptive. It is by means of this temporal lobe complex operating through a bipolar system that we are able both to project and introject. It makes of the temporal lobe and its intricate bilateral and autonomic connections, which MacLean has called the "visceral brain," the central nervous organ which can mediate the translation into somatic disturbances of those tensions which are generated on the level of psychological experience. It might even be called the psychosomatic organ (Kubie 1953:31f.).

The brief compass of the present essay precludes more than a suggestion of the articulations that are in process of formation between clinical psychology, psychoanalysis, and neurosurgery; the reader must be referred to the bibliography. Kubie finds that

. . . the symbolic process is a continuum from the conscious literal symbolism by means of which we ordinarily think, speak, act, and communicate with one another, through the preconscious allegorical symbolic forms of artistic and indeed of all creative thought, to the unconscious symbolism of the dream and of pathological symptoms. . . . Every symbol refers simultaneously to concepts which are derived from percepts of body needs and images, and to concepts which are derived from percepts of the outside world. Consequently, every symbolic unit hangs like a hammock between two poles, one internal or bodily (the "I") and one external (the non-"I"); so that whenever we consciously think and speak of the outer world, we are wittingly or unwittingly thinking and speaking of the inner world; and similarly when we are consciously thinking and speaking of the inner world, whether we realize it or not, we are simultaneously thinking and speaking of the outer world . . . (Kubie 1953:39, 42).

The speech function is so bound up with the symbolization processes that a special remark about its representation in the cerebral hemispheres is needed. With a possible exception of an area on the surface of the temporal lobe, the speech-areas now recognized occur elsewhere than in those regions involved in the foregoing discussion. In fact, the notion of speech as seated in the famous Broca's area is now known to be invalid. The activity itself—whatever be its involvement with the symbolic processes—includes vocalization, "word" formation, and silences; and these demand a coordination between at least five different cortical areas.[20] (In addition, the right and the left hemispheres are not equally involved.) We cannot say that these areas—and certainly this holds for the regions involved in symbolization—are lacking in the apes, although they lack the extreme development found in man.

The human brain mechanism thus appears as an intensified primate mechanism, with no visibly new structures. Between any postulated prehuman and his remote descendant, the protohuman, there could hardly have been anything but a gradual evolution of brain; between the night of no-speech and no-culture and the day of speech and culture, there could hardly have been anything but the twilight of a dawn. But the twilight men are all extinct.

CULTURE RECONSIDERED

In this article, we have assumed that culture is "man's way of living"—about as innocuous, and also nebulous, a definition as can be imagined. Kroeber and Kluckhohn (1952) have surveyed the semantic history of the term; they conclude that, while "we have a fairly well-delineated concept," "as yet we have no full theory of culture" (p. 181a). From their survey it appears that no serious attempt has ever been made to probe for the antecedents of culture in a prehuman substratum. The reason for this appears curiously complex. First, there is the Judeo-Christian culture tradition which postulates the uniqueness of man as primary and his similarities with other animals as of lesser significance. Translated to culture—its phenomena are so distinctive from the life-modalities of all other animals as to give ample room for their exploration while treating biological connections as irrelevant.[21] In recent years, some attempts at defining culture have been based upon concepts adapted from psychology. While this procedure has been fruitful, it necessarily cannot rise above its source; insofar, therefore, as psychology has likewise found it feasible to operate without serious exploitation of neurological data, culturology has shared the limitations. It is understandable that biological and cultural anthropology have consequently tended to become or to remain alien to each other.[22]

Hitherto we have tried to indicate the following points: (1) The biogram of a species (extensively if not completely) is a function of its physiological drama; (2) The primate biogram is a modified mammalian biogram, wherein a menstrual cycle has developed out of the oestral, with consequences for the social configuration; (3) A complex viviparity has fixed the basic familial pattern of mammals as that of mother-and-offspring, which relegates the adult male to a marginal or extrafamilial position; (4) The human has retained, practically unaltered, the physiology of the primate, but has developed the cerebral potential of the Order to an extreme degree.

In this regard there is nothing about the human brain that justifies its appraisal as anything other than the most intense expression of the primate potentiality. As compared with the "gap" between the reptilian brains without neopallial hemisphere and the mammal with such hemispheres, the discrepancy between ape and human brain is minor. This raises the paradox of a "minor discrepancy" making the difference between the nonsymbolizing ape society and the symbolizing, culturized human. This is not the occasion for discussing the point; suffice it to remark that we possess no yardstick whereby to judge that this difference is any greater than that between a reptilian and a mammalian psyche. The observation is a wholesome corrective if during our further comparisons of man and other animals we tend to become bemused by the human superlative. Our problem henceforth is that of a symbolizing brain operating upon a primate biogram.

We have noted that the societal configurations of insects are based upon individual statuses predetermined so thoroughly as to include anatomical polymorphism; while the vertebrate societal configuration is a matter of statuses compounded of an anatomical dimorphism limited to sex plus interreactions on a behavioral level. Thus vertebrate configurations possess one predetermined, unalterable facet and one exposed to the dynamics of change and social metabolism.

The symbolizing function operates upon both without favor, and within both the reproductive and nonreproductive phases of the biogram. Statuses and their roles become loaded with symbolism; that is, they become *eidolons* (see below). The nonreproductive phase proliferates both individual and group-reinforced eidolons. The familialism of the reproductive phase likewise converts statuses into eidolons. The male acquires a permanent eidolon within the familial field.

In this essay, "eidolon" means definition of status such that within a society it connotes certain associated activities, certain demand-rights and duties, privilege-rights and no-demand-rights, powers and liabilities, immunities and no-powers.[23] The simplest status possible, in man as well as other vertebrates, is geminal, involving a mutualism between two individuals. Human society is unique in that there is an endless multiplicity of possible statuses attached to an individual, and also in that it develops group-statuses with membership-statuses. A group-status is that of a group as such in the midst of a society; the members of the group hold corresponding statuses by reference to the group: i.e., they are derived statuses. The family itself obtains its eidolized group-status from the society within which it occurs. Since our subject is concerned only with eidolons which emerge from statuses already present in some form within prehuman society, we shall henceforth confine our attention to the evolution of human familialism because it is a prime example of the process. As compared with the wealth of statuses that a society can erect outside the familial circle, the number that can obtain within the familial circle is limited. It is a fundamental point that the very statuses within the family are reflexes of the group meaning of the family to the larger society. This will be analyzed presently.

1. *The social ontogeny of the human individual*. It appears that during the Pleistocene epoch the Hominid branch of the Anthropoidea lengthened its life-span and correlatively expanded the size of its brain. In the human brain, the cells cease to multiply in early infancy, but continue to increase in size; and there are certain electroencephalographic, histological, and biochemical alterations. During this ontogeny the nervous system is "malleable" in a way it ceases to be when growth is completed. Two kinds of learning go along with these processes: one that occurs only during ontogeny, one that sets in later and continues during maturity.[24]

These two kinds of learning certainly are not confined to man. They are characteristic at least of the higher mammals, and may well extend over a far wider range of the vertebrates. But in the case of man, the many years of growth provide both an extremely large amount of brain material for imprinting and plenty of opportunity for repeated impressions. It is a commonplace that the impressions of this early growth period in mammals and birds shape the animal's psyche for life. In the case of man, it is profoundly significant that his personality is one of multiple statuses which are acquired at various stages of maturity.

The long period of immaturity in man is followed by a long period of maturity. As yet, the full import of the fact that culture is a matter of interreactions between individuals having altogether a range of many decades of both kinds of learning has never been assayed by any method, whether anthropological, sociological, or other.

In both males and females, more in the former than the latter, the procreative period is lengthened—while the total life-spans of the sexes remain sub-equal. The prolongation cannot but be a factor in the evolution of familialism, and in the group-status of the family. This point will be brought out in the course of further discussion; introductorily, we may note again that the primate female, by virtue of her menstrual cycle, may conceive and therefore give birth at any time of the

year. With the ages of the young scattered thus desultorily over family
and society, and with the prolonged maturation of a superlative brain,
we have the setting for a rich and active psychic life; and parent-
young and young-young relationships become very complex. The
complexity includes multiple-status conflicts, frustrations, demand for
reciprocal adjustments among members of the primary group, elaborations of conduct that satisfy the motivations of the symbolizing
functions. A rich psyche engenders its own problems: it suggests the
operation of feedbacks.

We are now prepared for a further consideration of human statuses.
In man, dominance-subordinance and social hierarchialism are even
more strongly motivated than among other animals—which is saying
a good deal. In countless individuals they even become the focus of
life-pattern to the point of obsession. Obsessions are always loaded
with symbolism; and this fosters the suggestion that it is the symbolizing functions themselves that abet or even engender obsession.
Some cultures certainly encourage such life-patterns. We have noted
that vertebrate societal configuration includes a fixed and predetermined facet of sex dimorphism and a facet exposed to change, upon
both of which the symbolizing function operates. This means that
there is frequent intrasexual and rarely intersexual competition for
"eidolized" statuses. Leadership-followership is likewise institutionalized in many societies.

Multiple status is a human social characteristic. A human does not
cease to be a son or a daughter on becoming a husband or wife. That
is, not only can an individual A be the son or daughter of B and the
husband or wife of C, but B recognizes the A-C relationship and consequently enters a B-C relationship.

Let us look a little more closely at the A-B relationship. The mother-
offspring trophallaxis in mammals has already been mentioned, and
its eventual and necessitous rupturing as the offspring reaches a certain degree of maturity. At the human level, let us note that it is not
the biological relationship per se but the opportunity it affords for
psychological orientations that becomes socially significant. A mother-
offspring mutualism that endures for over a decade of maturative
learning in an animal with the endowment already noted does not
erase easily, even though other statuses meanwhile come into existence. Inevitably there arise occasions when the individual's statuses
conflict, and he has to make a choice. In other words—his own statuses become an environment to which he has to adjust. There opens
up to him a new world of sociopsychic inconsistencies, frustrations,
compromises, integrations. To this matter we shall return when we

discuss the topic of incest-definition. For the present we note that an earlier status may continue to influence personality as it tries to shape its newer statuses; and we may term this continuance a "reverberance."

Human statuses become socially generalized. It is not only B and C who recognize the sonship of A to B, but the whole group. And F is the son of G, K is the son of L: the group recognizes a common factor in A, F, K; yet the role-content of this common factor alters as A, F, K progress through their life-cycle. A is B's son for life, and even after the death of B. Moreover, B may persist as a parent even after death and collect ritualistic symbols. But, for all this to come into existence requires that the group be small. Had protohuman groups been as populous as those of penguins or flamingos, it is hard to see how these communal generalizations of status could have come about.

Other relationships—grandparents, cousins, uncles, aunts, and the like—are extensions of the primary group and must have emerged at the time when the primaries were being defined. It is imaginable that the definitions took many generations to materialize. A woman now a mother still lives in the presence of her own mother; her mother is in contact with her daughter. Siblings of several ages must deal with each other while each is orienting toward their common mother. The accidents of biology have furnished the setting for social definitions; only later may the biological fact be turned to a symbolic account: it is used to rationalize and sentimentalize and so reinforce the social relationship. Were this not so, there would be no adoption customs.

2. *Humanization of the primate family: familialization of the male.* Of all the new statuses that are involved in the human kind of society, none is as decisive as the familialization of the male. The sex which has but one orientation toward reproduction—the erotic toward a heterosexual partner—is brought to polarize many of his interests and skills upon the familial circle.

Malinowski (1927: Part IV; chs. 2, 3) promoted the romantic notion (although surely not original with him) that in the course of evolution the male assumed obligations toward the female he had impregnated, who had become less capable of fending for herself under the burden of pregnancy and parturition. This is a piece of modern folklore which would deserve no attention except for its apparent currency among laymen; yet it does throw into relief the theory offered here.

For one thing, female apes and female human primitives are quite capable of taking care of themselves; for another, male monkeys, apes, and primitive humans are a rampart for the whole group. Moreover, human primitives hunt for the whole group and distribute to a wide circle of individuals; this requires no blandishment from some female to whom one becomes attached. Finally, we have no evidence that the pre- and protohuman societies owed their subsistence to the hunting of large game that required male prowess.

It would be supererogatory to demonstrate that the male family status arose ages before there was any inkling of biological paternity. Present-day Australian natives do not see husband and father as two aspects of one thing; and the Pueblos, who are much more advanced culturally, still do not place upon the biological father and mother's husband the duties which we associate with those two roles. It has never been shown how the protohuman male could have accepted an obligation without first assenting to a moral and value code that could arise only by asserting the obligation. There is some circular reasoning here.

Too often, attempts to derive the human from the ape condition have speculated on too slender a basis. A factor seldom considered in speculations about the rise of human familialism is the fluctuating population-profile. The relations between males and females, males and males, females and females, vary in primate hordes with the absolute size of the groups and with the relative proportions of the sexes. Male baboons in a confined territory, with but a few females to go around, will fight savagely; in a large territory, with the sexes more nearly equal, intrasexual tolerance rises markedly. We have no right to assume that during some protohuman epoch relationships became stabilized and developed a standard set. Such things occur as consequences of a developed culture. As for monogamy and polygyny, brother-right coitus with a man's wife, marriage-dissolution, in-law rights and obligations—all these and many others are not among the prime requisites for defining human social origins. In a protohuman society, there must have been simultaneously single-couple consortings, polygynous ones, more or less stable unions, rapid turnover in mateships, bullyboys with harems, and a fringe of bachelors "hovering about and looking for a chance to commit adultery" (Hooton 1946:261). Another piece of folklore is the fancy of male sex-jealousy. True enough, a male actively in process of courting a female fights off other males—be they all fish, reptiles, sparrows, moose, or baboons; but this is far from the same thing as sex-monopoly.[25]

Male and female apes, and other animals as well, develop companionships out of sheer prolonged association. I have termed this "taking each other's rhythm."[26] On nonhuman levels, the extreme instances of this performance are the permanently monogamous matings of geese. Although it is exceedingly rare among mammals for such permanent unions to occur, there certainly are cases of males and females remaining together after the female has been impregnated and sexual relations have ceased. Thus, male foxes may remain with the vixen for some time after she has given birth, and establish a parental bond with her young. Bingham (1927, 1932; see also Yerkes and Yerkes 1929:247 seq.) gives a valuable account of the contrasting behaviors of male and female chimpanzee parents. Other instances could be cited. But when the male develops these bits of parental behavior, they appear only after a while, and they do not duplicate the maternal behavior. It has already been pointed out that, among the nonmammalian vertebrates at least, parental behavior is not a "built-in" ingredient of female sexuality; the mammalian situation has been indicated as a specialization attached to the peculiarities of mammalian gestation and postnatal care. At this juncture, we are faced with the fact that no human society is without the feature of social paternity and husbandhood in some form and to some extent, while no ape society has it except in the sporadic way just indicated; at the same time, these sporadic traces seem to be clues to the sources of male familialization in the evolving human line.

Nevertheless, it is a commonplace that even in the most evolved societies male activities are not as identified with the familial polarity as are those of the female. The male develops skills and interests which belong in that free-roving area where he is also the rampart of the entire society. The male elaborates his cultural inventions in that area where neither mating nor the rearing of young occurs. There have been two consequences. (1) In proportion as the male becomes familialized and so develops a stake in the circle that he comes to share with a female and their offspring, he brings to bear upon his domestic world the skills which he develops and elaborates outside that world. His mate has her own skills and inventions which she often can exercise simultaneously in the interests of her double orientation: that toward her mate and that toward her offspring. Extra-familial and intrafamilial activities are thus brought into mutual support: there is a cultural integration of the two vertebrate biogrammatic phases: the reproductive and the nonreproductive. (2) But most cultural inventions take shape outside the familial polarity; and it is out here that culture develops most elaborately. This reverses the relative complexity of the two biogrammatic phases; for, as we have had occasion to notice, it is in the reproductive phase that the non-human vertebrates display the more complex social behavior.

No matter what the readjustments between the sexes as to specific tasks and skills that can occur within societies in the course of time, sex moiety of interests and activities remains undiminished. Such division apparently obtains among all primates. This is not to say that males and females never engage in exactly the same kind of tasks. For example, foraging is done by both male and female monkeys; but the females sometimes share their forage with their young. Curiously, when in a human society a mixed-sex group engages in an identical common task, there develop in due course compensatory sex distinctions, often in the way the common task is broken down into parts per sex, or in the reactions of the one sex toward the other. To be sure, these procedures reflect cultural conditioning; but I would suggest that the simplest accounting for the situation is not the whole account, and that something deeper is involved. Men and women have different "rhythms." All vertebrates and many invertebrates as well (insects, arachnids) "take each other's rhythm" during sex activation; and adult primates are never without the tonus supplied by the sex glands. On this hypothesis, it is understandable that the group dances of primitives, where the sexes mass in complementary groups and thus give psychological emphasis to their sex dimorphism, should be powerful social cohesives. However, I know of no scientific study of this very meaningful phenomenon.

3. *Humanization of the primate family: the definition of incest.* In birds and mammals, other than man, once the parent has dismissed the offspring, they no longer are parent and offspring; their erstwhile relation remains a fact only to that bipedal mammal who tries to keep track of biological proveniences.

In man, the relationship continues to reverberate, and we have a source of intrapersonal conflict. Let us consider the mother-son mutualism. On the one hand, as a matter of psychological fact, suckling and coitus are mutually inhibitory, and between mother and son a suckling trophallaxis has in fact existed. On the other hand, here are a female and a male; sexuality has an existence at least from infancy on; and symbolic transfers are well known to the psychoanalyst.

A son is the only male whom a female puts through the weaning process, both from instinctual impulsion and reluctantly. He is also the only male other than the husband with whom there is immediate physical opportunity for coitus. The male consort is the other closely-contacted male, but she has not suckled and weaned him. At the same time, object-transference occurs in many ways among various animals. A human (and, presumably, a proto-human) female is capable of transferring her broodiness to her mate as well as her eroticism to her son. It is not unreasonable to see in the welter of conflicting attitudes the course for society's definition of mother-son status as a male-female relationship in which coitus shall never occur. This cannot be a resolution of a dilemma which all mothers and sons arrive at separately and autogenously; it is a resolution by society. But we are not to imagine it as occurring at some one time, and under some kind of decree. It "just grew": it must have come about gradually, without social self-consciousness.

The father-daughter relationship lacks the trophallaxis that involves the mother, so the weaning process is lacking; but the potential sexual situation exists. The daughter has been in an adult-immature relationship with the father, and within the family circle; but this is not enough to deter erotic orientations from developing on either side. However, the daughter's eroticism toward her father runs into intrasex competition with her mother, who has stood in a dominant position and also one of trophallaxis toward her. Since trophallaxis relationship between father and daughter is nonexistent, this kind of incest may be more frequent than the converse kind.

Between brother and sister opportunity for coitus is simpler, easier, and lacks the reverberances of the other two relationships. It probably occurs most frequently; in fact, although its tabu is very widespread, it is not universal.[27] Whether the fact that both siblings orient to the same parents has anything to do with the tabu, is uncertain. The situation is confusing, but several features seem involved: (1) The parents, and not society, enforce the incest tabu between siblings, whereas society and also the unimplicated parent are wards against parent-offspring incest. (2) Mother-son and father-daughter incest tabus do not have the same determinant circumstances behind them. Accidents of language have lumped them under the one term, together with that of a yet different situation, intersibling incest. When we treat them as a single phenomenon, we become prisoners of our semantics. However, some of the components in these disparate phenomena are similar. (3) The near-universality of these three kinds of incest tabu suggest that they are not culturally determined but involve subcultural, innate, psychobiological processes such as psychoanalysis is attempting to discover. (4) The fact that there are attitudes of disapproval or condemnation in all societies suggests that the psychic conflicts generated by the paradoxes of the situation do result in incest. (5) Any explanations of incest which start from the present-day rationalizations of primates as to why they disfavor or condemn it are to be discounted at face value. Moreover, explanations in which anthropologists attempt to use the advantages that have accrued to a so-

ciety from incest tabu as the reason for their coming into existence or
for their persistence, display a post facto logic and also are to be discounted.

From all this, we get the following definition of the human family in
terms of its phyletic emergence: It is a primary group within the society in which the status of heterosexual principals includes engagement
in coitus and all other members of the group are expected to refrain
from it. The definition is socially determined, and not by the family
itself. For, as we recall, the family is a group-status. This same situation defines the social status of being a child: an immature with a
familial reference. It defines the mutualism of parent-offspring. Every-
where the relationships of parent-offspring and of sibling-sibling are
normally irrevocable.[28] Not so the husband-wife bond, for the dissolu-
tion of which societies generally make ready provision.

Another set of relationships must have received their definitions at
the same time as those implicated in incest regulations: the isosexual
ones of father-son, mother-daughter, and isosexual siblings. In the organization of the human family, these isosexual relationships must
be the reverse of the coin to which the heterosexual relationships are
the obverse.

In final survey of the family, we may note: (1) Societies did not
take form by a confederation of families, since family is a stable
group recognized as such by the society; (2) From its earliest emergence in the vertebrate Classes, it has always represented a mood of
society, a phase in the biogram of the society; (3) It polarizes but a
portion of the society's repertoire of interests; (4) It is shaped by the
society much more than it shapes society; that is, its organization fits
the institutional demands of society, and it changes if the society
changes—it does not initiate societal changes but conforms to them;
(5) In no society is it more highly organized nor does it harbor
more complex social interchange than what is encountered in the area
outside the family (the non-reproductive area). For, in the family
the number of statuses is limited, while statuses can multiply indefinitely outside the family; the groups outside the family can become
indefinitely larger and so afford a wider range of behavioral expression.

FINAL APPRAISAL

If our hypothesis is valid, there must be consequences for a science
of man.

A patterned framework emerges for social anthropology and sociology, where hitherto there has been none: hitherto the writer of text-books has been free to list and develop his topics in any order he pleased. If he should now find that his descriptions must fit integrally into a natural scheme, our sciences would gain a coherence as yet lacking.

Furthermore, that there is a biological configuration from which social sciences may proceed, ties them into processes of organic evolution.

If a scheme appears for which zoology, psychology, neurology, and social science may together construct a common denominator, again there is gain.

As for culture itself—its many historical courses, its boundless web of mutual influences, its diffusions, its value-achievements, remain as amazing as ever. To the principle of cultural relativism, however, we may add another: biological determinism; although it is hoped that the limitations of its applicability have been implicit in all of the foregoing. The human organism combines innate processes of body and mind that demand to be elicited by favorable stimuli. Cultures are the idioms for eliciting and expressing this innate nature; they may be judged by their success in eliciting it optimally. Bantu or Balinese culture may not compete with the Occidental in technological triumphs, but they may stand much more favorable comparisons with it if the mature man, not the artifact, is the touchstone.

Notes

1. In the more detailed treatment, "coenonia" is used instead of "society" for technical reasons.

2. There are some land-dwelling Mollusca and Annelida, but it would be pedantic to insist upon this qualification. The Vertebrata are a subphylum of the phylum Chordata; but the "sub" may be dropped in this essay without a loss of information.

3. Technically, these are called "Kasper Hausers." See Katz 1953; Brückner 1933.

4. I use "personality" unabashedly à propos of any vertebrate individual as occasion demands, since this process is present in birds and mammals as truly as in man. It may be reasonably suspected to exist in other Classes.

5. For a comprehensive review of this subject, see Beach 1948; Ford and Beach 1951.

6. "Cold-blooded."

7. Certain salamanders have a most peculiar reversal of this order; sea-horses have a yet more bizarre arrangement.

8. For a careful study of social development among young chicks, see Brückner 1933.

9. We are disregarding the reproductive physiology of the Monotremata and the Marsupialia.

10. The fact is well attested, but its biodynamics are unresolved. Why, for instance, should the groups of some species break up more readily than others into smaller bands?

11. See Schaffner 1956.

12. This is not to deny that occasionally a monkey female may be soliciting a male while her youngster is trying to suckle.

13. See Carpenter 1934, 1940, 1942, 1952, 1955; Maslow 1936, 1937, 1939, 1940, 1942; Maslow and Flanzbaum 1936.

14. See Lorenz 1937; Tinbergen 1951; Fletcher 1957.

15. The example is from Tinbergen 1951: p. 49.

16. See Katz 1953; Dennis 1941; Spitz 1945, 1946.

17. See Beach 1937, 1938, 1942, 1951, 1953; Dennis 1941; Gesell 1945, 1948, 1949; Goldstein 1939; Halstead 1947; Hebb 1949, 1953; Lashley 1929, 1938, 1949, 1951.

18. Here is the fundamental philosophical assumption of the essay. The writer refuses to entertain notions of man as representing some kind of saltatory *nova* in the evolutionary scheme, until continuous gradation has been shown to be inherently inadequate for explaining human phylogeny over the entire gamut from anatomy to psychology. See also note 21.

19. For a lay account of modern knowledge about the brain, see Bello 1955. For basic information regarding the relation of the symbolic process to brain, see Kubie, MacLean, Magoun, Penfield and associates.

20. Approximately—these areas occur on the superior frontal gyrus, the inferior portions of the anterior and posterior central gyri, the opercular portion of the inferior frontal gyrus, the gyrus supramarginalis, and an indefinite and extensive area of the temporal cortex. See particularly, Penfield and Rasmussen ch. V.

21. Of course, practices attendant upon such biological phenomena as birth, menstruation, puberty, ingestion, and excretion are subject-matter for cultural anthropology. It should be obvious that this is beside the point to the present discussion.

22. Necessity for conserving space handicaps presentation at this point. In cultural anthropology and psychology there have been historical developments that are still likely to affect the receptivity toward the present approach. One is the tradition dating from Spencer's "superorganic," of which a gross consequence has been the belittlement of organic antecedents in the study of culture. A second is Lloyd Morgan's canon, about which there continues to be confusion in psychological circles as to its application. A third is the discrepancy between American and European approaches to comparative psychology. A fourth is the tendency, already noted in this essay, for many cultural anthropologists to go along with those psychologists who find it practicable to dispense with a neurological basis for their investigations.

The present essay subscribes in principle to Lloyd Morgan's canon, and applies it in the special sense that no human psychic phenomena may be given an explanation sui generis until it has been determined to what extent demonstrable factors in the psychology of related animals are etiologically deficient. Behavioral resemblances between man and other vertebrates do not lead to anthropomorphizing other animals; they do lead to "theromorphizing" man. Cultural conditioning is then viewed as an exploitation of the more generally vertebrate, and as a thing that tends to disguise the more basic and general.

23. These terms will be recognized as an extended application of the Hohfeldian system of legal concepts. See Hoebel 1954:48.

24. I am following Hebb 1949. He summarizes (p. 116) the phylogenetic

changes in the learning capacity thus: "(1) more complex relationships can be learned by higher species at maturity; (2) simple relationships are learned about as promptly by lower as by higher species; and (3) the first learning is *slower* in higher than in lower species." Learning in the mature animal is "heavily loaded with transfer effects" (p. 110). "It is of course a commonplace that the experiences of childhood have a permanent effect on one's attitudes, interests, and even abilities. Lorenz . . . has demonstrated the effect experimentally in birds. With mammals, everyone knows that taming is easiest in infancy, with a lasting effect . . . Hunt . . . has shown an effect of early hunger on later hoarding by the rat. . . . That the level of problem-solving at maturity, then, may be permanently influenced by childhood experience is an accepted psychological principle . . ." (p. 120).

The early type of learning is acquired during the time when the neural tissue is in process of growing. The physiology at this time is different from the adult condition; the electroencephalograms are patterned differently. The present essay has taken the view that psychological phenomena are the symptomatics of neurophysiological processes. Most experimental studies of rats, dogs, and other animals use the adult animal—after motivation and capacity to learn have matured. They are not useful at all in establishing how the definitive neuropsyche has developed.

Some actions, once learned, seem not to need further reinforcement, they resist extinction, they are but little influenced by set, and under normal conditions they are acquired very early in life. But studies of learning processes have tended to concentrate upon the later "voluntary," "learned" items of behavior.

25. In a personal communication, Sherwood Washburn informs me of stranger baboons copulating with females in full view of males who expectably might be jealous, without ever evoking any particular reaction.

26. The phrase analogizes with, but did not originate from, George H. Mead's "role-taking."

27. That there has been a fair number of brother-sister marriages among royalty is well attested. But there are also cases of entire societies where the tabu is absent (personal communication from Douglas Haring).

28. Those exceptional customs of child-borrowing or child-exchange hardly militate against this generalization.

A Selected Bibliography

ALLEE, W. C. 1952 Dominance and hierarchy in societies of vertebrates. See Colloques 157–183.

BEACH, F. A., JR. 1937 The neural basis of innate behavior, I: Jour. Compar. Psychol. 24:393–440.

—— 1938 The neural basis of innate behavior, II: Jour. Genet. Psychol. 53:108–148.

—— 1942 Central nervous mechanisms involved in the reproductive behavior of vertebrates. Psychol. Bull. 39:200–226.

—— 1948 Hormones and behavior. New York, Paul Hoeber.

—— 1951 Instinctive behavior: reproductive activities. See Stevens 1951:ch. 12.

—— 1953 Animal research and psychiatric theory. Psychosom. Med. 15:374–389.

—— 1955 Ontogeny and living systems. See Schaffner 1955:9–74.

BELLO, F. 1955 New light on the brain. Fortune, Jan., 104–133.

BINGHAM, H. 1927 Parental play of chimpanzees. Jour. Mammal. 8:77–89.

—— 1932 Gorillas in a native habitat. Carnegie Institution Washington Pub. No. 426.

BRÜCKNER, G. H. 1933 Untersuchungen zur Tierpsychologie, insbesondere zur Auflösung der Familie. Zeitsch. f. Psychol. 128:1–110.

CARMICHAEL, L., ed. 1946 Manual of child psychology. New York, John Wiley.

—— 1946a The onset and early development of behavior. See Carmichael 1946:43–166.

CARPENTER, C. R. 1934 A field study of the behavior and social relations of Howling Monkeys. Compar. Psychol. Monog. 10:2.

—— 1940 A field study in Siam of the behavior and social relations of the Gibbon (Hylobates lar). Compar. Psychol. Monog. 16:5.

—— 1942 Characteristics of social behavior in non-human primates. Trans. N.Y. Acad. Sc. II:4:8:248–258.

—— 1952 Social behavior of non-human primates. See Colloques:227–247.

—— 1955 Tentative generalizations on the grouping behavior of non-human primates. See Gavan 1955:91–98.

COLLOQUES INTERNATIONAUX DU CENTRE NATIONAL DE LA RECHERCHE SCIENTIFIQUE: XXXIV. Structure et Physiologie de la Société Animale. Paris, 1952.

CRAIG, W. 1918 Appetites and aversions as constituents of instincts. Biol. Bull. Marine Biol. Lab. Woods Hole, Mass. 34:91–107.

DENNIS, W. 1941 Infant development under conditions of restricted practice and minimum social stimulation. Genet. Psychol. Monog. 23:143–189.

DREVER, J. 1955 The concept of early learning. Trans. N.Y. Acad. Sc. 17:463–469.

FLETCHER, R. 1957 Instinct in Man. New York, International Universities Press.

FORD, C. S., and F. A. BEACH 1951 Patterns of sexual behavior. New York, Paul B. Hoeber.

GAVAN, J. A., ed. 1955 The non-human primates and human evolution. Detroit, Wayne University Press.

GESELL, A. L. 1945 The embryology of behavior. New York, Harper and Bros.

—— 1948 Studies in child development. New York, Harper and Bros.

—— 1949 Human infancy and the ontogenesis of behavior. Amer. Scientist 37:529–553.

GOLDSTEIN, K. 1939 The organism. New York, American Book Co.

HALSTEAD, W. C. 1947 Brain and intelligence. Chicago, University of Chicago Press.

HEBB, D. O. 1949 The organization of behavior. New York, John Wiley.

—— 1953 Heredity and environment in mammalian behavior. Brit. Jour. Animal Behaviour I:43–47.

HESS, W. R. 1944 Das Schlafsyndrom als Folge dienzephaler Reizung. Helvet. physiol. et Pharmacol. Acta 2:305–344.

HOEBEL, E. A. 1954 The Law of primitive man. Cambridge, Mass., Harvard University Pr.

HOOTON, E. A. 1946 Up from the ape. New York, Macmillan.

JASPER, H., C. A. AJMONE-MARSEN, and J. STOLL 1952 Corticofugal projections to the brain stem. Archives Neurol. and Psychiat. 67:155–171.

JEFFRESS, L. A., ed. 1951 Cerebral mechanisms in behavior. New York, John Wiley.

KATZ, D. 1953   Animals and men. Harmondsworth, Middlesex, Penguin Books.

KROEBER, A. L., and C. KLUCKHOHN 1952   Culture: a critical review of concepts and definitions. Cambridge, Mass., Papers of the Peabody Museum, Amer. Archaeol. Ethnol. 47:1.

KUBIE, L. S. 1948   Instincts and homeostasis. Psychosom. Med. 10:15–30.

―――― 1953a   The central representation of the symbolic process in psychosomatic disorders. Psychosom. Med. 15:1–7.

―――― 1953b   Distortion of the symbolic process in neurosis and psychosis. Jour. Amer. Psychoanal. Assn. I:59–86.

―――― 1953c   Some implications for psychoanalysis of modern concepts of the organization of the brain. Psychoanalyt. Quart. 22:21–52.

LASHLEY, K. S. 1929   Brain mechanisms and intelligence. Chicago, University of Chicago Press.

―――― 1938   Experimental analysis of instinctive behavior. Psychol. Rev. 45: 445–471.

―――― 1949   Persistent problems in the evolution of mind. Quart. Rev. Biol. 24:28–42.

―――― 1951   The problem of serial order in behavior. See Jeffress 1951:112–136.

LEVICK, G. M. 1914   Antarctic penguins. London, J. Heinemann.

LORENZ, K. 1937   Über die Bildung des Instinktbegriffs. Die Naturwissenschaften 25:289–300, 307–318, 324–331.

McGRAW, M. B. 1946   Maturation and behavior. See Carmichael 1946:ch 7.

MacLEAN, P. D. 1949   Psychosomatic disease and the visceral brain. Psychosom. Med. 11:338–353.

―――― 1954   The limbic system and its hippocampal formation. Jour. Neurosurgery 11:29–44.

MAGOUN, H. W. 1952   An ascending reticular activating system in the brain stem. Arch. Neurol and Psychiat. 67:145–154.

MALINOWSKI, B. 1927   Sex and repression in savage society. New York, Humanities Press.

MASLOW, A. H. 1936   The role of dominance in the social and sexual behavior of infra-human primates. Jour. Genet. Psychol. 48:261–277, 310–338; 49:161–198.

―――― 1937   Dominance-feeling, behavior, and status. Psychol. Rev. 44:404–429.

―――― 1939   Dominance-feeling, personality, and social behavior in women. Jour. Social Psychol. 10:3–39.

―――― 1940   Dominance-quality and social behavior in infra-human primates. Jour. Soc. Psychol. 11:313–324.

―――― 1942   Self-esteem (dominance-feeling) and sexuality in women. Jour. Soc. Psychol. 16:259–294.

MASLOW, A. H., and S. FLANZBAUM 1936   The role of dominance in the social and sexual behavior of infra-human primates. Jour. Genet. Psychol. 48:278–309.

MASURE, R. H., and W. C. ALLEE 1934   Flock organization of the shell parakeet Melopsittacus undulatus Shaw. Ecology 15:388–398.

NOBLE, G. K. 1931   The biology of the Amphibia. New York, McGraw-Hill.

PAPEZ, J. W. 1937a   The brain considered as an organ. Amer. Jour. Psychol. 49:217–232.

―――― 1937b   A proposed mechanism of emotion. Arch. Neurol. and Psychiat. 38:725–743.

———— 1944 Structures and mechanisms underlying the cerebral functions. Amer. Jour. Psychol. 57:291–316.

PENFIELD, W. 1952 Memory mechanisms. Arch. Neurol. and Psychiat. 67:178–198.

PENFIELD, W., and H. JASPER 1954 Epilepsy and the functional anatomy of the human brain. Boston, Little, Brown.

PENFIELD, W., and T. RASMUSSEN 1950 The cerebral cortex in man. New York, Macmillan.

SCHAFFNER, B., ed. 1955 Group Processes I. New York, Josiah Macy, Jr. Foundation.

———— 1956 Group Processes II. New York, Josiah Macy, Jr. Foundation.

SCHELDERUP-EBBE,TH. 1924 Zur Socialpsychologie der Vögel. Zeitsch. f. Psychol. 96:36–84.

SCHILLER, F. 1952 Consciousness reconsidered. Arch. Neurol. and Psychiat. 67:199–227.

SPITZ, R. A. 1945 Hospitalism. *In* The psychoanalytic study of the child, I. New York, International Universities Press.

———— 1946 Hospitalism: a follow-up report. The psychoanalytic study of the child, II.

STEVENS, S. S., ed. 1951 Handbook of experimental psychology. New York, John Wiley.

TINBERGEN, N. 1951 The study of instinct. London, Oxford University Press.

YERKES, R. M., and A. W. YERKES 1929 The great apes. New Haven, Yale University Press.

Selective Forces in the Evolution of Man

ERNST CASPARI

BIOLOGICAL PROBLEMS CONCERNING THE HUMAN MIND

With respect to every biological object or process two types of questions can be asked: the question of mechanism and the question of evolutionary origin (Mayr, 1961). The first question asks for the functioning of the object, the way it works; this question leads in the progress of analysis to an ever deeper understanding of the functional significance of the object. The great advances in biology which have taken place in the last few years, and which are clarifying rapidly the fundamental structure of genes, the coding of genetic information in the DNA molecule and the transfer of this information to cellular components, concern the fundamental mechanisms of living matter. In principle, every question of mechanism can finally be answered at the molecular level, even though at higher levels of integration a large number of fascinating problems concerning mechanisms remains to be solved.

A biological object is never completely described in terms of mechanism only. The specific way in which the mechanism functions in a certain species is the result of the unique evolutionary history of this species. While the fundamental mechanisms, genes, enzyme systems, etc., seem to be in principle very similar in all organisms, their specific arrangement giving rise to an organism adapted to a specific environment permits a large amount of variety. This variety has always attracted the interest of biologists. It can be understood, if its evolutionary history is described. But behind the evolutionary history in a descriptive sense there is a still more difficult problem, the problem to discern the evolutionary forces which have been responsible for bringing about the specific history of a particular organism.

A biological object which offers problems of particular attraction to

NOTE: This paper is dedicated to Professor L. C. Dunn in recognition of his many distinguished contributions to Biology and is based on a paper delivered at the Symposium "Genetics and Evolution of Human Behavior" of the American Psychiatric Association, December 27, 1961.

From *The American Naturalist*, Vol. XCVII, No. 892, Jan.–Feb. 1963, pp. 5–14. Reprinted by permission.

us is the human mind. About this object we can ask the same two questions. Most of the efforts in psychology and psychiatry have tried to analyze mechanisms. This is quite obvious in the new fields of psychopharmacology and electrode implantation in the brain where attempts are made to understand behavior in terms of biochemical and physiological processes. But it should be understood that most of the other methods used in psychology and psychiatry, including psychoanalysis, are fundamentally descriptions of mechanism, even though in these cases no attempt may be made to reduce these mechanisms to physical and chemical concepts. Besides this set of problems, the question of evolutionary origin has to be posed. It is in principle much more difficult to answer, since we cannot use the experimental method of analysis, and the historical record is in no case complete. Fundamentally, for the reconstruction of evolutionary history, we possess two methods: the comparison of related living organisms and the study of the remains of the past. All evolutionary history, as far as we can describe it, is derived from these two sources. The method of comparison has been applied to the problem of the evolution of the human mind in two ways: the observation of the cultural life of so-called primitive humans, and the study of the behavior of other primate species, as exemplified in the thorough investigation of the behavior of baboons in the wild carried out by Washburn and collaborators (Washburn and de Vore, 1961). Both methods have severe limitations, as has been known for a long time with regard to the use of the comparative method for the reconstruction of the phylogeny of morphological characters. More specifically, it is hard to know whether a simple cultural pattern in a primitive society is truly primitive or secondarily simplified as an adaptation to specialized ecological conditions (Blanc, 1942–43). But the method is valid in principle and has given a large amount of pertinent information. The paleontological method would appear primarily to permit conclusions concerning the evolution of morphological characters. But the presence of tools in old strata, the way in which they are deposited, and the contexts in which the fossils are found, have permitted us an increasingly clear insight into the behavior and activities of early humans and pre-humans (Clark, 1962). This recent knowledge enables us to ask the question of the evolutionary forces which may have led the evolution of man in the particular direction which it has taken; that is, the emergence of the human mind as we know it at present. It should be emphasized that such considerations are by their very nature speculative. Even though some general knowledge of the nature of the forces in evolution is available, we have no methods as yet to pinpoint the specific forces active in a particular species at a particular time, especially for organisms in the past where environmental conditions are insufficiently known.

EVOLUTION OF BEHAVIORAL CHARACTERS

Evolution consists of a change in the genetic properties of a population in time. We speak of the collection of genes present in the population as a gene pool, neglecting to consider the actual distribution of the genes in a gene pool to individuals. A gene pool will tend to remain stable in time, with a certain amount of variation in the frequency of genes due to chance which would not affect the gene pool of large populations over any length of time. The foremost mechanism by which changes in a gene pool come about is natural selection; some genes in a gene pool have under certain conditions a larger chance of being transmitted than their alleles. If, in a gene pool, two alleles of a gene are present, and one of these alleles has less of a chance of being transmitted than the other, the first one will gradually diminish in frequency and disappear.

The probability of a gene's being transmitted to the next generation depends on the phenotypic characters it produces in its carrier organisms in homozygous and heterozygous condition. Insofar as these phenotypic characters influence the viability of the carriers of a gene, i.e. their probability of surviving to reproductive age, their fertility, i.e. their probability of reproducing, and their fecundity, i.e. the number of offspring produced by them, they will determine how many copies of a particular allele will be present in the gene pool of the next generation.

The relation of these genetically controlled characters which determine the frequency of a gene in a population to the nature and mode of action of the genes involved has been elucidated in only a few cases. We know that the material basis of the genes is deoxyribonucleic acid (DNA), a high molecular substance whose structure permits identical reproduction, and which can carry in the sequence of bases a message in coded form which is transmitted by the process of identical reproduction. This message is known to be decoded in the cytoplasm of the cell, and is apparently translated into the structure of proteins. These proteins have, then, specific structures depending on the message which was coded in the gene, and their specific structures determine the activities of the proteins.

Because the cell and the organism are integrated systems a change in the activity of one protein may have secondary effects on a number of physiological processes. Secondary gene effects of this kind, which are called pleiotropic effects, have actually been frequently found. They become the more important, the more highly complex a biological system is (Caspari, 1952). With respect to particular phenotypic characters, pleiotropic gene effects will become more important, the farther removed a character is from the primary gene action. We would expect a particular protein to be influenced by a very low number of genes, one or at the most two. In the formation of pigments, several enzymes are involved, therefore effects of several genes may be postulated. Furthermore, we might expect at this level further pleiotropic effects of genes to play a role, acting through, for example, the amounts of substrates available. Actually, the number of gene loci known to affect eye pigments in Drosophila and coat colors in the mouse is of the order of 50. The characters on which adaptive value depends, probability of survival and fertility, are very far removed from the primary gene action, and would therefore be expected to be influenced by the pleiotropic effects of a large number of genes. As a matter of fact, it has been found that no mutant gene which has been thoroughly investigated does not have at least some effect on one of the characters composing adaptive value.

The adaptive value of a gene is not only dependent on the structure of the gene itself; it is also dependent on its environment. The environment in this respect can be divided into internal and external environment. The adaptive value of a gene is certainly dependent on the other genes with which it is associated, its genotypic environment. Dobzhansky has contributed a large amount of material which shows clearly that it is not particular genes which affect the selective values, but certain combinations of genes are superior to others (Dobzhansky and Pavlovsky, 1958). This is to be expected under the hypothesis of genic interaction in the production of characters removed from primary gene action which has been presented above. Even more important is the dependence of the adaptive value of genes on the external environment. It has been known for a long time that the viability and fertility of organisms of a specific genotype depends strongly on external conditions, such as temperature, food, humidity, and that a gene or gene combination which is at a disadvantage under one set of conditions may be at an advantage over another set of conditions.

This means that when a change in environmental conditions occurs, the adaptive value of some components of the genotype will change, and as a consequence the composition of the gene pool will change. More than that, it will change in the direction of adaptation to the new environment, since the genes causing better adaptation will become predominant in the altered gene pool. This change in the gene pool as a result of changed environmental conditions supplies a very powerful mechanism for genetic adaptation to changes in environmental conditions. How powerful this method is has been demonstrated recently by the response of insect populations to the invention of special poisons, the insecticides, by man. The alleles for insecticide resistance, apparently present in low numbers in the original population, have become accumulated due to their drastically increased adaptive value.

This last example shows one aspect of selection which should be briefly mentioned. If adaptation by genetic mechanisms is to occur, genes endowing the organism with the specific properties required by the new environment have to be present from the start, if only in low numbers. Genetic polymorphism is therefore a prerequisite for adaptability to changes in environments. Several mechanisms are known by which a certain amount of polymorphism is maintained. All genes mutate, even though with low frequencies, and for genes which under one set of environmental conditions are unfavorable, a mutation-selection equilibrium will become established, in which the frequency of the gene in the population is determined by the mutation rate and by the rate at which the gene is eliminated from the gene pool by natural selection. Another important method is heterozygote superiority, heterosis. In this case, the heterozygote has a selective advantage. Since a heterozygote contains two different alleles, it follows that both alleles will be maintained in the population. The case of sickle cell anemia in man, where the heterozygote is perfectly viable and resistant against malaria, is a well known example. Further possible mechanisms have been suggested. For the present purpose it may suffice to point out that a store of genetic variability in a species is necessary for evolutionary changes to occur, and that all organisms investigated show a large amount of genetic polymorphism.

EVOLUTION OF HUMAN CRANIAL CAPACITY

In the evolution of man, large physical changes have taken place, particularly with respect to the lower extremities and the pelvis, and with respect to the skull. We may relate the changes in the lower extremity to the acquisition of bipedal gait, and the increase in the size of the skull and the brain to the increase in the mental capacities of man. The latter conclusion may be criticized because of Lashley's (1949) finding that, inside a species, brain size does not seem to be correlated with learning ability. But Rensch (1956) has demonstrated that in comparing different related species, brain size appears to be proportionate to the ability to solve complex problems. In view of the fact that the function of the brain consists in the control of behavioral activities, it seems reasonable to assume that a conspicuous increase in relative brain size would be accompanied by effects on behavioral capacities.

The paleontological evidence gives us some clues on the sequence of the events which have taken place in the evolution of man. It shows particularly that the changes in the pelvic region, indicating the acquisition of bipedal gait, preceded, at least to a large degree, the acquisition of a brain of fully human size. This contradicts the assumption put forward by some earlier anthropologists, notably Weidenreich (1946), that the development of a large brain is a direct consequence of the forward tilting of the base of the skull accompanying the development of an upright position. While a connection between these two evolutionary trends cannot be excluded, they seem to have occurred independently of each other in time. Another important contribution of paleontology to our understanding of human evolution is the indication that the genetic changes responsible for the growth of the brain of man must have gone on at a very fast rate. In the time range from Australopithecus to the present, the cranial capacity of the human line has increased from an essentially apelike size to the brain size of modern man, that is, by a factor of roughly two. Leakey, Evernden and Curtis (1961) have estimated the age of the Australopithecus remains from Olduvai Gorge, as 1.75 million years, on the basis of potassium-argon determinations. This estimate has been doubted by Straus and Hunt (1962), but their own estimate tends towards a lower rather than towards a higher age. From the point of view of this argument, it can be accepted as certain that the evolutionary rates for changes in the cranial capacity of man were rapid. Kurtén (1959) points out that the evolutionary rates for the human cranial capacity during the Pleistocene period are paralleled by changes in other animals during the same period, for example, the size of bears, and he includes them together in the Type B rate of evolutionary change. It should be mentioned, however, that the changes in the gene pool underlying morphological changes depend on the number of generations rather than years, since recombination of genes and the effect of selection are expressed in the transmission of genes from one generation to the next. Modern man has an exceptionally high age of maturity, and a relatively long reproductive life. If we assume that modern man produces four generations per century, the number of generations produced in one million years would be about 40,000 generations. This corresponds to the number of generations produced by a very fast breeding organism, such as Drosophila or mosquitoes, since about 8000 B.C. Even if we admit that the early hominids bred faster than modern man, we must assume that this period of immaturity was somewhere in-between that of the present day apes and of modern man (Schultz, 1956). Modern apes, though they are not as slow breeders as humans, still have a long period of immaturity; the female chimpanzee becomes mature at about eight years. The number of generations since Australopithecine times may therefore be regarded as at the most 2–3 times higher than the above mentioned estimate. This would still constitute a very fast rate of evolutionary change, and would approach the value of Kurtén's type A rather than B.

EVOLUTION OF HUMAN BEHAVIOR

According to the previous discussion of the nature of evolutionary changes, it may be concluded that these changes have gone on under very strong selective pressures. The question may then be asked what the selective pressures favoring genes for increased brain size may have been. As pointed out earlier, the answer must necessarily be speculative, but it may lead to consequences which can be subjected to further verification.

The differences in mental abilities between man and his nearest relatives are very large. It is impossible to enumerate them and point to their interrelations. Suffice it to point to the increased ability for and dependence on learning in all behavioral activities, the ability to communicate by speech, and the ability to make tools. Anatomists have attempted to obtain evidence for the existence of speech in prehuman hominids from examination of the jaw and the brain case; but these attempts have been unsuccessful, and the problem may turn out to be insoluble in principle (Du Brul and Reed, 1960).

Another aspect of human behavioral activities, however, has left a record which can be investigated, tool making. And in this connection it seems well established that prehuman organisms had already made tools long before their brains reached an essentially human size. In other words, the acquisition of the ability to make tools proceeded parallel with acquisition of a human brain.

As stated earlier, changes in the gene pool may be regarded as a reaction, mediated by natural selection, to changes in environmental conditions. A few remarks should therefore be made on the presumptive environmental conditions under which the prehuman organisms lived. It seems to be generally agreed that these organisms were plains-living, not forest-dwelling, animals. Furthermore, it may be assumed that they lived in goups of individuals of relatively small size, since social organization is very widespread among Primates. It should be said here, that according to the evolutionary models of Sewall Wright (1931) such an organization, involving division of a species into small endogamous groups with occasional exchange of genes by migration, is particularly conducive to fast evolutionary changes, since genes may accumulate in the separate breeding populations due to chance, that is, irrespective of adaptive value, or as adaptations to the peculiar characters of their special habitat. In this way, such a population structure would result in an increase in genetic potentialities of the species. But to account for the actual trend human evolution has taken, additional factors must be considered.

At some stage of their evolution human ancestors must have gone over from a primary vegetarian existence to predation on game; early man at some time became a hunter, and more specifically a social hunter, that is, an organism of which several individuals cooperated in killing the prey (Clark, 1962). This type of life favors the ability of organisms to communicate with each other, and as a consequence, other social predators, such as the wolf and the domesticated wolf, the dog, also show the ability to communicate with each other to a high degree. A factor favoring the acquisition of the ability to speak may therefore be found in the better communication in hunting offered by this ability. Tool making, also may have had an adaptive value in hunting or eating game.

INTERACTION BETWEEN CULTURE AND MORPHOLOGY IN HUMAN EVOLUTION

These factors alone, indicating an adaptive value for some of the mental abilities of man under prehuman environmental conditions, cannot account for all the fast changes which must have gone on in the history of the gene pool of man. I would therefore like to make a further suggestion which appears to me to be a logical consequence of what has been stated earlier, and for which a small amount of factual support may be available. It has been pointed out that the selective process has the property of adapting the population to changes in the environment. The mental activities of man, on the other hand, enable him to adapt actively to his environment, to chose a variety of different environments, and to actively change his environment by cultural activities. The second and third point are of importance because they imply that if a population changes its environment actively, the selective value of the genes contained in the gene pool may be changed, and consequently the population will undergo a genetic change. It is, then, proposed that in the evolution of man genetic change and cultural change have been in a positive feedback relation with each other: genic changes have caused an increased ability for active adaptation by cultural means, and adaptation by cultural means has changed environmental conditions in such a way that different selective pressures have arisen, giving rise to further genetic changes in the population.

This model stands in contrast to the classical idea that genetic adaptation in man has been replaced by cultural adaptation; it rather postulates that these two processes go hand in hand, supplementing each other. There are some facts which seem to favor the picture presented here. As Dobzhansky and Allen (1956) have emphasized, genetic changes are still going on in human populations, and are proceeding in a direction adapting the population to present conditions, not to conditions of the past. It is in agreement with this picture that the first beginnings of cultural activities, tool making, are found at a stage of human evolution that was probably not yet endowed with all human mental capacities.

It may be inferred from this hypothesis that, as in most positive feedback relations, both components of the process should have proceeded with increasing velocity in time. This is certainly the case with human cultural activities. The largest part of the time of human evolution was spent in the pebble tool and hand axe cultures, each lasting about 600,000 years and showing little diversity in space and time. Since the neolithic, cultural changes have gone on with ever increasing speed (Clark, 1962).

The situation with respect to morphological changes is more difficult. The Australopithecine stage seems to have lasted for a long period, and the increase in cranial capacity may have been more rapid at the Pithecanthropus level, as indicated by the difference between Java and Peking man. Nevertheless, these conclusions are based on small statistical samples, and may very well be changed when additional material becomes available. Furthermore, the conclusions are highly dependent on the dating of the fossils, which, as pointed out earlier, may be subject to a large degree of uncertainty.

Kurtén (1959) has presented a curve for the evolution of human cranial capacity from Java man to recent man which does not fit the expectations from a positive feedback model, since it rises steeply in the early parts and tends to flatten out gradually in recent times. The curve is of course subject to the limitations mentioned above, small sample size for the fossil material and large possible error in dating. In addition, the shape of the curve may be compounded by an increase in generation time during the period covered. Nevertheless it appears that the fundamental observation is probably valid, since there is no evidence for further increase in in cranial capacity since the last glacial period, that is, in about 200,000 years. If the Australopithecines are added to the curve, and it is assumed that this stage was a relatively long duration, the curve for the evolution of cranial capacity would become S-shaped, corresponding to the expectation up to the level of Peking man, and flattening out from there on. This could be explained by assuming that the growth of the human brain case has reached an upper limit which cannot be immediately exceeded under the genetic and physiological conditions of the species.

Finally, it should be mentioned that evidence bearing on the problem of a feedback relation between cultural change and genetic evolution might be obtained from the study of recent history. It is well established that morphological changes in human populations have taken place during historical times. But their genetic basis and the adaptive values of the genetic conditions involved have not been thoroughly studied.

It appears, then, that a model involving a positive feedback relation between cultural and genetic evolution in man does not contradict the facts as known at present, and ought to be further tested by additional investigations. It seems to be able to account for a number of puzzling phenomena which have occurred in the evolution of man.

SUMMARY

It is proposed that in human evolution a positive feedback relation existed between cultural and genetic change. Cultural activities enable man to change his environment, and may be assumed to change in this way the adaptive values of genes in human populations. If these genetic changes enable man to carry out further adaptive changes in his environment, both cultural and genetic changes may be assumed to have proceeded at increasing speeds. The fact that the Australopithecines, with an essentially ape-sized brain, were tool makers, and that cultural changes have occurred at increasingly fast rates, are in agreement with the hypothesis. The rate of the evolution of brain size seems to agree with it up to the stage of Peking man, as far as can be judged from the small number of fossils available, but the brain has apparently increased at much lower rates in relatively recent times.

Literature Cited

BLANC, A. C. 1942–43 Cosmolisi. Interpretazione genetico-storica delle entita e degli aggrupamenti biologici ed etnologici. Riv. Antropologia 34:1–114.

CASPARI, E. 1952 Pleiotropic gene action. Evolution 6:1–18.

CLARK, J. D. 1962 The evolution of culture in Africa. Am. Naturalist 96:15–28.

DOBZHANSKY, TH., and G. ALLEN 1956 Does natural selection continue to operate in modern mankind? Am. Anthropol. 58:591–604.

DOBZHANSKY, TH., and O. PAVLOSKY 1958 Interracial hybridization and breakdown of coadapted gene complexes in *Drosophila paulistorum* and *Drosophila willistoni.* Proc. Natl. Acad. Sci. U.S. 44:622–629.

DU BRUL, E. L., and P. A. REED 1960 Skeletal evidence of speech? Am. J. Phys. Anthropol. 18:153–156.

KURTÉN, B. 1959 Rates of evolution in fossil mammals. Cold Spring Harbor Symp. Quant. Biol. 24:205–214.

LASHLEY, R. S. 1949 Persistent problems in the evolution of the mind. Quart. Rev. Biol. 24:28–42.

LEAKEY, L. S. B., J. F. EVERNDEN, and G. H. CURTIS 1961 Age of Bed I, Olduvai Gorge, Tanganyika. Nature 191:478–479.

MAYR, E. 1961 Cause and effect in biology. Science 134:1501–1506.

RENSCH, B. 1956 Increase of learning capability with increase of brain size. Am. Naturalist 90:81–95.

SCHULTZ, A. M. 1956 Postembryonic age changes. *In* H. Hofer, A. H. Schultz, D. Starck [eds.], Primatologia 1:887–964.

STRAUS, W. L., JR., and P. B. HUNT 1962 Age of Zinjanthropus. Science 136:293–295.

WASHBURN, S. L., and I. DEVORE 1961 Social behavior of baboons and early man. pp. 91–105. *In* S. L. Washburn [ed.], Social life of early man. Viking Fund Publ. Anthropol. 31.

WEIDENREICH, F. 1946 Apes, giants and men. Univ. Chicago Press, Chicago.

WRIGHT, S. 1931 Evolution in Mendelian populations. Genetics 16:97–159.

Cranial Capacity and the Evolution of the Human Brain

RALPH L. HOLLOWAY, JR.

INTRODUCTION

The matter of cranial capacity or brain size has occupied a central position in most of the writings of anthropologists concerned with human evolution. This parameter, measured in cubic centimeters, has been used to make taxonomic identifications, to discuss behavioral complexity and intelligence, and to discuss dissimilar rates of somatic evolution. While it is generally appreciated that this parameter is a poor one for explaining behavioral differences, there is almost no discussion in the anthropological literature regarding the reasons behind the unsuitability of this parameter for either taxonomic or behavioral correlations. The range of variation of cranial capacity for modern *Homo sapiens* is about 1000 c.c., and no correlation between capacity and behavior has been demonstrated. Such a figure represents almost the total amount of increase in capacity from the Australopthecine level to that of modern man. This parameter has also been one of the major stumbling blocks for almost forty years in the acceptance of the Australopithecines as true hominids. It has been mainly the discoveries of stone tools, as well as the postcranial material (the pelves) which have been the most weighty factors in interpreting these early fossils as true hominids. With present-day emphases on behavior and selection in primate populations both past and present, and the increasing focus upon culture as an adaptive process and ecological

NOTE: I am very grateful to Dr. Mark Rosenzweig and Dr. Marion C. Diamond for giving me the opportunity to pursue this study and for providing the facilities for experimental work related to their own project. To Dr. T. D. McCown I owe a particular debt for his understanding, encouragement, and support in undertaking neurological studies. Finally, I am very much in debt to T. D. Lanagan for his many helpful suggestions and comments. Naturally, I am to be held entirely responsible for the views put forth in this paper.

Much of the data on which this paper were collected while under a NIMH fellowship (Predoctoral) MPM-17, 171-C1 1961–62 while at the Department of Anthropology, University of California, Berkeley. The experimental work on dendritic branching was carried out under a Post-doctoral NIMH fellowship, 1-F2-MH-17, 171-01, 1964, Department of Anatomy, University of California, Berkeley.

From *American Anthropologist*, Vol. 68, 1966, pp. 103–21. Reprinted in revised form by permission.

niche, it seems critical to have a better understanding of both the meaning of this parameter and its unsuitability with respect to behavioral differences.

This paper has an exceedingly simple point to make: a comparison of different taxonomic forms based on cranial capacity is *not* a comparison of equal units. Showing just *why* this is the case may aid in understanding other aspects of neural organization which are of more importance in relation to behavior, and pave the way for a clearer formulation of hypotheses which can eventually be tested through experimentation. While I have provided a much more thorough presentation of this problem elsewhere (Holloway 1964, 1967, 1967a), it has been suggested that a presentation of the basic problems in a format containing a minimum of neurological technicalities might be of value for those anthropologists interested but without the necessary neurological training. Thus the following treatment is not meant to be an exhaustive review of either all the problems in this area or a compilation of data relating to comparative neuroanatomy. Following a brief discussion of methods of study, a tentative beginning toward a hypothesis is offered to illustrate one possible approach to the evolution of the brain which partially overcomes the essentially dead-end views based on cranial capacity per se. It should be appreciated that the hypothesis is not offered in complete form, and needs considerable reformulation. It does serve, however, as a heuristic device for exemplifying one possible approach and the kinds of relationships which need experimental explication.

METHODS OF STUDY

There are but two approaches to the study of the evolution of the brain and behavior. The first is what Edinger (1949) has referred to as "paleoneurology," i.e., the study of fossil endocasts. The second method is that of comparative neurology, a study of the brains of extant animals arranged in some order approaching general ideas concerning phylogenetic levels. With respect to the primates, such comparisons have usually been between man, apes, monkeys (Old and New World), lemurs, and tree-shrews. Neither of these methods are without serious drawbacks. In the case of paleoneurology, one can only study the external surface features, which in life were covered with varying amounts of tissues and fluid, and which are obscured in the endocast. Furthermore, those features which are distinguishable are related to only the grossest behavioral functions. In the case of animals lower on the phylogenetic scale than primates, there is generally an increasing return on the amount of information which can be gained from studying the surface markings. One reason for this is that subcortical structures are more often exposed since the cortical covering is less extensive. On the other hand, statements regarding behavior involve categories gross enough to be correlated with surface features, such as olfactory prominance, visual and auditory abilities related to the general size of the subcortical nuclei concerned with such functions, and general degrees of motor control and proprioception, related to relative increase in size and complexity of the cerebellum. With the primates, such gross correlations can be carried out at the familial or higher taxonomic categories, and categories such as memory, "foresight," attention, and perception, "symbolism," language, etc., which are of primary interest to the anthropologist, are not correlatable with the outside configurations. The various attempts which have been made in the past to obtain such correlations have been based on assumptions which current knowledge would relegate to the limbo of phrenology. For example, the eminent neuroanatomist Smith (1926) had concluded after examining the Piltdown endocast that its sulcul pattern was extremely primitive, more so in fact, than Pithecanthropus. Keith (1931) regarded the Galley Hill endocast as very primitive, and Shellshear and Smith (1934) concluded that Peking Man was more primitive than Java Man on the basis of endocranial markings. Levin's (1937) summary of so-called "inferior" characters such as the lunate sulcus, less fissuration, small temporal lobes, etc., found in the brains of distinguished men, highlights the fallacies of such approaches. Certainly Schepers's (1946, 1948, 1952) analyses of Australopithecine cytoarchitecture and psychological functioning on the basis of fissural homologies with Brodmann's (1909) maps must be excluded from any true scientific consideration.

Perhaps one of the sole exceptions to the usefulness of surface features in terms of hominid endocasts is the matter of the lunate sulcus in the Taung specimen, the significance of which was realized immediately by Dart (1925). This sulcus separates the posterior visual cortex from the parietal lobe, and in apes and monkeys is much more anteriorly placed than in man's or his homologous sulcus, if one is present at all. While there is no real consensus at present regarding this feature, since it has been claimed by Keith (1931) that the sulcus appearing on the Taung endocast is related to the parietal lobe, the importance of this feature remains. If it could be unambiguously demonstrated that this endocranial marking was indeed the lunate sulcus, it would prove that there was neural reorganization in the Australopithecine cortex, and that it was something more than simply an ape's brain. A clear demonstration of this backward migration would indicate that there had been an expansion of the so-called "association cortex" of the parietal lobe, and a reduction of primary visual cortex. Even if this were so, what could be said with any certainty regarding the behavior of Australopithecus? Would we say that the animal was capable of handling more complex stimulus relationships in its environment? Would we conclude that such an expansion would allow for greater concentration upon visual gestalts? Would we conclude that the expansion of parietal association cortex meant that reception for communicational behavior was enhanced? For this writer, each of the above speculations has reasonableness behind it, based both on experimental neurological evidence and on the adaptive significance of the Australopithecines, tool-making and an incipient hunting adaptation probably requiring considerably more co-operative, socially integrated behavior (Montagu 1967). As reasonable as some of these suggestions might appear, there is no way at the present time of proving any of these possibilities. This example does illustrate, however, the paucity of information to be gained from endocasts, yet at the same time it illustrates how important even a simple demonstration such as this would be in discussing the possible adaptations of the early hominids and the fact that evolution had already worked on a basic ape-like set of features to produce important changes.

Another aspect of the study of endocasts, particularly with primates, has been the overemphasis on the frontal lobe as a sort of hallmark of Man. Boule and Anthony (1911) used the relative size of the frontal lobe as a measure of behavioral level, particularly in reference to Neanderthals and modern *Homo sapiens*. Their methods were strongly criticized by Weidenreich (1936). More recently, Le Gros Clark (1961) and Vallois (1961) have asserted that this aspect of cerebral anatomy is the main factor in differentiating human from ape behavior. Weil (1929), Tilney (1928), and Schepers (1946, 1948, 1952) have also claimed that the frontal lobe in man is significantly greater than in lower primates. Rensch (1959) and Washburn (1959) apparently accept this judgment also. In all cases measurements have been made on endocasts. Much of this work goes back to Brodmann's (1912) measurements of relative surface area of the regio frontalis of the frontal lobe (not including areas 4 or 6) for a series of primates. Unfortunately, Brodmann never published his cytoarchitectonic results for Man, and his maps were based on work done on the monkey and transferred to man on the basis of sulcal homologies. In many endocasts, it is not even possible to clearly define the central sulcus,[1] which serves as a convenient dividing boundary between frontal and parietal lobes, and which also defines the separation between motor and sensory cortex. The extent of these functional areas depends on the application of electrical or chemical stimuli on the exposed brain and observation of motor activity. Stimulus parameters are of great importance in delineating the functional areas, and Bonin and Bailey's (1961) summation makes it clear that the delineation is anything but simple. Neither the cytoarchitectonic nor stimulating studies are able to delineate the sulci and gyri to any extent which allows quantitive estimate of so-called "association" cortex from motor cortex. In almost all cases where actual primate brains have been measured rather than endocasts, the quantitative data are clearly against the interpretation of a relatively larger frontal lobe in Man. Brodmann (1912), Lebouq (1928), Brummelkamp (1938), Brummelkamp and Offringa (1940), have shown the relative size of the frontal lobe in Man and apes to be the same. Even if it were possible to show a definite increase in this aspect of cerebral anatomy for Man, it would remain unclear as to how such information could be related to behavior. A much better case can be made for relative increase of the parietal lobe, a fact early appreciated by Brodmann (1912) and also Weidenreich (1936). Even this fact does not give one any basis for coming to grips with significant behavioral differences between members of the Primate Order, unless one is willing to work at the level of speculation given above relative to the lunate sulcus in Australopithecus, or is willing to reduce his view to one of rather strict localization of functioning for particular areas of the cerebral cortex, as does Geschwind (1964, 1965) when he relates the inferior parietal lobe to speech reception and increase in associations between cortical areas which are free from limbic or noncortical involvements. Here, the reader should consult Lennenberg (1967) for a general review of this problem.

The second method, comparative neuroanatomy, is also beset with difficulties. The brains studied are not those of ancestors to Man, but rather the results of separative lines of evolution. Thus, in addition to any problems which might arise out of interpreting the actual hardware, there is an epistemological problem which necessitates that there at least be made explicit a set of assumptions under which one can operate. Outside of divine revelation, however, *these are* the two methods available, and it is clear that the first, paleoneurology, is unsuitable with respect to primates, particularly hominids. On the other hand, comparative neuroanatomy does allow for closer investigation into the internal structure of the brain and its relation to behavior. The assumptions to be made explicit are as follows: (1) that extant ape and monkey brains provide insights only if the assumption be accepted that these forms are close to ancestral forms in terms of overall organization; (2) that neural organization in these forms today is not radically altered from that of the past forms at the same level of organization.

In reference to the Taung specimen above, the term neural reorganization was introduced, and it is necessary to explain what is meant by this phrase. It has long been appreciated that no new neural structures have appeared in the evolution of higher primates. Basically, the human brain contains all the same structures as any mammal. On the other hand, the usual interpretation based on cranial capacity has assumed that the human brain is simply a fourfold multiplication of an ape brain, which then in turn is simply a fourfold increase over a macaque brain. Such a view is incorrect, since relationships between the "parts" have altered in the course of evolution and are specific to the particular species studied. *Neural reorganization* here means that quantitative shifts between components or substructures of the brain, as measured in terms of area or volume, have taken place under natural selection such that the outputs of the systems are different between the species. By shifting interactions between components in quantitative ways, the product of the whole is altered. How much it is altered, however, is a difficult problem and one of the central concerns of comparative psychology as well as anthropology.[2]

Some examples of this aspect will make the problem of neural reorganization more salient. For example, consider the cerebral cortex, that portion of the brain which has been and is such a target for speculation regarding behavior. The general assumption, usually implicit when comparing ape and human behavior, is that the human cortex is four times the size of that of a chimpanzee, and thus has at least four times as many neurons. Studies of microstructure of the cortex show that cell density, the packing distance between neurons, decreases as the size of brain increases (Shariff 1953; Tower 1954). That is, the distance between adjacent neurons increases. There is also some suggestion that the cells themselves are somewhat larger in larger brains, and that the amount of dendritic branching increases also (Rensch 1959). By changing spatial relations in the direction mentioned, a fourfold increase in volume does not mean a fourfold increase in neuron number. Comparative cell counts for primates (Shariff 1953) suggests that the increase in cell number in the cortex of man is of the order of $1\frac{1}{4}$ that of the chimpanzee's rather than four. In absolute numbers, this amounts to about 1.4 billion neurons, which is still a significant increase when one considers permutation possibilities. The problem of relating such numbers to behavioral transforms remains, however. It is interesting to note that during brain surgery, more than this number can be removed without converting the patient into a new species. There is also evidence that up to one-third of the cortical neurons in man are lost during aging, amounting to about 2 billion neurons (Brody 1955).

Actually, many more quantitative studies are needed to provide comparisons in the Primate Order with respect to cerebral complexity. Pakkenberg (1967) has recently shown that when shrinkage factors resulting from fixation of brain materials are taken into account, the total number of neurons in the human cortex was 2.6×10^9, in comparison to the usual figure of about 10×10^9 found throughout the literature. Comparisons of primate cortices at this molar level are very difficult unless sampling of the different areas are extensive. Mathematical extrapolation methods (see Jerison, below) are full of pitfalls unless sampling is complete and allowance is made for reorganization at the level of types of cortical tissue such as granular, agranular, and koniocortex (roughly, motor, associative, primary sensory). For example, if Shariff's (1953) values for the volume of different cortical tissue types are used, the well-known "A/S" ratio suggested by Hebb (1949) can be roughly calculated as follows: man = 27.8; chimpanzee = 20.8; macaca = 4.8. (These are not true A/S ratios, however; motor cortex has been ignored in the calculation because Shariff gave values for areas 4 and 6 combined.) Furthermore, what is seldom appreciated is that such reorganization of cortical tissue also means that there has been reorganization of subcortical structures. This is particularly true in the case of the thalamus, particularly those nuclei in feedback or two-way connections with the more expanded associational areas of the cortex such as frontal and parietal lobes; thalamic nuclei such as the dorsomedial and pulvinar.

Cases of microcephaly *vera* offer another example of reorganization although the precise location of the alteration in organization is unknown. Many of these *people,* with brain sizes that even a few gorillas would disdain, are able to talk and interact in a manner which indicates a peculiar human specificity of behavior which other primates do not have. While we know nothing about this specificity, except that it exists beyond parameters such as cranial capacity, cerebral cortex volume, or numbers of nerve cells, microcephaly offers an interesting test cause for certain notions regarding human behavior in terms of "rubicon" models. For one thing, considering the small size of the microcephalic brain (400–600 c.c.), histological studies suggest that in addition to there being more distance between neurons, there are also large numbers of cells that are either morphologically immature or nonfunctional. This opens the interesting possibility that these people possess the human specificity of behavior while possessing less neurons in the cortex that a healthy chimpanzee. Whether the explanation might rest on a particular kind of neurochemistry, or systems arrangement, remains a problem for future research.[3] The reader should also consult Lennenberg (1964, 1967) for a discussion of nannocephalics, a pathological condition where the body is dwarfed as well as the brain, yet the human specificity of behavior develops.

In addition to these considerations, there is good evidence that the number of neuroglial cells in the cortex increases with brain size (Hawkins and Olszewski 1957). These elements, the neuroglia, are in a metabolic symbiosis with the neurons and partly fill the spaces between the neurons in the cortex (Hyden 1962). Studies by Hild and Tasaki (1962) and Tasaki and Chang (1958) have shown that the neuroglia are capable of motility and have electrical properties which possibly couple in with the neuron. Galambos (1961) and Hyden (1962) have suggested that the true neural unit is the neuron *plus* its neuroglial cells and have attempted to explain some aspects of memory on the basis of coupling and symbiotic activities between these two derivatives from neural ectoderm. It may be at this level that some interesting aspects of human specificity may emerge. Thus the comparative studies show that the primate cortex has undergone reorganization of its microstructure in a number of ways. This suggests something very obvious that has a direct relation to anthropology. A comparison of cranial capacities of extant forms, or those based on endocasts, will not be a comparison of equal units. One c.c. of chimpanzee cortex is not equivalent to one c.c. of human cortex, nor is it likely that any equivalent measure can be found.

In this same vein, Jerison has provided a number of interesting calculations which attempt to relate cranial capacity in hominids to numbers of cortical nerve cells in terms of numbers necessary to maintain vital functions, and those which might be regarded as "extras" related to "behavior mechanisms in response to the challenge of the environment" (1963:289). These calculations are based on known parameters of neural density and cortex volume in the primates, as well as upon certain assumptions regarding "vital functions" in primitive mammals. It is assumed that, on the basis of these mathematical relations, one can calculate the number of neurons in a hominid from a knowledge of its cranial capacity and approximate body weight. While space requirements militate against a thorough critique of this method and its underlying assumptions (see Holloway 1966 for a fuller critique), a few points should be made. In the first place, variation in these parameters is high, and it seems extremely unlikely that we will ever have an adequate sample of hominid skulls and skeletal materials from any one level to permit anything more than the most crude approximation of these necessary parameters. Secondly, Jerison's results based on mathematical extrapolations from brain weight-body relationships and cortex-density relationships do not fit the empirical data provided by Shariff (1953). Thirdly, such an attempt overlooks the fact of glial components in the primate brain. Fourthly, and perhaps more important, is that it seems impossible to relate in any realistic way the advances in numbers of "extra neurons" with behavioral differences. For example, between rhesus and baboon monkeys, the difference in this parameter is 0.9 billion cortical neurons of the "extra" variety; between gorilla and Australopithecus africanus, it is 0.8 billion; between Zinjanthropus and *Homo erectus*, 1.7 billion; between two forms of *Homo erectus* with equal body weight but 100 c.c. capacity difference, the amount of "extra" neurons differs by 0.6 billion. One wonders then how many billions of neurons separated Turgenev from Anatole France, whose capacities differed by some 1000 c.c. As I have tried to show elsewhere (Holloway 1964, 1967, 1967a) we do not provide a plausible framework with which to explain the transforms in behavior on the basis of added cortical neurons. As the preceding paragraphs have tried to show, various rubicon models do not account for specificity of behavior or the added complexity of interactions between glia and neurons.

This type of evidence makes clearer the peculiar relationship between cranial capacity and behavioral ability. The use of cranial capacity to explain behavior has occasioned much criticism due to the poor correlations of ability with size, as well as the extreme variability. Appreciation of the internal reorganization of the cortex allows one to realize that increase in capacity is only the outward manifestation of internal changes rather than mere increase in neuron number. For example, Garn (1963) and Gerard (1959, 1960) favor an explanation based purely on simple increase in neuron numbers, which, while significant for increased complexity of behavior, cannot be the whole story. Hopefully, a more complete knowledge of the internal changes will give some parameters which are more meaningful in terms of behavior than c.c.'s of volume. For example, increased space between the neurons or decreased neural density is attended throughout both the comparative and ontogenetic series, and experimental work by increased ramification of dendrites. There is also the suggestion of a relative increase per neuron of neuroglial cells, which are necessary for the proper metabolic functioning of the working neurons. The first parameter, dendritic branching, can easily be related to permutations and cortically-mediated behavior when quantified (Clendinnon and Eayrs 1961; see also Sholls 1956, and Uttley 1955). Eayrs (1955, 1961) has shown that thyroidectomy of rats will decrease dendritic ramification in the cortex and increase neural density, with concomitant decrease in behavioral attributes mediated by the cortex. On the other hand, administration of growth hormone to pregnant rats has a positive effect on their offspring in the opposite direction, resulting in decreased neural density and increased dendritic branching as well as increased adaptive behavior mediated by the cortex (Clendinnon and Eayrs 1961). Studies on dendritic branching by myself on rats given extra-environmental stimulation as against isolated controls, suggests that certain changes in cortical structure described elsewhere (Diamond et al. 1964; neural density, glial/neuron ratio) might be related to increased dendritic branching. A replication study (Holloway 1966a) has shown that environmental training probably does effect the brain structure at the microscopic level, since dendritic branching was increased in eleven out of fifteen pairs. If these results can be substantiated with a yet larger sample, they will tie dendritic branching, decreased density, increased neuron size, and increased glial/neuron ratios into one tight package, and also help explain increased adaptability of cortically-mediated behavior. (A fuller treatment of this aspect appears in Holloway 1964, 1967, 1967a.)

Reorganization of the primate brain has involved structures other than the cortex. It has been known by neuroanatomists for some time that structures related to emotional behavior have also changed in terms of quantitative relationship to the whole brain, a fact taken into consideration thus far only by Chance (1962) in his discussion of primate behavior. The amygdaloid nucleus, for example, shows a proportional increase in man over lower primates (Crosby and Humphrey 1941). This structure is clearly implicated in the expression of rage as certain ablation experiments have shown. Stephan and Andy (1964, 1966) have shown that the relative and absolute amounts of telencephalon, diencephalon, cerebellum, change in different levels of primate evolution, as well as quantitative shifts in the primate septum, which comprises a number of nuclei associated with the mediation of emotions (see Olds, 1965, for example). In addition, there are clear quantitative data regarding certain fibers in the midbrain which are considered to be involved in hypothalamic-thalamic-cortical mediation of emotional attributes. Daitz (1953) has shown that in man there is a fivefold increase in the fibers of the hypothalamic portion of the fornix in comparison to the monkey. Papez (1937) formulated a mechanism of emotion which still finds considerable agreement today (Green 1960). Papez theorized that emotive processes of cortical origin would be built up in the hippocampus, hippocampal gyri, dentate gyrus, and amgydala. From these centers, efferents would both ascend and descend, the former to the anterior thalamic nuclei through the mammillothalamic tracts, and then to the cingulate cortex. The fornix would relay the pulses from the former structures to the mammillary bodies in the hypothalamus and thence through the mammillothalamic tracts. Daitz (1953) found roughly five times as many fibers in the human subcallosal fornix than in the macaque, while in the hypothalamic portion, the number of fibers was about equal for the two species. Powell *et al.* (1957) showed that the ratio between the number of fornix fibers in the hypothalamus and the cell number in the mamillary nucleus was 1:1 in the monkey and 2:1 in man. Rothfield and Harmon (1954) confirmed the observation that placidity results from neocortical ablation provided the limbic system is not interfered with. Intercepting the fornix fibers *lowered* rage threshholds in their neocorticate preparations, although Green (1960) lists several studies where no behavioral change was noted after section of the fornix. Bard and Mountcastle (1948), using cats as experimental subjects, demonstrated that neocortical ablations which did not interfere with any of the limbic structures resulted in placidity. With subsequent removal of certain of these latter structures, such as the amygdaloid, rage reactions were considerably lowered. Such experiments have been duplicated by a number of other workers (see Brady 1960 for extensive review), and Rosvold *et al.* (1954) found that hierarchical positions in eight male Rhesus monkeys were altered by the effects of amygdalectomy. Chance (1962) has utilized these observations concerning evolutionary change in the primate amygdaloid nucleus and behavioral changes with experimental evidence to suggest that part of man's rage-controlling ability is the result of shifts in the components of this system. Unfortunately, the limbic system is extremely complex involving many nuclei, neuroendocrine balances, the temporal cortex as well as the frontal, and the hypothalamus. Knowledge of the interactions between each of the structures is not yet explicated to the extent that one can use a systems theory to advantage, and there is not yet any real body of comparative, quantitative data available for extending the type of analysis Chance has undertaken. Such evidence as has been presented, however, is not only interesting in demonstrating that neural reorganization in primates has taken place during evolution, but that the changes have been far more extensive than the simple view of only cortical elaboration. Such changes are not accessible through study of endocasts. With respect to hominid evolution, the task of demonstrating behavioral changes related to such changes of balance between the limbic and cortical systems is almost hopeless. At best, one can learn more fully about the interrelations of these components, their relationship to behavior using the comparative approach until both aspects are more completely known. Once the comparative picture is known and the structures more clearly related to behavior, it might be possible, on a logico-deductive basis, to comment about probable behavioral evolution in hominid evolution or the earliest transition period. At this stage, any such attempt must be highly speculative, as I have indicated elsewhere (Holloway 1966, 1967, 1967a).

It is worthwhile to consider sensorimotor systems as well, since these too have become reorganized during primate evolution. Indeed, this aspect of brain evolution is seldom considered, except at the motor level, in terms of the representation of the hand, and more particularly the thumb and tongue on the motor cortex (see discussion below). It stands to reason that animals achieving a behavioral adaptation in the direction of greater control over their environments, in terms of both motor manipulability and perception of ever-increasing complexity of stimuli, would gain not only in their central strategic operations but in their afferent and motor sectors also. While there is considerable data accruing from behavioral studies of free-ranging primates (see DeVore 1965), it is sometimes difficult to accept the perceptions of the human observer as being exactly the same for the monkeys or apes studied. The stimuli observed by the human are assumed to be exactly the same for the animals studied, an assumption which is seldom spelled out by the field-worker. Yet there is certainly clear evidence for reorganization of the visual cortex, geniculate bodies, and almost all way stations of neural interactors between the proximal stimulus and final action pathway. Tilney (1928) demonstrated that there had been considerable reorganization (in the sense defined in this paper) with respect to structures related to motor activity and control. He provided a series of quantitative measures of various motor neural components throughout an extensive primate series, and used these indices to elaborate his conception of "neokinesis." Neokinesis was, in Tilney's view, the development of elaborate, individuated activity related to simultaneous co-ordination of hand, head, and eyes. Striking quantitative changes were given for the pyramids, cerebral peduncles, inferior olive, dentate nucleus of the cerebellum, and cuneate nucleus of the cord, each increasing in areal extent up the phylogenetic scale. It is surprising how few attempts there have been to synthesize this material with the present comparative primate picture regarding motor abilities.

All of these examples, and these are but a few, stress the fact of structural reorganization in the primate brain, and underline the fact that man's brain is *not* simply a fourfold explosion of a chimpanzee brain. It shows that comparing cranial capacities between forms is without logical foundation, since the comparisons are between unequal units. Recently, Noback and Moskowitz (1962, 1963) have underlined this fact of reorganization of interaction between components in their discussions of encephalization and corticalization and the increasing severity of disturbance to motor functions as one shifts higher up in the primate scale.

This aspect of neural reorganization as defined here is of considerable importance to our understanding of primate evolution. If nothing else, it should indicate clearly that appreciation of function on the basis of cranial capacity is almost nonsensical. It underlines the fact that our appreciation must rather be based on more intricate analyses of the skeletal and archeological remains of the early hominids and a more complete understanding of comparative neuro-anatomy. As shown earlier, much of the reticence concerning the hominid status of Australopithecines was related to a simplified view of cerebral rubicon models. It should likewise be appreciated that current statements regarding the rates of neural evolution (Washburn 1959, 1960) relate only to cranial capacity and not to the evolution of the brain.

Another approach to understanding differences between primate brains has used electrical stimulation of certain areas of the cortex and plotting these results on a sort of unfolded cerebral map. The "homunculi" usually figured show that the area for the hand and thumb as well as the tongue (Woolsey 1958; see also Washburn 1959, 1960 for figures) is larger in man than monkey, a hardly surprising result, considering that it has been known in functional terms for some time, and the subcortical basis demonstrated quantitatively by Tilney in 1928. Such illustrations have had the effect of possibly over-emphasizing the cortex at the expense of needed comparative information on the total neural picture. One must be extremely careful with the interpretation of such mappings, however, beyond the essentially simple and well-known fact of the importance of thumb and tongue to human affairs. The areas depicted will depend naturally on the stimulus used and its intensity, and great care must be exercised not to confuse involvement of an area with a function as the locus of that function, otherwise one is back to a sort of phrenology, and sight is lost of the extensive neural interactions in any behavior and its complexity. Such maps are complicated by the seldom-appreciated fact that one can obtain motor responses from the sensory areas in the postcentral gyrus and sensory responses from the motor cortex of the precentral gyrus (Pribram 1958). Nor is it likely that behavioral differences such as between man and monkeys can be gained from such maps. Count (1964) for example, claims that stimulating in the lower portion of the human precentral gyrus produces vocalization but that this will not happen with monkeys. However, Kaada (1951) demonstrated that monkeys will vocalize when stimulated there. It is not the motor aspects of vocalization one is after since it is a common mammalian pattern to have motor fibers and cells at such a location, but rather the basis for combinations of units, and the hierarchical strategies in the cognitive sense.

It seems most reasonable to assume that total brain organization is somehow related to the specificities of human behavior in terms of language behavior, which includes not only simple motor and receptive aspects of sound production and reception, but also the cognitive patterns relating symbolism to all aspects of the universe, real or not, and the specificity of such quantum organization (see Lennenberg 1967). It seems hardly possible that any one simple expansion, such as the inferior parietal lobe (see Geschwind 1964, 1965), will explain the human emergence of language behavior in its full richness of cognitive patterning and strategies, the involvements of emotions or motivating structures, the affect interplay between adult and child in maturation, the species-specific rhythms of orientation, babbling, and the intellectual development of the human child, which cannot be reduced to one simple piece of cortex on the side of the brain, or to a set of particular cortico-cortical connections. Indeed, it is questionable whether such behavior can ever be explained in anatomical terms alone except at the exceedingly complex level of system interactions, where one chain of neurons would be a system interacting with thousands more—thousands in the cortex, thousands in the thalamus, limbic lobe, reticular formation, and so on, all interacting together, whose metasystemic patterning in time is a matter of emergence.

Finally, but not least in importance, is the matter of defining what is essentially human behavior as against other primate behavior. It is the problem of behavior of degree as against behavior of kind. Whether or not labels such as "symboling," symbolism, conceptual thought, sign vs. signal behavior, etc., etc., bring one any closer to understanding and defining the difference is debatable. Since there is no access to subhuman experience, closure can never be put on this problem about which so much has been written. As Osgood (1953) has plainly summarized, there is considerable evidence to suggest that animals other than Man have thoughts, i.e., relationships in time and space can be computed, without the stimulus being made available in the immediate environment. It seems, rather, to be the manner in which experience is organized that sets the human line apart from other animals. The activity is organized by sequential concatenations which have an arbitrary (non-iconic) symbolic makeup, the arbitrariness being dictated by social rules rather than strictly innate or biological limits of the vocal apparatus. The latter sets boundaries and conditions probabilities, but is not determinative in the sense that it probably is in other subhuman primates. The issue is far more complex than simple perception vs. conception (Oakley 1957). Much of the human brain executes behaviors that we share with the apes, but the exact neural correlates of that evasive human specificity, which even a microcephalic has, remain to be explained as well as defined. As I have tried to argue throughout this paper so far, neither cranial capacity, neuron number, homunculi on cerebral maps, or whatever "rubicon" model is offered, will explain the transform of behavior of kind. In terms of hominid evolution the only evidence that allows a discussion, even speculative, of behavioral change, are the stone tools, skeletal evidence, and the context in which they occur. I am here assuming, of course, that making stone tools according to a set pattern is an example of arbitrary symbolism and an index of human behavior, i.e., one of a kind rather than degree. Elsewhere (Holloway 1964) I have suggested a number of hypotheses based on neural data which might explain such differences. In no case is the information adequate to provide but the roughest sort of hypothesis. One is based on neuron-glial interaction, emphasizing the notion of sustained activity using short and long term memory as an intervening construct to handle orders of difficulty in retaining non-iconic or arbitrary configurations. A second hypothesis suggested a systems approach based on subcomponent activities in maintaining a vigilance or "set" of the cortex to complex configurations and perceptual acts of an efferent sort. As shown before, the comparative data on these components of the primate brain are only sketchily known. A third hypothesis suggested a modulatory schema based on known quantitative estimates of cortical enlargement in terms of cell number and permutations. Neither hypothesis was meant to be independent of the other necessarily, nor is it held that human behavior in its manifold complexity could ever be reduced to such terms. These hypotheses were actually only orientations toward new perspectives, and the reader may check these for detailed discussions.

TOWARD A HYPOTHESIS

Consider now the Australopithecines and the problem of brain size and behavior. If the assumptions made explicit above are granted, one is faced with understanding the significance of the almost 1000 c.c. increase in capacity since this stage of hominid evolution, in terms of behavioral complexity.

If one thinks in terms of cranial capacity and not neural reorganization, it is difficult to understand how the transform to symbolic behavior came about within the confines of an ape-sized brain. Indeed, Schultz (1962) has found a gorilla skull with a cranial capacity of 752 c.c., which exceeds the capacities known for Australopithecines (Tobias 1963). As these discoveries have shown, the increase in *cranial capacity* was the final great change in hominid morphology, following basic reorganization of the locomotor apparatus, dentition, and skull (Washburn 1959, 1960). While this last point is obvious, and has been since Dubois's discovery of Pithecanthropus, it would be another matter entirely to assert that the evolution of the brain followed the other changes. For one thing, considering possible body weight and cranial capacity, Jerison (1963) has shown that relative brain weight is greater in those early hominids. Thus the relationship between brain and body weight has been reorganized at least at this general level and early time in hominid evolution, a fact clearly appreciated by Dart (1956). The skeletal evidence for the hand, foot, pelvis, and jaws of these hominids shows that the musculoskeletal apparatus had been changed or reorganized according to some adaptive pattern. Clearly, unless it is to be supposed that behavior issues forth from a structural vacuum, it must be granted that neural structures have likewise been altered to allow for the behavioral differences that the evidence of the remaining anatomy demands. In addition to locomotory activity, the stone tools show that finer degrees of manual dexterity had been attained by the time of the Australopithecines. The stone tools also indicate that these hominids were capable of organizing experience in a more human manner. To say that the brain evolved first or last is greatly oversimplifying matters. Dart (1956) clearly appreciated this fact, as shown by his analysis. As the comparative neurological evidence shows, there was a reorganization of components or subsystems in the brain, a fact not appreciated with the emphasis incorrectly placed on cranial capacity as the single parameter, as Straus (1953) also appreciated. The brain as well as the rest of the body have evolved together; this is only the logical extension of the musculoskeletal evidence and the archaeological remains.

The tremendous increase in neural mass since the Australopithecines can be partly explained, I believe, by the reorganization of the microstructure of the cerebral cortex. The shifts in neural density, increased dendritic branching, and increased ratio of glial cells to neurons could account for much of the increase in capacity. In addition, of course, there would be an increase in number of cortical neurons. It is suggested here that the major part of the increase parallels the changes discussed early in the experimental evidence which related increases in cortically-mediated adaptive behavior to shifts of reorganization in the microstructure of the cerebral cortex. Obviously, it will be forever impossible to show exactly what the changes were, since there are no Australopithecine brains to dissect. The only arguments one can advance must be of a logico-deductive nature, relying on assumptions regarding behavior and structural continuity, and interpretations of the archaeological record.

Such a process is filled with dangers, to be sure. It is suggested here, on the basis of the fact that stone tools are continuous throughout the Pleistocene, that there is no real evidence of any significant shift in behavior of kind since the Australopithecines, unless, perhaps, the cave-paintings qualify. This would mean that from the Australopithecines on, the major changes in the brain would have involved increasing degrees of complexity resulting through the increase in connectivity. This increase in connectivity would allow for greater degrees of discrimination of both the social and physical environments, prediction, and memory *control,* as well as capacity. That is, it would mean increasing adaptability or plasticity along essentially continuous lines. It would mean essentially changes in degree rather than kind. I prefer to call this aspect of behavioral adaptation "complexity-management" (see Holloway 1967a for fuller development); that is, an ongoing adaptation of increasing neural complexity to handle the ever-increasing complexity of the environment, that both perceived and produced by the hominids. Furthermore, and most importantly, such a process in terms of evolution would be a deviation-amplification (Marayuma 1963) process, one of positive feedback in the cybernetical sense. One of the delicate problems of the intellectual heritage resulting from the numerous discussions throughout the literature of environment vs. nature has been the limited definition of environment. In a very real sense, the early hominids must have been their *own* environment, and their actions within the more passive context of environment must have in fact *become* an integral part of their environment in the total sense. Concretely, for example, the making of a stone tool, the witnessing of another hominid making one, or its use would then be part of the environment, as much as the social behavior of a fellow hominid would be a part of environment. With a cultural niche (in the ecological sense) there is the capacity and the probability of generating ever-increasing degrees of improbability, or relatedness. It is important to realize that within the niche, the environment is expanding precipitously. Thus the selection pressures for better "hardware" to handle the ever-increasing complexity of the total environment is built into the process to a much increased degree in comparison to nonhuman environments. Information-processing thus becomes critical. One aspect of handling information is to have either a perfect means of accurately registering signal inputs, or by relying on redundancy of the message so that "noise" does not mask the information of the signal completely. The first method has never been attained in any mammalian sensory apparatus, as far as we know. One way of looking at such a mass of neural elements in the cortex would be as a hardware stratagem for handling redundancy and blocking "noise" (See also Garn 1963). It would be quite interesting to know whether behavior becomes more redundant as it becomes more complicated. If so, there are a number of neural information models from neurophysiology to correlate fairly closely the microstructure with redundancy and noise-masking operations. This interpretation, although incomplete, fits well our present models of natural selection as well as the increasing brain size of later hominids and the increasing degrees of complexity of their material and socio-cultural environments. One aspect of the increasing complexity of the hominid environment is the increase in tool complexity, involving greater numbers of basic operations, and also an increasing repertoire of *different* operations (for example, a Chellean hand axe as against a Levallois flake). This was an activity extending through time, in which sustained control over motor patterns, apperception of the tool process, and realization of criteria were dependent on sustaining a concentrated task for a lengthy period of time. Increased neural complexity would be necessary to maintain such tasks, to block out the redundant stimuli and surrounding noise. The same neurological hardware acting to inhibit extraneous perceptions or unnecessary activities would also enhance memory storage and recall.

This explanation allows for a considerable degree of synthesis of fairly disparate notions. Not only does it better relate the brain with behavior, but it also offers the possibility of synthesizing the above ideas with endocrinological and growth changes. In the first part of this paper it was indicated that the experimental alteration of endocrine balances would affect the neural structures along the lines mentioned in this hypothesis. The differing growth rates of genera within the Hominidae suggest that the balance between endocrines and target tissues was altered a number of times in the course of evolution. As I have tried to show elsewhere (Holloway 1967a), shifts in neuroendocrine control and their pathways would have been attendant upon shifts of the aggressive-co-operative axis of behavior from an early ape-like group to the hominid condition, where there was co-operative sharing of food, probable division of labor, full receptivity of the female, domestication of the male, and patterned symbolic methods of social control and interaction. Thus selection pressures would have favored behavior related to more co-operative forms of social behavior and at the same time favored that apparatus most capable of handling greater environmental complexity in terms of social and material stimulus discriminations. The neuroanatomical evidence mentioned earlier regarding certain divisions of the limbic lobe suggested that there have been shifts in this system within the Primate Order. It seems probable that this system underwent reorganization during the early Pleistocene to a hunting hominid type of existence. The observation of Koikegami *et al.* (1958) that bilateral destruction of the amygdaloid nuclear region had effects of an inhibitory nature on the growth rates of infant rats is of particular interest in this respect. Such evidence provides a most welcome link between neural, endocrine, and behavioral systems. For one thing, no truly synthetic theory of human evolution can overlook the profuse number of anatomico-physiological systems related to behavior which Count (1958) shows in his primate "biogram." For another, there is some difficulty in suggesting that natural selection kept favoring larger brains if there is no connection made between the neural structures of the cortex and increasing behavioral adaptation. That is, the very units which comprise the gradual increase in cranial capacity over the span of the Pleistocene, cubic centimeters, cannot be demonstrably linked with real differences in behavior. The modern condition, where there is almost 1000 c.c. of variation without behavioral difference that can be analyzed, warns that in attempting to explain the increase in cranial capacity during hominid evolution, some other parameter(s) must be used. It is suggested here that changes in the time schedule of interaction between somatic and endocrine pathways, that is, epigenesis, would tie-in social behavior and natural selection closer together and possibly account for some of the increase in neural mass. As Clendinnon and Eayrs's (1961) experiments have shown, administration of growth hormone to the pregnant mother has effects on the ontogenetic development of the offsprings' cerebral mass.

Washburn and Hamberg (1965) point out that the ". . . adaptive function of prolonged biological youth is that it gives the animal time to learn" (p. 613). Another function of prolonged youth or growth is that it allows an organ—the brain—to develop to do the learning. Going further, perhaps another adaptive function of a prolonged biological youth is that the affective ties that develop between the supporting group and growing individual are binding in both a contractual and emotional sense, with biological advantages accruing to those with more heightened sentiments in terms of co-operative tasks, protection, etc. Humans are not less dependent upon warmth and mutual affect-interaction with parents and peers than are monkeys. Whatever the actual nature of the early hominid adaptation at the level of social behavior within the group, it must have included a number of reorganizations involving emotive and cognitive components. If the suggestion is accepted that a sort of endocrine revolution took place in early hominid evolution to effect a number of processes in the directions mentioned above, such as permanent receptivity of the female, prolonged growth of offspring, prolonged growth of brain, reduction in sexual dimorphism, decrease in intragroup aggressiveness, etc., then the function of the group is not only to transmit learning but also to protect the most important organ of adaptation, the brain. Perhaps one can take the synthesis further. At about the same time this reorganizational shift was going on, the hominids were adapting to an increased intake of meat, or better, high-energy proteins. Perhaps this adaptation was necessary for the increased period of growth and dependency and of advantage in providing a type of nourishment of added value in maintaining resistance to disease. It seems not unfeasible that a social revolution led to closer group densities which slightly enhanced the possibility of lowered disease resistance. Here, protein-intake and dispersal of part of the group in hunting activities might be seen as positive adaptive strategies. While one should not underplay the importance of behavior and learning to successful adaptation, it should be obvious that the changes that took place in the early hominid period were very complex and included a number of elements at the anatomical, physiological, behavioral, and ecological levels. Whether these changes can be explained in such simple terms as concatenated adaptations one after the other (see Hockett and Ascher 1964) or as simple learning within the group (Washburn and Hamberg 1965) seems doubtful. The framework offered here is extremely speculative, but attempts to put together the behavior with structures, both social and physical, which require analysis. It becomes obvious that the brain cannot be left out of such a scheme when some later development comes along. There exists the real possibility that many of the other adaptations centered about the evolution of this organ, and that group co-operation, decrease in intra-group aggression, full-time receptivity of female, domestication of the male, hunting, meat-eating, etc., might even be seen as a set of adaptations to enhance one major strategy of adaptation: a more complex neural organ.

This type of explanation, while it admittedly needs more working out, suggests one escape from the position which relates small shifts through time of cranial capacity to increasingly adaptive behavior. It does this by focusing not on cranial capacity as a valid parameter in itself which can be related to behavior, but by focusing on the resulting effects which make up the increase in cranial capacity. That is, other parameters such as dendritic branching, neuron density, glial/neural ratios, etc., become available for study and experimental manipulation. In short, it drains attention off the unusable, overly-gross parameter of cranial capacity, that parameter of so much anthropological concern, and permits new hypotheses to be formulated and tested in the laboratory. It may well turn out in the future that such testing will not provide positive evidence for the hypothesis given above. If not, that would be a very real gain alone, and one could then turn to some other hypothesis.

Admittedly, this is a very partial explanation of the relationships between brain and behavior. The interpretation is certainly not free of problems, but it is hoped that it more realistically relates actual structure to aspects of behavior which may be further analyzed from a neural viewpoint. I have suggested that a study of comparative neural microstructure is one promising way of appreciating the relationships between behavior and structure at the neural level. It is not held, naturally, that all of human behavior can ever be explained at the level of neurology. This would be an unfortunate reduction. We still need a framework which can segregate effects and then reintegrate in a synthesis of process those aspects which can be explained on the basis of structure and those relatable to the cultural factors behind motivations, reinforcements, and the particular human code, symbolization at the extrinsic level. The problem requires an eclectic approach, and what is mentioned here relates to but a small part of that approach. An appreciation that a comparison of cranial capacities for different forms is a comparison of unequal units is a beginning in such a direction.

SUMMARY

This paper discussed the methods available to those interested in the evolution of brain and behavior. Two methods are possible: paleo-neurology, and comparative neurology. It has been argued that paleo-neurology is of little or no use with respect to hominid evolution. The latter method, while more useful, must rest on carefully delineated assumptions. Cathecting on cranial capacity as a parameter is a defeating process since the variability is so great, and the parameter masks the changes in cortical microstructural reorganization which have taken place. It was shown that the human brain has undergone significant reorganization in a number of components and subsystems of the entire brain. It was suggested that other parameters such as dendritic branching, neural density, glial/neural ratios, and shifts in fiber tracts to the whole might be more profitable for examination and understanding behavioral differences. The evidence from the case of microcephaly demonstrates clearly that it is possible to construct neural hardware that permits for the development of human behavioral specificity without adhering to any known "rubicon" model. It was also argued that models suggesting a vast relative increase in human frontal lobe will not stand against the actual anatomical evidence. Experimental evidence was cited which demonstrated an interplay between cortical parameters and endocrine balances and that shifts in cortically-mediated behavior follow reorganizational changes in cortical microstructure, which parallels the hominid increase in cranial capacity.

A hypothesis was offered which linked these changes with the fossil and archaeological record, based on explicit assumptions regarding behavior of degree and kind. The hypothesis claimed that by the time of the Australopithecines there was neural reorganization of such an extent as to permit the shift into essentially human behavior, and that subsequent neural changes were related to behavior of degree rather than kind, with the emphasis on complexity and a new kind of ecological niche which guaranteed ever-increasing complexity, both socially and materially. An initial attempt was made to tie in behavioral changes of a social nature, in terms of aggression and co-operation, with changing neuroendocrine balances such that the increase in cranial capacity through most of the Pleistocene could be economically explained. This circumvented the difficulty of explaining and relating small changes in cranial capacity per se to behavioral differences. It was also pointed out that these relationships are amenable to experimentation. The evidence provided by the Australopithecine remains, in terms of musculoskeletal apparatus and stone tools, indicated that changes in neural structure had probably taken place by the time of the Australopithecines, and that to indicate priorities of somatic evolution based simply on cranial capacity is grossly oversimplifying important aspects of hominid evolution.

Notes

1. It might be pointed out that in a number of cases it is sometimes extremely difficult to identify this sulcus in whole human brains taken from the cadaver.

2. No attempt here is made to undertake a discussion of neurochemistry. At the time of this writing, the author is not aware of any study which has been based on neurochemical, quantitative studies within the Primate Order. With the ever-accelerating progress being made in unraveling the genetic code, immunochemistry, and neurochemistry, the future offers great promise in providing additional parameters which, when coupled with the quantitative anatomical data, will provide a more sure base for hypothesis-building and experimentation.

3. It is worth while making explicit the point that there are limits regarding the use of teratological material in terms of anatomical structure and behavior, particularly within the evolutionary framework. The use of microcephaly as an example is not meant as an assertion that possibly some fossil form went through a microcephalic "stage." What this example does establish is the important point that it is possible to construct a neural apparatus within ape-size limits which permits the peculiar specificity of human behavior to operate. In addition, it indicates that the neural hardware permits this specificity without a number of cortical neurons in the normal human range, and perhaps beneath that of a healthy pongid.

References Cited

ANDY, J. O., and STEPHEN, H. 1966 Primate septum in phylogeny. Anat. Rec. 154:310 (Abstract).

BARD, P., and MOUNTCASTLE, V. B. 1948 Some forebrain mechanisms involved in the expression of rage, etc. Research Publications Association of Nervous Disorders, 362–404.

BONIN, G. VON, and BAILEY, P. 1961 Patterns of the cerebral isocortex. Primatologia. II, Teil 2, Lief. 10.

BOULE, M., and ANTHONY, R. 1911 L'encephale de l'homme fossile de La Chapelle-aux-saints. L'Anthropologie 22.

BRADY, J. V. 1960 Emotional behavior. Handbook of Physiology, Section I, Vol. 3. Edited by J. Field, *et al.,* 1529–52.

BRODMANN, K. 1909 Vergeichende lokalisationslehre der grosshirnrinde. Leipzig, J. A. Barth.

———— 1912 Neue ergebnisse uber die vergleichende histologische lokalisation der grosshirnrinde mit besonderer beruchtsichtigang des stirnhirns. Anatomisch Anzeiger, Bund 41. (Erganzungsheft)

BRODY, H. 1955 Organization of the cerebral cortex. III. A study of aging in

the human cerebral cortex. Journal of Comparative Neurology 102:511–56.
BRUMMELKAMP, R. 1938 Ueber das verhaltnis des oberflache des frontalhirns zu der deijenigen des ganzen Gehirns bei hoheren affen und menschen. Kon. Nederl. Akad. v. Wetensch. 41 (10):1127–33.
BRUMMELKAMP, R., and OFFRINGA, J. 1940 The relative growth of the frontal brain during human onto- and phylogenesis. Acta Neerlandica Morphologica 3:202–8.
CHANCE, M. R. H. 1962 Social behavior and primate evolution. *In* Culture and the Evolution of Man. Ed. M. F. Ashley Montagu. New York, Oxford University Press.
CLARK, W. E. LeGros 1961 The humanity of man. British Association Advancement of Science 18:213.
CLENDINNEN, B. G. and EAYRS, J. T. 1961 The anatomical and physiological effects of prenatally administered somatotrophin on cerebral development in rats. Journal Endocrinology 22:183–193.
COUNT, E. 1958 The biological basis of human society. American Anthropologist 60:1049–85.
—— 1964 Comments on Hockett and Ascher's "The human revolution." Current Anthropology 5:156–7.
CROSBY, E. C., and HUMPHREY, T. 1941 Studies of the vertebrate telecephalon. II. Journal of Comparative Neurology 74:309.
DAITZ, H. 1953 Note on the fibre content of the fornix system in Man. Brain 76:509–12.
DART, R. A. 1925 Australopithecus africanus: The man-ape of South Africa. Nature 115:195–9.
—— 1956 The relationship of brain size and brain pattern to human status. South African Journal Medical Science. 21:23–45.
DeVORE, I. ed. 1965 Primate Behavior. New York, Holt, Rinehart and Winston.
DIAMOND, M. C., KRECH, D., and ROSENZWEIG, M. R. 1964 The effects of an enriched environment on the histology of the rat cerebral cortex. Journal of Comparative Neurology 123:111–19.
EAYRS, J. T. 1955 The cerebral cortex of normal and hypothyroid rats. Acta Anatomica 25:160–83.
—— 1961 The possible significance of neuropil for the mediation of cortical function. *In* Regional Neurochemistry. Proceedings 4th International Neurochemical Symposium, Varenna, Italy. Ed. Kety, S. Oxford, Pergamon Press.
EDINGER, T. 1949 Paleoneurology versus comparative brain anatomy. Confina Neurologica 9:5–24.
GALAMBOS, R. 1961 A glia-neural theory of brain function. Proceedings National Academy Sciences 47:129–36.
GARN, S. 1963 Culture and the direction of human evolution. Human Biology 35:221–36.
GERARD, R. W. 1959 Brains and behavior. *In* The Evolution of Man's Capacity for Culture. Ed. J. Spuhler. Detroit, Wayne State University Press, 40–53.
—— 1960 Neurophysiology: an interpretation. *In* Handbook of Physiology, Section I, Vol. 3. Ed. J. Field *et al.* 1919–66.
GESCHWIND, N. 1964 Development of the brain and evolution of language. Georgetown University Monogr. Ser. Lang. & Ling. 17:155–70.
—— 1965 Disconnexion syndromes in animals and man. Brain 88:237–94 and 586–644.

GREEN, J. D. 1960   The hippocampus. *In* Handbook of Physiology, Section I, Vol. 2. Ed. J. Field, *et al.*

HAWKINS, A., and OLSZEWSKI, J. 1937   Glial nerve cell index for cortex of the whale. Science 126:76–7.

HEBB, D. O. 1949   The Organization of Behavior. New York, J. Wiley Co.

HILD, W., and TASAKI, I. 1962   Morphological and physiological properties of neurons and glial cells in tissue culture. Journal Neurophysiology 25:277–304.

HOCKETT, C. F. and ASCHER, R. 1964   The human revolution. Current Anthropology, 5:135–52.

HOLLOWAY, R. L., JR. 1964   Some aspects of quantitative relations in the primate brain. Unpublished Doctoral Dissertation. University of California, Berkeley.

———— 1966   Cranial capacity and neuron number; critique and proposal. American Journal of Physical Anthropology 25:305–14.

———— 1966a   Dendritic branching: some preliminary results of training and complexity in rat visual cortex. Brain Research 2:393–6.

———— 1967   The evolution of the primate brain: some aspects of quantitative relations. Part I of a two-part review article to appear in Brain Research. (In press).

———— 1967a   The evolution of the human brain: some notes toward a general theory. To appear in General Systems Yearbook, Vol. 12. Society for Research in General Systems.

HYDEN, H. 1962   A molecular basis of neuron-glia interaction. *In* Macromolecular Specificity and Biological Memory. Ed. F. O. Schmitt. Cambridge; M.I.T. Press.

JERISON, H. J. 1963   Interpreting the evolution of the brain. Human Biology 35:263–91.

KAADA, B. R. 1951   Somato-motor, autonomic and electrocorticographic responses to electrical stimulation of "rhinencephalic" and other structures in primates, cat and dog. Acta Physiologica Scandinavica, 24, supplement 83.

KEITH, A. 1931   New Discoveries Relating to the Antiquity of Man. London, Williams & Norgate, Ltd.

KOIKEGAMI, H. S., FUSE, S., HIROKI, S., KAZAMI, T., and KAGEYAMA, Y. 1958   On the inhibitory effect upon the growth of infant animals on the obesity in adult cat induced by bilateral destruction of the amygdaloid nuclear region. Folia Psychiatrica et Neurologica Japan 12:207–23.

LEBOUCQ, G. 1928   La rapport Poids-Surface dans le cerveau des singes. Compte Rendue Assoc. Anatomie, Prague.

LENNENBERG, E. H. 1964   A biological perspective of language. *In* New Directions in the Study of Language. Ed. E. H. Lennenberg. Cambridge, M.I.T. Press, 65–88.

———— 1967   Biological Foundations of Language. New York, John Wiley & Sons.

LEVIN, G. 1937   Racial and "inferiority" characters in the human brain. American Journal Physical Anthropology 22:345.

MARAYUMA, M. 1963   The second cybernetics: deviation-amplifying mutual-causal processes. American Scientist 51:164–79.

MONTAGU, A. 1967   The Human Revolution. New York, Bantam Books.

NOBACK, C., and MOSCOWITZ, M. 1962   Structural and functional correlates of "encephalization" in the primate brain. Annals N.Y. Academy Science 102:210–18.

———— 1963 The primate nervous system: functional and structural aspects in phylogeny. *In* Evolutionary and Genetic Biology of Primates, I. Ed. J. Buettner-Janusch. New York, Academic Press.

OAKLEY, K. P. 1957 Tools makyth man. Antiquity 31:199–209.

OLDS, J. and M. 1965 Drives, rewards, and the brain. *In* New Directions in Psychology, II. Ed. F. Barron. New York, Holt, Rinehart, Winston, 327–410.

OSGOOD, C. E. 1953 Method and Theory in Experimental Psychology. New York, Oxford University Press.

PAKKENBERG, H. 1966 The number of nerve cells in the cerebral cortex of man. Journal of Comparative Neurology 128:17–20.

PAPEZ, J. W. 1937 A proposed mechanism of emotion. Archives Neurology & Psychiatry 38:725–43.

POWELL, T. P. S., GUILLERY, R. W., and COWAN, W. M. 1957 A quantitative study of the fornix-mammillothalamic system. London, Journal of Anatomy 91:419–37.

PRIBRAM, K. H. 1958 Neocortical function in behavior. *In* Biological and Biochemical Bases of Behavior. Ed. H. F. Harlow and C. Woolsey. Madison, University of Wisconsin Press.

RENSCH, B. 1959 Trends toward progress of brains and sense organs. Cold Spring Harbor Symposium Quantitative Biology 24:291–303.

ROSVOLD, H. E., MIRSKY, A. F., and PRIBRAM, K. H. 1954 Influence of amygdalectomy on social behavior in monkeys. Journal of Comparative and Physiological Psychology 47:173–8.

ROTHFIELD, and HARMON, P. 1954 On the relation of the hippocampal-fornix systems to the control of rage responses in cats. Journal Comparative Neurology 101:265–82.

SCHEPERS, G. W. H. 1946 The South African Fossil Ape-Men: the Australopithecinae. R. Broom. Transvaal Museum Memoir 2, Pretoria.

———— 1948 Problems in brain evolution. *In* Robert Broom Commemorative Volume. Ed. L. DuToit, Cape Town.

———— 1952 Part II. The brain casts. *In* The Ape-Man of Swartkrans. Broom, Robinson, Schepers. Transvaal Museum Memoir 6, Pretoria.

SCHULTZ, A. H. 1962 Die schadelkapazitat mannlicher gorillas und ihr hochstwert. Anthropologisch Anzeiger 25:179–203.

SHARIFF, G. A. 1953 Cell counts in the primate cerebral cortex. Journal Comparative Neurology 98:381.

SHELLSHEAR, J. L. and SMITH, G. E. 1934 A comparative study of the endocranial cast of Sinanthropus. Philosophical Transactions Royal Society London. (B) 223:469–87.

SCHOLL, D. A. 1956 The Organization of the Cerebral Cortex. London, Methuen & Co.

SMITH, G. E. 1926 Casts obtained from the brain cases of fossil men. Natural History, Vol. XXVI.

STEPHAN, H. and ANDY, O. 1964 Quantitative comparisons of brain structures from insectivores to primates. American Zoologist 4:59–74.

STRAUS, W. L. 1953 Comments in chapter 15, *in* Reappraisal of Anthropology Today, Ed. S. Tax. Chicago, University of Chicago Press.

TASAKI, I., and CHANG, J. 1958 Electric responses of glial cells in cat brain. Science 128:1209–10.

TILNEY, F. 1928 The Brain from Ape to Man. Vols. I and II. New York, Hoeber & Co.

196 *Ralph L. Holloway, Jr.*

Tobias, P. V. 1963 Cranial capacity of Zinjanthropus and other Australopithecines. Nature 197:743–6.

Tower, P. V. 1963 Structural and functional organization of mammalian cerebral cortex. The correlation of neurone density with brain size. Journal Comparative Neurology 101:19–53.

Uttley, A. M. 1955 The probability of neural connections. Proceedings Royal Society London (B), 144:229–40.

Vallois, H. V. 1961 The social life of early man: the evidence of skeletons. *In* Social Life of Early Man. Ed. S. L. Washburn. Viking Fund Publication Anthropology. No. 31:214–35.

Washburn, S. L. 1959 Speculations on the interrelations of the history of tools and biological evolution. Human Biology 31:21–31.

———— 1960 Tools and human evolution. Scientific American 253:62–75.

Washburn, S. L. and Hamberg, D. 1965 The implications of primate research. *In* Primate Behavior. Ed. I. DeVore. New York, Holt, Rinehart, Winston, 607–22.

Weidenreich, F. 1936 Observations on the form and proportions of the endocranial casts of Sinanthropus Pekinensis, other hominids and the Great Apes: A comparative study of brain size. Palaeontologia Sinica, Series D, Vol. 7; Fasc. 4:1–50.

Weil, A. 1929 Measurements of cerebral and cerebellar surfaces: comparative studies of the surfaces of endocranial casts of man, prehistoric men, and anthropoid apes. American Journal Physical Anthropology 13:69–90.

Woolsey, C. N. 1958 Organization of somatic sensory and motor areas of the cerebral cortex. *In* Biological and Biochemical Bases of Behavior. Ed. H. F. Harlow, and C. Woolsey. Madison, University of Wisconsin Press.

Self, Society, and Culture in Phylogenetic Perspective

A. IRVING HALLOWELL

When man is considered in evolutionary perspective, primary emphasis is usually given to his biological attributes, the morphological features that can be dealt with comparatively in other members of the primate order, living or extinct, and in organisms more distantly related. In the intellectual climate of the post-Darwinian period, however, human evolution was conceptualized in much broader terms. The advent of Darwinism helped to define and shape the problems of modern psychology as it did those of anthropology. An evolution of "mind" within the natural world of living organisms was envisaged. Now a bridge could be built to span the deep and mysterious chasm that separated man from other animals and which, according to Descartian tradition, must forever remain unbridged. Darwin himself explicitly set processes of reasoning, long considered an exclusively human possession, in an evolutionary perspective; he also advanced an evolutionary interpretation of the facial and postural changes of man when expressing emotion.[1] He argued that mental differences in the animal series present gradations that are quantitative rather than qualitative in nature. A. R. Wallace, who had had more intimate contacts with primitive peoples than Darwin, was immensely impressed with their abilities. To him, the evolution of the brain represented a sharp mutational development in man that permitted adaptive capacities far beyond those he thought were necessary for survival on a primitive level of human existence. The position he took was a challenge to the theory of natural selection as espoused by Darwin himself. "Natural Selection," Wallace wrote, "could only have endowed the savage with a brain a little superior to that of an ape, whereas he actually possesses one but very little inferior to that of the average members of our learned societies." [2] Eiseley points out that, in 1864, Wallace "set forth the idea that with the rise of man, natural selection was ceasing to act upon the body and was coming to act almost solely upon the human

From *The Evolution of Man,* Sol Tax (ed.), 1960, pp. 309–71. Reprinted by permission of the University of Chicago Press.

intelligence. Man, he contended, was old and had attained the upright posture long before the final changes in the skull and brain which characterize our living species. Other animals had continued to change and modify under evolutionary pressures; in man, by contrast, all but mental evolution has largely ceased." [3]

Although Darwin was later accused of gross anthropomorphism by some of his critics, he did stimulate scientists to think and write about mental evolution. Wallace's views, on the other hand, were discounted because, in the end, he fell back upon a theological explanation. Romanes, a disciple of Darwin coined the term "comparative psychology," [4] and it was not long before a phylogenetic dimension had been added to the program of scientific psychology. In its early stages, however, comparative psychology had little interest for anthropologists. In reaction against anecdotalism, more rigorously controlled observations were demanded by psychologists, and lower mammals, like the rat, and insects too, became preferred laboratory subjects. The results of these observations, even though highly reliable, did not throw much light on the phylogenetic roots of human psychology. Laboratory studies of infrahuman primates like the chimpanzee, initiated by Köhler, Yerkes, and Schultz, only developed to a point where they engaged anthropological interest in the twentieth century.[5] Even today, as Nissen points out, "of the 50-odd living genera of primates, only a very few have been studied to any extent in regard to behavior: man, chimpanzee, the macaques, and cebus monkeys." [6]

It was also under the stimulus of Darwin's ideas as applied to man that historians, economists, sociologists, linguists, cultural anthropologists, and others began to apply evolutionary ideas to human institutions on a wide scale. Language, religion, art, marriage and the family, law, and economic organization were studied comparatively in order to discover whether orderly developmental sequences could be established. But the fact should not be overlooked that these efforts were chiefly confined to developments in a single species of the Hominidae—*Homo sapiens*. Fossil material and archeological remains were scanty at the time and field studies of non-hominid primates living in their native state were non-existent. Besides this, the evolutionary hypothesis was closely linked with the older idea of progress as applied by social scientists and humanists. This re-enforced the reconstruction of series of unilinear stages which somewhat paralleled the concept of orthogenesis in biology. In this form theories of social and cultural evolution persisted into the early years of this century.

Since it was assumed that processes of evolution were not confined to the organic sphere alone, a corollary psychological question arose in conjunction with the attempts that were being made to establish stages of cultural evolution which had taken place in the course of man's long struggle upward from savagery to civilization. Could it be shown that in the cultures of primitive peoples there was a reflection of primitive mind? J. G. Frazer, who adhered to the recapitulation theory, was among those who explicitly linked this problem with the generic question of mental evolution. He thought that not only ethnographic data were relevant but likewise studies of patients in mental hospitals and of the ontogenetic development of the child. He said that "this comparative study of the mind of man is thus analogous to the comparative study of his body which is undertaken by anatomy and physiology."[7] But when unilinear stages of cultural evolution were rejected by most twentieth century anthropologists, the notion of "primitive mind," as applied to non-literate peoples, collapsed with them; the conclusion was drawn that culture change and development in *Homo sapiens* are not primarily linked with evolution in mentality. Outside of anthropology, the more inclusive concept of genetically determined mental evolution—insofar as it sought support in the theory of recapitulation in its original extreme form—became generally defunct with the rejection of this theory by biologists.[8] Thus the psychological dimension of evolution which to Darwin himself was an integral part of the total evolutionary process and of vital significance for our comprehension of man's place in nature fell upon evil days.[9] It is true that animal psychologists continued to investigate some problems comparatively; but special areas of investigation, such as learning behavior in rats, emerged to the foreground, while a primary focus on evolutionary questions as such receded. Schneirla, in a review of trends in comparative psychology (1952), emphasizes the fact that "most American animal psychologists at present seem to be *really* non-evolutionary minded, in the sense that they show no special zeal to find how man differs mentally from lower animals and vice versa, but rather focus strenuously on general problems without much attention to phyletic lines."[10]

So far as anthropology is concerned, the rejection of nineteenth century unilinear theories of cultural evolution along with the notion of a demonstrable level of primitive mentality in *Homo sapiens* meant that evolution, once so inclusively conceived, was reduced in effect, to investigations in the area of physical anthropology. Physical anthropologists, moreover, concerned themselves chiefly with morphological problems, not behavior. Thus, the question arises whether, in the centenary year of the publication of the *Origin of Species,* our thinking about human evolution must remain confined to the investigation of morphological facts? I do not think so. I believe that, in the light of contemporary knowledge, it is both possible and desirable to reconsider human phylogeny in a more inclusive frame of reference than has prevailed in the immediate past, without returning to pseudo-evolutionary problems and theories of an earlier day. For, in addition to the reappraisal of problems in the area of human culture history, undertaken by other contributors to these volumes, we still are faced with the question, What were the necessary and sufficient conditions that made possible, through evolutionary processes, adaptation at the level of primate existence that we find culminating in *Homo sapiens?* Simpson has pointed out that "the generally accepted modern theory of evolution is called 'synthetic' but comparative psychology has been an element not yet fully incorporated in the synthesis." [11]

What I am suggesting is that we more boldly extend the synthetic principle by probing more deeply the *anlagen* of the psychological, social, and cultural dimensions of man's existence, in order to define with more precision the relevant continuities, as well as the discontinuities, which link the behavior of *Homo sapiens* with his predecessors in the evolutionary process. The reason it seems worthwhile to consider human evolution afresh in a wider frame of reference is that now we have sources of information at our disposal which were not available in the nineteenth century, or even in the earliest decades of this century.

1. In the field of human paleontology new fossil material of importance has turned up while, on the other hand, the confusion created by the fake fossil, once known as Piltdown Man, has been resolved. Of the new material, the remains of the australopithecines are of paramount importance. Their over-all dental morphology conforms to that found in more advanced hominids such as Pithecanthropus. And besides this, although their cranial capacity is lower than that of the latter, they had achieved bipedal locomotion. Consequently these primates, associated with Villafranchian fauna of lower Pleistocene date, are now placed among the Hominidae. Structurally and behaviorally they represent an earlier level of hominid development than the Pithecanthropus group, once considered to represent the earliest known hominid type.[12] We now know that the earliest hominids were small-brained and newly bipedal. Large brains did not announce the advent of hominid evolution, as Sir G. Elliot Smith argued in 1912 and as Sir Arthur Keith repeated with reference to Piltdown. "Recent finds of fossil men and other primates," writes Straus, "indicate that it is the brain that was the evolutionary laggard in man's phylogeny; indeed,

the studies of Tilly Edinger of the phylogeny of the horse brain suggest that this may well be a general rule in mammalian evolution." [13] Darwin himself remarked: "We must bear in mind the comparative insignificance for classification of the great development of the brain in man." [14]

In the light of this new knowledge it is now apparent that the familiar terms "man" and "human" are colloquial terms. They are *not* equivalent to the zoological term Hominidae, or to the adjectival form, "hominid." The australopithecines were early hominids, but they were not "human" in the sense that we are human. We represent the terminal product of hominid development. It is difficult now to make use of the colloquial term "man" in discussing evolution. [15] Our temporal predecessors within the zoological family Hominidae were not all "men" in the usual lay meaning of the term. This situation is indicative of a broadening of our knowledge as well as the reality of the evolutionary process itself. In current zoological classification, the subfamily Homininae, as distinguished from the subfamilies Oreopithecinae and Australopithecinae, serves to differentiate later from earlier groups of hominids. And the term "euhominid" is coming into use to designate "men" both living and extinct, belonging to the most evolved group of the family Hominidae, the Homininae. [16]

2. Beginning with the pioneer field observations on chimpanzees by Henry Nissen, published in 1931, shortly followed by the studies of C. R. Carpenter (1934, 1940) on New and Old World monkeys and the gibbon, a new body of information on non-hominid primates began to accumulate. We now have reliable data on a few samples of the ecology and organization of primate societies, [17] supplementing behavioral observations made under laboratory conditions. [18] While hitherto both kinds of studies were made by psychologists, a few anthropologists have now begun to study non-hominid primates in the field.

3. Another source of relevant data comes from what psychoanalytic theory has been able to tell us about the structure and functioning of the human personality and from cross-cultural studies of the relation of cultural variability to personal adjustment. By directing attention to the conditions under which primary processes in human adjustment occur in *Homo sapiens,* these have raised further questions of general anthropological and psychological interest. [19] As case studies these investigations have been mainly concerned with specific differences in personality structure and functioning which can be shown to be related to cultural differences, but implicit in these data are indications that universal dynamic processes are involved which are related to the

psychobiological nature of modern man as a species. Likewise, capacities are implied which must be related to generic psychological attributes of *Homo sapiens* that have deeper roots in the evolutionary process. All human individuals, through learning processes, become psychologically structured for participation in concrete sociocultural systems. On the other hand, hominids considered as an evolving group became the "creators" of culture in the generic sense.

In conventional terminology the psychological dimension of evolution has long been phrased as the evolution of "mind." But this terminology reflects the mentalistic concepts of an older period of psychology when "mind," "intelligence," and "reason" were key terms. One of the seminal contributions of the psychoanalysts—daily faced with persons who need concrete help in readjusting to their life situation—was to hypothecate a model of personality organization, conceptualized in "structural" terms. Whether we accept their particular model or not, it is one which has proved useful in clinical practice. It has likewise been fruitful in analyzing the dynamics of human behavior in sociocultural contexts of all sorts. In phylogenetic perspective, the psychoanalytic model of personality structure suggests that one of the things we must account for in human evolution is not simply a "human mind" in the abstract, but a generic type of personality organization which did not exist, perhaps, at the earliest hominid level. In terms of the psychoanalytical model, too, the "rationality" of the human mind is counterbalanced by an irrationality, linked with the constant play of biologically rooted forces which are intelligible in an evolutionary perspective. Furthermore, with the advent of a cultural mode of adaptation, the biological adaptation of human individuals becomes subordinate to their psychological adjustment.[20] They become an integral part of the perpetuation of sociocultural systems to the extent that variations in personality structure and the roles which human beings are groomed to play become a necessary condition for the survival and functioning of such systems.

4. Kroeber has said that "the most significant accomplishment of anthropology in the first half of the twentieth century has been the extension and clarification of the concept of culture."[21] Without considering formal or elaborated definitions here, the essence of the concept as originally developed is that learned behavior, socially transmitted and cumulative in time, is paramount as a determinant of human behavior. The cultural systems which characterize human societies are products of social action and, at the same time, are conditioning factors in further action. It was the application, as Kroeber

points out, of the culture concept by twentieth century anthropologists, among whom it assumed central importance, that "immensely advanced the growth of anthropological science."

With respect to the evolution of man, this emphasis on culture led to a somewhat paradoxical situation in the early decades of this century. While continuing to give lip service to organic evolution, although rejecting nineteenth century theories of cultural evolution, a crucial evolutionary issue was held in abeyance. Culture was taken for granted and stressed as the unique possession of *Homo sapiens* and earlier types of hominines, dating far back into the Pleistocene. The chief evidence was the association of tools with these early euhominids. In the 1920's Kroeber's paper, "Sub-human Cultural Beginnings," was practically unique. So far as *Homo sapiens* was concerned, it was assumed that all living races shared equally the necessary psychological capacities for acquiring culture. Culture in its concrete manifestations, considered as an attribute of all human societies, was abstracted and studied as such. Culture traits, complexes, and patterns became key terms. In effect, this preoccupation with culture led to a *re*-creation of the old gap between man and the other primates which, it was once thought, the adoption of an evolutionary frame of reference would serve to bridge. The repeated emphasis given to speech and culture as *unique* characteristics of man sidestepped the essence of the evolutionary problem.[22] Distinctive characteristics of the most highly evolved primate were asserted without reference to prior capabilities, conditions, and events in the evolutionary process that made this characteristic mode of adjustment possible. For unless culture and speech be conceived as sudden and radical emergents, they must be rooted in behavioral processes which can no more be considered apart from the general framework of behavioral evolution than the distinctive structural characteristics of man can be considered apart from morphological evolution. Without the establishment of the nature of such linkages the question arises, how far has the emphasis given to distinctive attributes of man advanced our understanding of man's evolutionary position in the animal series beyond the descriptive epithets of an earlier day? One thinks of such characterizations of man as the "rational animal," the "tool-making animal," the "cooking animal," the "laughing animal," the "animal who makes pictures," or *animal symbolicus*. All these characterizations stress man's differences from other living creatures. Like the criteria of culture and speech, they emphasize discontinuity rather than the continuity, which is likewise inherent in the evolutionary process.

A statement made by Carpenter a few years ago clearly articulates an opposition to any such sharp descriptive dichotomization between man and other primates. He said he found untenable a number of assumptions that seemed acceptable to many of his colleagues. One of these was "that the phenomena known as 'mind,' language, society, culture and 'values' exist exclusively on the level of human evolution." [23] And Hebb and Thompson say that "exposure to a group of adult chimpanzees gives one the overwhelming conviction that one is dealing with an essentially human set of attitudes and motivations." [24] Thus, while cultural anthropologists have continued to render formal homage to the idea of evolution, at the same time the full range and depth of its significance has not been actively pursued. The statements of Carpenter, and Hebb and Thompson, should remind us that there remain crucial evolutionary questions which transcend the old problem of unilinear stages of cultural development and those problems which are dealt with by physical anthropologists. [25]

In phylogenetic perspective, we must ask: Did all the aspects of culture as observed in *Homo sapiens* come into being together at an early hominid stage? Did the australopithecines *manufacture* tools, speak, pray, exercise property rights, draw, paint, and recognize moral values? Is there any relation between the expansion of the brain and cultural adaptation? Are "half-brained" hominids as capable of cultural adaptations as those with an expanded cortex? Is speech a necessary condition for the earliest phases of cultural adaptation? And is there any relation between tool-making, as contrasted with tool-using, and speech? Do non-hominid primates show any traces of what has been called culture in *Homo sapiens*? And what of the dimension of psychological structure? What kinds of psychological capacities and mechanisms underlie a cultural mode of adjustment? And what is the relation between the development of systems of social action in the primates and the emergence of cultural systems, characterized by a normative orientation?

What I have attempted in this paper are the broad outlines of a conjunctive approach to human phylogeny in which the organic, psychological, social, and cultural dimensions of the evolutionary process are taken into account with reference to the necessary and sufficient conditions that underlie a human level of existence. At the same time, I have devoted some attention to earlier opinions, in order to bring the problems needing reconsideration into sharper focus in the light of contemporary knowledge. Behavioral evolution is, perhaps, the term which best defines the framework of a conjunctive approach. Biologists, too, are now taking an increasing interest in behavioral evolution. Some years ago Nissen remarked that "one of the weakest links in the sciences dealing with evolution, the one most needed to strengthen its facts and theoretical framework is that dealing with behavior." [26] It is in behavioral perspective that we can best conceptualize the major categories of variables that must be examined with reference to the evolutionary status of *Homo sapiens*. Whether we consider hominid evolution in an ecological, a social, a psychological, or a linguistic frame of reference, behavior is the unifying center to which we must constantly return at each adaptive level. As we proceed to higher levels we must consider new integrations of determinants brought about by potentialities for behavioral adaptations that did not previously exist, for example, the consequences of bipedal locomotion, the adoption of new food habits, the use and manufacture of tools, the expansion of the brain, the effects of a new level of psychological integration in the later hominids, and the role of speech in the symbolic mediation and coordination of social relations. In the evolutionary process, differential behavior patterns provide major clues to significant variables.

Any attack on problems of behavioral evolution, of course, involves inherent methodological difficulties. A direct observational approach at all stages is not possible. With respect to the past, we can only make inferences and deductions from non-behavioral data. But we can observe and compare the behavior of different species of living primates, with full appreciation of the fact that they represent their own specialized modes of adaptation. In the case of the hominids, archeological data provide us with both the material products of individual activity and the consequences of social interaction as expressed in traditional usage where the manufacture of tools can be established. But the archeologist, as such, is not concerned with the problem of behavioral evolution. His attention is chiefly directed to the forms, distributions, and temporal relations of objects from which the early cultures of the euhominids can be inferred. Questions of behavioral evolution, on the other hand, force us to look behind the tool and ask questions which neither the archeologist nor the physical anthropologist can answer by a direct appeal to their data. Tools as products of behavior raise questions of another order. To account for a tool-making tradition by one creature and not another we have to consider the psychobiological capacities which are a necessary condition of tool-making; intervening variables have to be inferred. Problems of this kind must be faced sooner or later, and, indeed, behavioral criteria frequently have been invoked in dealing with questions of human evolution but without sufficient discussion of all the psychological implications involved.

While it is inevitable that there will be differences of opinion in the interpretation of the facts of behavioral evolution, the areas which involve dispute will be narrowed with the accumulation of new data.

THE PSYCHOCULTURAL DIMENSION OF EVOLUTION

Some years ago LeGros Clark, referring to the question of the zoological classification of the australopithecines,[27] said:

Taxonomic difficulties of this sort, of course, are bound to arise as discoveries are made of fossils of a seemingly transitional type, and with the increasing perfection of the fossil record, probably the differentiation of man from ape will ultimately have to rest on a functional rather than an anatomic basis, the criterion of humanity being the ability to speak and make tools.

We must ask, then, what special capacities and conditions underlie the phenomena of speaking and tool-making? Effective use of such criteria is hardly possible without considering what these capacities and conditions may be. We cannot depend on the evidence from human paleontology and archeology alone. Insofar as speech is concerned, it is now known that reliable inferences cannot be made from brain anatomy.[28] Furthermore, it seems doubtful that speech as observed in *Homo sapiens* possesses properties as a system of communication which can be treated as a phenomenal unity in phylogenetic perspective. The question is, How far can speech actually be projected into the past?[29] Do we not have to know more than we now know about the properties of non-linguistic systems of communication at subhuman levels in order to understand the position of speech in behavioral evolution?[30]

Hockett has recently pointed out that "part of the problem of differentiating Man from the other animals is the problem of describing how human language differs from any kind of communicative behavior carried on by non-human or pre-human species. Until we have done this, we cannot know how much it means to assert that only Man has the power of speech."[31] He has approached the problem by identifying seven "key properties" of the speech of *Homo sapiens* and compared them with the available data on non-human systems of communication. Hockett discovered that there was considerable overlapping in the properties selected, although they did "not recur, as a whole set, in any known non-human communicative system."[32] This suggests that the combination of properties that characterize speech, those "design-features" which "seem to be of crucial importance in making it possible for language to do what it does,"[33] did not arise full-blown. It is argued that this assemblage of properties, considered with reference to man's lineage, "could not have emerged in just any temporal sequence. Some of them either unquestionably or with high likelihood imply the prior existence of some of the others."[34] Consequently, Hockett is led to suggest a tentative evolutionary reconstruction.

Since one of the key properties of a human system of communication is "cultural transmission,"[35] a property absent in the communication systems of primates and other animals, this factor becomes highly significant chronologically and, I think, has wider implications than those developed by Hockett. The latter suggests, in effect, that, although learning and the social transmission of habits, or what he calls a "thin sort" of culture, may have existed at a very early stage in the development of the higher primates, the associated system of communication that prevailed may have operated without "cultural transmission."[36] In other words, what I prefer to call a "protocultural" stage may have been chronologically prior to speech but not, of course, to some other system of communication. The evolutionary significance of this chronology as adapted to communication lies in the fact that the conditions which permitted a protocultural stage to develop were, at the same time, among the necessary prerequisites of a communication system characterized by the total assemblage of properties considered by Hockett.

This kind of evolutionary inquiry is, of course, a far cry from earlier approaches, particularly those which began by concentrating on the problem of "primitive" languages spoken by *Homo sapiens.* These proved as fruitless as attempts to discover evidence of "primitive mind" in our species. These failures, however, may have helped to expose genuine evolutionary problems more clearly. Hockett's approach permits us to have a fresh look at speech in greater evolutionary depth. And by direct observation we know that whereas some of the great apes have been able to acquire a "thin sort" of human culture when closely associated with members of our species, they do not have the capacity to acquire and use our distinctive form of linguistic communication, even when systematically motivated.[37] There seems little reason to doubt that, in the course of behavioral evolution, psychological capacities of crucial importance lay back of the ultimate emergence among the hominids of a characteristic system of communication. While this system shared some "design-features" with that of non-hominid primates, capacities that transcended those of other primates permitted the development and integration of novel features.

These, in turn, resulted in the functional potentialities of speech as we know it in *Homo sapiens.*

Man has long been defined as the "toolmaker," yet, if tools are taken as an index of a human status, considerable preliminary analysis is required to make this criterion useful. Oakley [38] has been more precise than previous writers in his *Man the Tool-Maker,* but, nevertheless, an English biologist, Pumphrey, has remarked that " 'Subman, the Implement Maker' would have been a more accurate if less impressive title at least for the first half of his book." Pumphrey sees "no valid reason for assigning intellect to a maker of implements. . . . The web of a garden-spider and the nest of a chaffinch are highly fabricated implements," whereas genuine tools, which he thinks cannot be assigned to early members of the Hominidae, "were made in order to make something else with them" [39] Even if we define the tool concept in terms of some very general adaptive function, without further analysis it is not very useful for making distinctions in an evolutionary frame of reference. Bartholomew and Birdsell say, "In contrast to all other mammals, the larger arboreal primates are, in a sense, tool-users in their locomotion [since,] as they move through the maze of the tree tops, their use of branches anticipates the use of tools in that they routinely employ levers and angular movements," [40] which is a very broad interpretation of tool-using. These authors draw the conclusion, moreover, that "protohominids were dependent on the use of tools for survival."

There is ample evidence that both biologists and psychologists have had their own difficulties in dealing with the question What constitutes tool-using? [41] And because the phenomenon of "tool-using" is not confined to the primates alone, it is necessary to understand the varying factors that underlie what has been called tool-using in other animals, in order to interpret properly the phenomenon of tool-using in the behavioral evolution of the primates and the differential factors that made tool-*making* possible as a unique development within the hominids.

In psychological experiments with infrahominid primates, "instrumentation," as it is usually called, includes piling boxes to secure food, the manipulation of sticks to achieve a similar goal, or pole vaulting! What is interesting is that high proficiency in instrumentation under laboratory conditions appears to be a function of previous experience in related situations.[42] However, it is individual learning rather than social learning that is involved in "tool-using" of this order. Sultan's success in "making" a tool was a unique individual achievement.[43] While there would seem to be no question of the capacity of some primates to use tools as a means of achieving a desired goal when sufficiently motivated, this poentiality alone is only one of the necessary prerequisites to a more highly developed stage of tool-using. However, it seems quite likely that, under natural conditions, some rudimentary habits of tool-using in the narrower rather than the broadest sense may have been individually learned and socially transmitted in non-hominid or early hominid groups. If so, this would exemplify what I have called a *protocultural* stage.[44] Nevertheless, the conditions operative at such a stage in primate groups are not in themselves sufficient to account for the still more advanced level of *tool-making*. If the latter is invoked as a functional criterion for human status we need to do more than differentiate between tool-using and tool-making. We must ask whether tool-making presupposes a higher order of psychological structuralization and functioning than tool-using; whether it implies a social system different from that of non-hominid primates; or a different system of communication.[45] Tool-making as observed in *Homo sapiens* is a skilled act—learned in a social context where speech exists, and usually performed with reference to a purposeful use at some *future* time.[46] Therefore, do we not have to make up our minds, when interpreting the archeological evidence, whether tool-making necessitates a sense of self-orientation in time, and, possibly, institutionalized property rights which assure continued control over the tool in the interval? When we have direct evidence of the persistence of characteristic techniques of manufacture and tool styles as well as evidence of innovation of invention (i.e., a tool-making tradition), we do have indices to a human level of cultural adaptation. But this involves far more than tool-making per se or mere social transmission.

The more perplexing evolutionary problems arise in cases where the material evidence is ambiguous. The problem is particularly difficult where the early hominids responsible for the archeological remains had a smaller cranial capacity than later hominids of the Middle Pleistocene and after. At first, the general opinion prevailed that the bipedal australopithecines of Villafranchian age were not toolmakers, although Dart maintained that, in addition to their hominoid anatomical characters, "they were human in employing skeletal parts to subserve the function of implements in the business of obtaining and preparing . . . food, in getting and dividing it."[47] With the Leakeys' recent discovery of *Zinjanthropus boisei*, however, dated as upper Villafranchian and classified as a new genus of the Australopithecinae,[48] the fact of tool-making in one genus of this group is now established. For, in this case, the discovery is unique in that the hominid remains were excavated from a living site, where they were associated with pebble tools of Oldowan type, along with the broken bones of small animals which had apparently been eaten. Consequently, as Howell says, "the new australopithecine from Olduvai Gorge represents the oldest, fully authenticated tool-maker so far known." [49]

These new empirical facts serve to sharpen an old question What is the relation between brain size and the psychological capacities for cultural adaptation as we know it in *Homo sapiens?* Although no final answer can be given at present, LeGros Clark, writing prior to the discovery referred to above, has reminded us that the range of variability in the cranial capacity of modern man is very wide (900 cc.–2300 cc.) and that "while the cranial capacity of fossil hominids can give information on the brain volume, it provides no information on the complexity of organization of the nervous tissue of which it was composed." [50] Washburn has indicated that there may be chronological questions that will have to be considered, that is, the sequential developments of tool-using, tool-making, speech, and a fully developed cultural mode of adaptation. It may be, he says, [51] that tool-using may require

much less brain than does speech and might have started as soon as the hands were freed from locomotor functions. Oral traditions essential for complicated human society probably were not possible with less than 700 or 800 cc. of brain, and there is no likelihood that elaborate traditions of tool making are possible at lesser capacities, although simple pebble tools might well be.

This brief discussion of speech and tools as behavioral criteria of a human status has, I hope, indicated some of the preliminary problems met with in applying them. The evolutionary problem becomes even more complicated if, to begin with, we attempt to operate with the concept of culture as the criterion of a human status—that "complex whole" of Tylor's classic definition which, he said, is acquired by individuals as members of society. How can we apply such an abstract generic concept, derived from empirical observations of a very concrete nature, in any meaningful analysis of the developmental aspects of human evolution and adaptation?

Wissler tried to solve the problem by assuming the phenomenal unity of what he called a "universal pattern" of culture. [52] His solution was reductionistic. He projected this pattern—including speech—full-fledged from the properties he conceived the "germ plasm" to possess. "The pattern for culture is just as deeply buried in the germ plasm of man as the bee pattern in the bee," he said. "The human

pattern . . . is a part, if not the whole, of man's inborn behavior.
. . . Man builds cultures because he cannot help it, there is a *drive* in
his protoplasm that carries him forward even against his will." [53]
Wissler, however, did not specify any particular genus or species of
the Hominidae. He did not say whether the same universal pattern
for culture was imbedded alike in the genes of Pithecanthropus and
Homo, and, at the time he wrote, the problem presented by the australopithecines had not yet arisen. While it is doubtful that any simple
biologistic approach to the evolutionary roots of culture can be any
more fruitful than preformationistic theories in biology, at the same
time, it must be recognized that Wissler was grappling with a genuine problem. It seemed clear to him that, despite the plasticity of the
behavior of *Homo sapiens* and the varying traits, complexes, and patterns of different cultures, there were constant and recurrent categories
of culture that transcended any particular mode of cultural adaptation.

Thirty years later Kluckhohn, discussing the question of universal
categories of culture,[54] pointed out that, although in the earlier history of anthropology there were those who recognized universal categories for a decade or more before Wissler and for an even longer
period subsequently,

the attention of anthropologists throughout the world appears to have been
directed overwhelmingly to the distinctiveness of each culture and to the
differences in human custom as opposed to the similarities. The later,
where recognized, were explained historically rather than in terms of the
common nature of man and certain invariant properties in the human situation.

The point I wish to stress here is that there are inescapable psychological as well as evolutionary questions raised by "cultural universals," once such phenomena are in any way thought to be related to
the nature of man and the human situation. Even if we do not accept
Wissler's "universal pattern" concept as such or his reductive explanation, he was correct in viewing universals in phylogenetic perspective.
It seems probable that some of them at least point directly to the
functioning of basic features of a human personality structure that
would appear to be a necessary condition for the existence of many
aspects of cultural adaptation. For instance, categories of Wissler's
"universal pattern" were subsequently elaborated by Murdock, who
itemized a long list of what he called "common denominators" of culture which occur, he says, "in every culture known to history or eth-
nography." [55] Among the many items he lists is *eschatology*. It is a

particularly interesting item when its underlying psychological implications are considered. For concepts concerned with a future life, in order to become functionally significant, require a concept of self as being, in some sense, indestructible and persistent in future time. Consequently, a capacity for self-awareness and self-identification must be assumed as psychological universals. Furthermore, since this future existence of the self requires a locale, a level of personality organization is indicated which not only implies ego functioning but a capacity for symbolizing self in space, as well as in time.[56] In phylogenetic terms the evolutionary status of *Homo sapiens* implies common psychological potentialities. These would appear to be as necessary for the functioning of notions of eschatology as for the manufacture of tools and other forms of cultural adaptation.

In the light of our present anatomical and archeological evidence we oversimplify the problem of human evolution if we do not press beyond such general categorical correspondences as, man: speech: tools: culture. Without qualification and further analysis, we cannot associate every aspect of the kind of cultural adaptation we find in *Homo sapiens* with all members of the Hominidae, any more than we can attribute to them a common "human nature." This latter concept always has proved difficult.[57] Sometimes it has been given a purely biological content. Among anthropologists it often has received a relativistic connotation, despite lip service to the "psychic unity of mankind."[58] Spiro has given the concept a more precise meaning by asserting that "the structure and functioning of human personality constitutes man's universal human nature, psychologically viewed. Its universality is not only descriptively true; it is analytically true, as well. In the absence of human personality there could be no human culture."[59] In phyletic perspective "human nature" is, then, the consequence of an evolutionary process. However conceptualized, it cannot be attributed to the earliest hominids in any meaningful sense. In a psychological frame of reference, a human personality structure did not arise as a sudden mutation in the evolution of the hominids any more than a saltatory constellation of anatomical traits suddenly gave rise to "man." Howells[60] said a number of years ago:

> Heretofore we have been given to talking about 'the appearance of man'—the tyranny of terminology—as if he had suddenly been promoted from colonel to brigadier general, and had a date of rank. It is now evident that the first hominids were small-brained, newly bipedal, proto-Australopith hominoids, and that what we have always meant by 'man' represents later forms of this group with secondary adaptations in the direction of large brains and modified skeletons of the same form.

Analogically, it is equally doubtful whether we should any longer talk in terms of the "appearance of culture," as if culture, along with "man," had suddenly leaped into existence. Moreover, if the ancestral hominids were at all like the australopithecines, it seems unlikely that they could have had a system of communication that was fully the equivalent of human speech.[61] There is no positive evidence, it might also be noted, that they had fire.[62] Further discoveries and analysis, no doubt, will illuminate the nature of their tool-making, particularly with respect to the degree of tool differentiation and standardization of technique and form which prevailed. In the light of our present knowledge, we can attribute neither a fully developed cultural mode of adaptation nor a human personality structure to all the Hominidae.

Thus, instead of assuming that culture possesses a phenomenal unity from the start and trying to identify its existence in the past, it seems more fruitful to consider certain aspects of behavioral evolution that are non-cultural in nature, but which are among the indispensable conditions that made cultural adaptation possible in the later phases of the evolution of the hominids. The most important of these conditions are sociopsychological in nature. Our empirical data are derived from observation on subhominid primates in their natural habitat or under laboratory conditions, for deductions from comparative behavior are as methodologically legitimate as those from comparative anatomy.[63]

THE DIMENSION OF SOCIAL STRUCTURE

Social systems are not unique to *Homo sapiens*. And, even at this highly evolved level, "social structure" is now frequently differentiated analytically from culture or personality organization. Eggan, for example, has expressed the opinion that "the distinction between society and culture, far from complicating the procedures of analysis and comparison, has actually facilitated them." He goes on to say that "social structure and culture patterns may vary independently of one another, but both have their locus in the behavior of individuals in social groups." [64]

In approaching the sociopsychological dimension of primate evolution, a distinction of the same order is useful. Life in structured social groups is characteristic of primates and long antedated anything that can be called a cultural mode of adaptation among the more advanced hominids. Social structure can thus be treated as an independent variable. While at the highest level of primate behavioral evolution there are no organized societies without culture (or the reverse), at lower levels there were societies without culture. In phylogenetic perspective a necessary locus and an indispensable condition for a cultural system is an organized system of social action. It likewise seems reasonable to assume that systems of social action at lower primate levels require some system of communication for their operation. To characterize such a system as "language" is ambiguous and even misleading without further analysis of the "design-features" of the system. Then, too, consideration of the sensory mode of communication is required.[65] Among primates both visual and acoustic modes appear to be extremely important. Schultz [66] speaks of the intricate "silent vocabulary" of the non-hominid primate.

Crouching down, presenting buttocks, exposing teeth, shaking branches, pounding of chest, dancing in one place, etc. are all actions full of definite meaning. [Although] the long lists of different postures, gestures and facial movements characteristic of monkeys and apes have not yet been compiled, . . . any careful observer realizes that they represent an intricate "silent vocabulary" of great aid in social intercourse. In the perfectly adapted arboreal life of monkeys and apes the limited variety of sounds, together with the great variety of meaningful gestures and facial expressions, is fully adequate for all social life within such close contact as permits seeing and hearing these detailed means of expression.

So far as the utterance of sounds is concerned, Schultz says they "are the essence of primate life . . . ; the simian primates are by far the noisiest of all mammals." In species that have been closely investigated, like the howling monkeys of Panama and the lar gibbon, differentiated vocalizations have been shown to have functional significance in the social coordination of the individuals belonging to a group.[67] According to Schultz,

The primatologist regards language not as something radically new and exclusively human, but rather as the result of a quantitative perfection of the highly specialized development of man's central nervous control of the anatomical speech apparatus in the larynx, tongue and lips, the latter being as good in an ape as in man. . . . As soon as the early hominids had ventured into open spaces, had begun to use and even made tools and had cooperated in hunting, the total variety of all means of expression needed additions which could come only from an increase in sounds, since the practically unchanged anatomy had already been fully used for all possible gestures etc. The latter have never been lost in human evolution, but merely overshadowed by the infinitely greater variety of sounds in increasing numbers of combinations.

Oakley and others have suggested that early hominids may have depended primarily on gestures, "mainly of mouth and hands, accompanied by cries and grunts to attract attention" and that speech may have been a comparatively late development.[68] If so, a mode of communication, infrahominid in origin, would have persisted into the protocultural phase of hominid evolution. Unfortunately this interpretation must remain speculative. Yet it may be that, when the neurological basis of speech is clarified, we may be in a better position to make chronological deductions.[69] It is difficult to imagine, however, how a fully developed cultural mode of adaptation could operate without speech. If one of the necessary conditions for the functioning of a typically human system of communication is a speech community, an organized social system is as necessary for human language as it is for a cultural mode of adaptation. This condition was present even at the non-hominid level. So what we can discern in primate evolution is a behavioral plateau which provided the necessary context but, at first, not all the sufficient conditions for speech and culture.

It will be unnecessary here to consider the structure and functioning of infrahuman primate societies in detail. But a few general comments and interpretations may be ventured, despite the limitations of our present knowledge, for our samples of reliable observations on primate societies in their natural state are woefully small, particularly for prosimian groups.[70] Besides this, it is not yet possible to consider non-hominid primate societies systematically in the larger perspective of mammalian societies.[71] There are terminological difficulties, also. Descriptive terms like "family," "polygamy," "harem," "clan," and even "culture" and "acculturation," familiar enough when employed with reference to *Homo sapiens,* sometimes have been applied to primates at the infrahominid level. Since no systematic terminology has been developed, these labels must be used with caution, especially when evolutionary questions are at issue.

We do have considerable empirical data on what appears to be a characteristic association of organized primate groups with territories,[72] despite wide variation in the size of the group and the mating patterns that prevail in different species. There also seems to be some significant connection between arboreality and small groups and the occurrence of larger groups in open country.[73] Since the bipedal australopithecines were not forest dwellers, increase in size of organized groups, associated with an ecological adjustment to open country, may have evolutionary implications.

Variations in type of mateship, of course, have suggested the closest human analogies. Since lar gibbons, for example, live in groups which consist of one male and one female and their young, we have a close analogy to the "nuclear family" in man,[74] which likewise represents a monogamous type of mateship. Some biological writers have applied the term "family" exclusively to this kind of primate social unit, despite the fact that in anthropological writing the connotation of the term "family" is never limited to the nuclear family. The gibbon type of mateship, in which the sexual drive of the male is low, would seem to be a limiting case in the range of social units found among the more evolved primates, and without evolutionary implications. In *Homo sapiens* we find two types of polygamous mateships, polygyny and polyandry, and social structures based on these are ordinarily called "families." Relatively rare in man in an institutionalized form, polyandrous mateships appear to be absent in infrahuman primates. On the other hand, polygynous mateships are common in both monkeys and apes. In chimpanzee and gorilla this type of mateship seems to furnish the basis of independent social groups. In some monkeys, for instance, the baboon, "harems" occur as subgroups within the larger "troops" or "bands" found in these animals. Monogamous mateships, on the other hand, do not occur in groups of larger size because females in heat mate with more than one male. Past attempts to establish any regular evolutionary sequence of mateship within *Homo sapiens* have failed, as have attempts to link any *particular* type of mateship in the infrahuman primates with early man, as Westermarck tried to do in the belief that there was evidence to show that the gorilla was monogamous. He urged that this "fact" was of significance in the study of sexual relationships and marriage in man.[75]

Perhaps it might be better to recognize that, since there are only a limited number of possibilities in mateships, it is not surprising to find them recurring at both the non-hominid and hominid levels of evolutionary development in the primates and in social units of varying size and composition. Whatever form they take, all these mateships serve the same reproductive ends. Their importance lies in this constancy in biological function rather than in any direct relation that can be shown to the evolution of group organization. They all lie close to biologically rooted central tendencies and continuities in behavioral evolution which link *Homo sapiens* to his precursors. What we find as the common social core of all but the lowest primate groups, despite their variation, is the continuous association of adults of both sexes with their offspring during the portion of the latter's life cycle that covers the period from birth to the threshold of maturity. This core pattern of associated individuals, when considered with reference to their interrelated roles, is linked with the fact that basic functions are involved—the procreation, protection, and nurture of offspring—born singly, relatively helpless at birth, and dependent for a considerable period thereafter. Variations in mateship or size of the group may occur without affecting these functions. Besides this, the sex needs of adults and the food needs of all members of the group can be taken care of. The role of the female in relation to her young does not seem to vary widely nor the behavior of infants and juveniles. The protective role of the male in relation to infants and juveniles is similar in gibbon and howler, even though the young of the group in the latter case are not all his own offspring and the actual zoological relationship between these two species is remote. Among monkeys and apes, the adult males never provide food for juveniles or females. After weaning the juveniles always forage for themselves. Whether we call non-hominid primate groups "families," "clans," "troops," or "bands," their basic social composition can be expressed by the same general formula:

$$X \text{ males} + X \text{ females} + X \text{ infants} + X \text{ juveniles.}$$

Whatever the mating types or size of early hominid groups may have been their social composition must have conformed to this fundamental pattern. This generic type of social structure, associated with territorialism, must have persisted throughout the extremely long temporal period during which major morphological changes occurred in the species of the primate order, including those which ultimately differentiated the Hominidae from the Pongidae and later hominids from earlier ones. Underlying it, physiologically, was the type of ovarian cycle characteristic of practically all the primates. In contrast with some mammalian species in which females have only one oestrus period a year, primate females along with those of a limited number of other mammalian species, are characterized by the recurrence of successive oestrus cycles in the course of a year. The primates belong to this group of permanent polyoestrus species.[76] Breeding is not seasonal but continuous.[77] In the course of primate evolution, however, as Beach has pointed out,[78] some emancipation from strictly hormonal control of sexual behavior occurred, which further distinguished the higher primates from other mammalian species. Cortical control came to play an increasing role in sexual behavior, and, in hominid evolution, with the remarkable expansion of the brain, this tendency reached its culmination. Thus, the way lay open for the development in human societies of a normative orientation toward sexual behavior.

The evolutionary significance of the social organization of primate groups cannot be fully appreciated, however, without considering behavior patterns other than those directly connected with reproduction, for the structuralization of these infrahuman societies is by no means a simple function of differential roles determined by sex and age. Of central importance, particularly in groups with a terrestrial habitat, and the Old World monkeys as compared with New World species, we find inter-individual behavior influenced by an order of social ranking in the group, a dominance gradient. Males are, quite generally, dominant over females and the females associated with them may outrank other females. While it appears that in different species the "slope" of the dominance gradient varies considerably, some kind of rank order occurs. The importance of this factor in the operation of the social structure lies in the fact that it serves to reduce aggression between males, it determines priorities to mates and food, it influences the spatial disposition of individuals within the group, affects the socialization of group habits, and may determine the relations of groups adjacent to one another.

The ranking position of individuals, nevertheless, is not fully determined once and for all; an individual's role in the dominance hierarchy may change. Psychological factors such as individual experience in inter-individual relations and social learning become involved in its functioning and affect the motivation of behavior, for one of the basic conditions of the operation of infrahuman structures is a *socialization* process, as Carpenter has indicated.[79] Individuals become socially adjusted from birth through the mediation of learning processes. "Descriptions of mother-infant relations in monkeys and chimpanzee leave no doubt as to the importance of learning in the filial responses of immature primates. The infant learns to obey gestures and vocal communications given by the mother and derives considerable advantage from her tuition and guidance," Beach says.[80] Indeed, modern research is showing that the primates are by no means unique among gregarious animals with respect to the importance of social learning and a dominance gradient. J. P. Scott[81] asserts:

In animals which are capable of learning, social behavior becomes differentiated on the basis of mutual adaptation and habit formation as well as on the basis of biological differences. As shown by Ginsburg and Allee (1942) the formation of a dominance order is at least in part related to the psychological principles of learning. Once such a relationship is formed and firmly established by habit, it may be extremely difficult to upset it by altering biological factors, as shown by Beeman and Allee (1945). . . . Experiments which modify the social environment have tended to bring out the general principles of socialization. Any highly social animal that has been studied so far has behavioral mechanisms whereby, early in development, an individual forms positive social relationships with its own kind and usually with particular individuals of its kind.

With respect to the socialization factor in behavioral evolution, Collias points out: "In both insect and vertebrate societies, maintenance of cooperative relations depends to a large extent on socialization of the young. Among vertebrates, this trend reaches its climax in the primates." [82] It seems reasonable to assume, therefore, that the intimate relation between learning and social structure, so fundamental to the functioning and elaboration of cultural adaptation, as well established in the non-hominid primates prior to the anatomical changes that led to both erect posture and the expansion of the brain.

Furthermore, by direct observation of both monkeys and apes, we know that learned habits may be socially transmitted, even in the absence of speech. The most striking cases have been reported by observers who have been studying *Macaca fuscata* at the Japanese Monkey Center during the past decade. These "Japanese Apes" have been lured from their forest habitat into open feeding places, where, among other things, they have been offered new foods. Systematic observation has shown that newly acquired food habits, such as eating candies, became quite readily socialized. Imanishi points out, moreover, that young macaques acquire the candy-eating habit more quickly than adults and that some mothers learned to eat candies from their offspring, rather than the other way round.[83] It has likewise been observed that the spread of a new food habit may be directly related to the dominance gradient which is a central feature of their social structure. Adult females of high rank were observed to imitate the wheat-eating of a dominant male very quickly and the habit was passed on to their offspring. Females of lower rank, in a more peripheral position in the group, only later acquired the habit from their offspring who, in turn, had picked it up through association with their playmates. The rate of transmission was extremely rapid in this case, the entire process occurring within two days.[84] In another instance, a young female initiated the habit of washing sweet potatoes before eating them. This habit, having been transmitted to her playmates, as well as to her mother, was slowly transmitted to a number of groups during the next three years. The same class of phenomenon in the anthropoid apes is illustrated by nest-building in chimpanzee [85] and the transmission of the technique of working the drinking fountain at Orange Park, which chimpanzees learned from each other.[86]

The social transmission of culture has sometimes been stressed as one of its chief earmarks. But to my mind it is only one of the necessary conditions of cultural adaptation rather than a distinguishing characteristic. Social transmission is a prerequisite of culture and an earmark of a protocultural behavioral plateau. Concepts of culture that lay primary emphasis on shared and socially transmitted behavior without qualification do not enable us to make a necessary distinction of degree between different levels of behavioral evolution.[87] Voegelin has made the acute observation that while there is a general agreement that all culture involves learned behavior, "additional conditions are generally invoked before learned behavior is granted the status of culture," and that "if ever the converse statement were made (*that all learned behavior is culture*), it would necessarily imply that infrahuman animals have culture." [88] The fact that even some animals other than primates may learn from each other,[89] that in primate groups there seems to be good evidence that social learning and socially transmitted habits do occur, and that some chimpanzees in social interaction with members of our species have acquired "culture traits," does not indicate that a full-fledged level of cultural adaptation has been reached in these species.[90] Other capacities and conditions were required before this higher level could be realized. Indeed, neither learning nor the socialization and transmission of learned habits seems to have reached an optimum level of functioning in any nonhominid species.

Perhaps this limitation may be attributed to the absence of a psychological capacity of a higher order than was necessary for the transmission of relatively simple habits in the groups described. Learning could not acquire paramount social importance until it could function in social structures of a higher order and wider range than those represented in the infrahominid primates. In social structures of this latter type, the phenomenon of territoriality which, according to Carpenter, "reduces stress, conflict, pugnacity, and non-adaptive energy expenditure" [91] within each group by isolating it from other groups, sets up a barrier at the same time to the integration of groups and the development of social structures of a wider range and more complex order.[92] Speaking more generally, in the case of the Japanese macaques, for example, groups are almost totally isolated from each other in their natural state. It is said that "even where several groups live in contiguous territories, the inter-group relations are practically non-existent. Encounters between distinct groups are extremely rare, and even when they occur both groups keep at a safe distance from each other." [93] Offspring do not associate with parents after sexual maturity has been reached. They leave their primary group and form new ones. Individuals of two or more generations are not continuously associated in the same group during their lifetime. Consequently continuity in learned habits is strictly limited. There is no way for experience to become cumulative, either spatially or temporally, beyond the narrowest range. In order for a cultural level of adaptation to be reached, structures of a wider range were required as a necessary social setting. This further step was contingent upon the development and functioning of psychological capacities that transcend those sufficient to account for the dynamics of the narrow-range social structures described. In short, the social integration of groups larger in size, distributed more widely in space, and characterized by a greater diversity in roles required a transformation in psychological structure.[94]

THE BIOLOGICAL DIMENSION
NEOTENY AND BRAIN ENLARGEMENT

A concomitant condition for the maximization of the sociopsychological importance of learning appears to have been the extension of the period during which the young become socialized. In the late nineteenth century John Fiske, an ardent follower of Spencer and Darwin, linked such an extension of the learning period in man directly with evolution through what he called the "prolongation of infancy." In this fact alone he thought he had discovered the essential key to man's distinction from other animals and the explanation of human psychological, familial, and cultural development. Fiske was impressed both with A. R. Wallace's account of the behavior of an infant orang raised by hand after its captured mother died[95] and by Wallace's suggestion "that natural selection, in working toward the genesis of man, began to follow a new path and make psychical changes instead of physical changes."[96] Fiske developed the thesis that the human being was born "in a very undeveloped condition, with the larger part of his faculties in potentiality rather than in actuality."[97] The period of helplessness is the period of "plasticity. . . . The creature's career is no longer exclusively determined by heredity . . . it becomes educable . . . it is no longer necessary for each generation to be exactly like that which has preceded."[98] Thus, "man's progressiveness and the length of his infancy are but two sides of the same fact"; "it is babyhood that has made man what he is." Infrahuman primates approached the point where "variation in intelligence" came to be "supremely important, so as to be seized by natural selection in preference to variations in physical constitution." But in a remote period "our half-human forefathers reached and passed this critical point, and forthwith their varied struggles began age after age to result in the preservation of bigger and better brains, while the rest of their bodies changed but little. . . . Zoologically the distance is small between man and the chimpanzee; psychologically it has become so great as to be immeasurable." [99]

We can see from these passages that Fiske anticipated a number of points frequently emphasized later in cultural anthropology and in evolutionary biology. But the theory he develops, while emphasizing the important role of learning in human experience and the potentialities of man for cultural development, does not account for the biological foundations of the extended period of dependency. He likewise makes "bigger and better brains" chronologically subsequent to the distinctive human condition that fired his imagination. Nor could he have anticipated the fact that later knowledge of the social organization of the non-hominid primates would fail to support his conviction that the prolongation of infancy "must have tended gradually to strengthen the relations of the children to the mother, and eventually to both parents, and thus give rise to the permanent organization of the family." For in Fiske's view, when this step was accomplished, "the Creation of Man had been achieved." [100]

While Fiske's theory, although once so widely known, is seldom referred to today, the fact should not be overlooked that the relations between the factors dealt with by him have not yet been satisfactorily resolved. Even now it is sometimes forgotten that an extended period of dependency and opportunities for social learning in man do not explain the genesis of cultural adaptation, even though these conditions may be of primary categorical importance in understanding the adjustment processes that relate an individual to his culture. While we now know more about the phylogenetic basis of what Fiske called the "prolongation of infancy," its precise psychological significance is a matter of dispute.

From comparative anatomy the fact seems well established that the larger apes, and particularly the gorilla, develop adult characteristics much earlier than does *Homo sapiens*. The latter has been called a "fetalized" animal; [101] that is, certain features that are characteristic of the fetal stages of apes persist in human adults. It is an example of a well-known evolutionary process which, generically, is usually referred to as "neoteny": fetal and/or juvenile features of an ancestral form persisting in the adult stage of descendants. [102] In man, the rate of development of some characters has been retarded. On the other hand, says De Beer, [103]

The reproductive glands have probably not varied their rate of development, for the human ovary reaches its full size at the age of about five, and this is about the time of sexual maturity of the apes and presumably of man's ancestors. The human body is, however, not ready for the reproductive glands to function until several years later. The retardation is due to the action of hormones which play an important part in regulating the speed of development. . . . At the same time, of course, in other directions, the evolution of man has involved progressive changes of vast importance, some of which however, might not have been possible (e.g., the development of the brain), had it not been for certain features of neoteny (e.g., the delay in the closing of the sutures of the skull).

It is the combination of various characters, considered with reference to their rate of ontogenetic development, that is peculiar to man.[104]

While such anatomical facts are well established, the psychological inferences drawn from them have varied in emphasis. Roheim maintains that the temporal disharmony between the development of what he calls the Soma and the Germa is the crucial point. Human sexuality becomes precocious because it develops at about the same rate as in other higher primates, but in our species full bodily growth is delayed. The consequence is that unconscious psychological mechanisms have come into play to repress, project, or transform sexual impulses before the individual is mature enough in other respects to engage in actual sexual activities. The Oedipus complex is universal not because it is derived from past events that have become inherited,[105] but because it "is a direct derivative of our partly premature, partly conservative (prolonged or retarded) rate of growing up." [106] "Our sexual ethics are based on juvenalization." [107] Montagu, on the other hand, sees in neoteny an evolutionary step whose major psychological significance is related to man's potentialities for learning.[108] He says:

The shift from the status of ape to the status of human being was the result of neotenous mutations which produced a retention of the growth trends of the juvenile brain and its potentialities for learning into the adolescent and adult phases of development. It is clear that the nature of these potentialities for learning must also have undergone intrinsic change, for no amount of extension of the chimpanzee's capacity for learning would yield a human mind.

Besides this, account must be taken of the biological fact that in primate evolution the life span of individuals became progressively lengthened while the onset of puberty and the beginning of fertility became more and more chronologically delayed. Culminating in man, the outcome was that the interval between generations became greater. This fact, then, needs to be considered both with reference to the association of individuals in larger social groups and in relation to the need for the development of the kind of psychological structure that would permit the co-ordination of the behavior of individuals of both sexes and widely differing ages over a large time period, in order that inter-individual relations in these more complex social systems might be successfully integrated.

While it is impossible to sustain the view that fetalization is completely responsible for all of modern man's distinctive psychocultural characteristics, perhaps we may follow Sir Julian Huxley's view [109] that while

> it will not account for all the special characters we possess, notably the special enlargement of the association areas of our cortex, and the full adaptation of our feet and legs to bipedal terrestrial existence, it has certainly helped us to escape from anthropoid specialization. It is this possibility of escaping froom the blind alleys of specialization into a new period of plasticity and adaptive radiation which makes the idea of paedomorphosis [fetalization, neoteny] so attractive in evolutionary theory. Both its possibilities and its limitations deserve the most careful exploration.

If so, important steps in sociopsychological evolution beyond the non-hominid or early hominid level may have been contingent upon the situational effects produced by biological factors which prolonged dependency of the young, delayed reproduction, and increased the life span in an already advanced hominid whose psychological functions were, at the same time, being greatly enhanced through the enlargement of certain areas of the brain.[110]

With respect to this particular development, there may well have been a critical transition period; however, an arbitrary Rubicon of 750 cc.[111] between the higher apes and the australopithecines on the one hand, and the early Homininae and recent man on the other, while perhaps of some crude taxonomic value, does not in itself permit significant behavioral inferences. "It is quality of brain rather than quantity, absolute or relative, that is all important," as Straus says.[112]

Today we know considerably more than we did a generation ago about the functioning of various parts of the cortex as well as other parts of the brain. And new insights and hypotheses with evolutionary reference are coming to the fore. Washburn, referring to the diagram in Penfield and Rasmussen (1950), showing the way the body is represented on the cortex, points out that there is unequal representation but that "the areas which are largest are the ones of greatest functional importance." Thus, "when the brain increased in size, the area for hand increased vastly more than that for foot," a fact which "supports the idea that the increase in the size of the brain occurred after the use of tools, and that selection for more skillful tool-using resulted in changes in the proportions of the hand and of the parts of the brain controlling the hand." The areas concerned with speech are also large and so are the frontal lobes which have been said to be connected, in part, with foresight and planning.

Our brains are not just enlarged, but the increase in size is directly related to tool use, speech, and to increased memory and planning. The general pattern of the human brain is very similar to that of ape or monkey. Its uniqueness lies in its larger size and in the particular areas which are enlarged. From the immediate point of view, this human brain makes culture possible. But from the long-term evolutionary point of view, it is culture which creates the human brain.[113]

In recent years, too, as a consequence of rapid advances in neuroanatomy and physiology, there has been a revival of interest in, and many discussions of, the brain mechanisms which underlie the phenomena of awareness, consciousness, attention, memory, and the functional integration of experience.[114] So far as integrative functions are concerned, the present weight of evidence appears to focus upon the influence exercised by the masses of nerve cells in the upper part of the brain stem upon the more recently evolved cortical areas. An older notion that the cortex itself was of prime significance because it was somehow the "seat of consciousness" no longer seems to make complete neurological sense. Although no unanimity of opinion has been reached, hypotheses should emerge in time which will lead to further clarification of the relations between neurological evolution, psychological functioning, and cultural adaptation. Of central importance in this complex web of relationships is the distinctive psychological focus of consciousness in *Homo sapiens*—the capacity for self-objectification which is so intimately linked with the normative orientation of all human societies.

SOCIOPSYCHOLOGICAL EVOLUTION AND NORMATIVE ORIENTATION

Although we can never check developmental stages in the enlargement of the brain by direct observation of behavior, we do know what the behavioral outcome was in the most highly evolved hominid. Here, along with a greater diversification in the forms of social structure in *Homo sapiens,* we are confronted with a radical change in their underlying dynamics. At this more advanced stage of normative orientation becomes an inherent aspect of the functioning of all sociocultural systems, since traditionally recognized standards and values are characteristic of them. Techniques are appraised as good or bad; so are the manufactured objects themselves. Property rights are regulated according to recognized standards. Knowledge and beliefs are judged true or false. Art forms and linguistic expression are brought within the sphere of normative orientation. Conduct is evaluated in relation to ethical values. All cultures are infused with appraisals that involve cognitive, appreciative, and moral values.[115]

It has been said by a biologist that the foundation of any kind of social order is dependent upon role differentiation.[116] The general principle underlying social organization at any level is that role behavior on the part of individuals is, within limits, predictable in a wide variety of situations.[117] This is what makes it possible to establish empirically characteristic patterns of behavior interaction whether in invertebrates, vertebrates, or primates, despite the fact that the relative importance of innate versus learned determinants may vary widely at different levels. Normative orientation in man implements regularities in social systems at a more complex psychological level of development through role differentiation that is mediated by socialized values and goals. While some contemporary biologists, like Darwin a century ago in his *Descent of Man,* have given particular emphasis to the moral sense of man,[118] this aspect of social adjustment is but one facet of man's normative orientation. If the total ramifications of the normative orientation of human societies are taken into account, we have a major clue to the kind of psychological transformation that must have occurred in hominid evolution which made this level of adaptation possible and some measure of its depth and significance for an understanding of the dynamics of human systems of social action.

In their analysis of the functional prerequisites of a human society, Aberle and his associates introduce the concept of an "actor," with cognitive, affective, and goal-directed orientation, but do not discuss the psychological prerequisites of this actor. While this is irrelevant in their frame of reference, in phylogenetic perspective the capacities of the actor are crucial. For the functioning of a system of action as a normatively oriented social order requires a capacity for self-objectification, identification with one's own conduct over time, and appraisal of one's own conduct and that of others in a common framework of socially recognized and sanctioned standards of behavior.[119] Without a psychological level of organization that permits the exercise of these and other functions, moral responsibility for conduct could not exist, nor could any social structure function at the level of normative orientation. Learning remains important, of course, but it functions at a higher level of sociopsychological integration. The relations between needs, motivation, goals, and learning become more complex. The analysis of Aberle and his associates inevitably includes the "normative regulation of means," the "regulation of affective expression," and the "effective control of disruptive forms of behavior." Value systems have an ordering function in social interaction; they promote the broad behavioral expectancies which are of the essence of role differentiation in a *sociocultural* system.

Man, for example, has departed very radically from his primate forerunners in ecological development through the invention and use of technological devices of all kinds and in economic organization. A normative orientation in these spheres of activity is epitomized by the standards applied to the distribution of goods and services and to the ownership of property. One of the universal functions of all systems of property rights, which are among the common denominators of culture, is to orient individuals in human societies toward a complex set of basic values which are inherent in their day-to-day operation. This kind of value orientation is just as crucial in relation to the motivation and interpersonal relations of individuals as are the values associated with sexual behavior. Property rights are not only an integral part of the economic organization of any human system of social action; they likewise implement the functioning of the social order in relation to the resources of the physical environment through normative means. Discussions of "property" among infrahuman animals have centered around such phenomena as food-sharing, the defense of the nest, prey, territorial domain, and so forth. The question is: In what sense are such phenomena comparable with the socially recognized and sanctioned rights in valuable objects that characterize property in human societies? In the latter the basis of ownership is the correlative obligations others have to allow me to exercise *my* property rights. *A* owns *B* against *C,* where *C* represents all other individuals. It is an oversimplification to omit *C* and simply say *A* owns *B*.[120] Among infrahuman animals, we meet with entirely different conditions. All we observe is the utilization, or possession (in the sense of physical custody or use) of certain objects which bear some relation to the biological needs of the organism or group of organisms. We cannot properly speak of rights, obligations, and privileges in societies where there is no normative orientation. We can only refer to such abstractions when a cultural system as well as a system of social action exists. "Use-values" may exist at a protocultural stage in the primates, but they function in social systems with different properties.

Another example of normative orientation in human societies is the well-known phenomenon of incest avoidance. With its associated manifestations of shame, guilt, and anxiety, it long presented a puzzling sociopsychological problem because the underlying psychological structure was not thoroughly understood.[121] Such patterns of avoidance, with both constant and variable features, do not and could not operate at a non-hominid level where genealogical relations between individuals are not known, where socially sanctioned value-systems are not present, and where the phenomena of self-identification and moral responsibility for conduct does not exist. Kroeber has pointed out that "the incest taboo is the complement of kin recognition." Abstraction, in turn, "involves ability to symbolize, in other words, speech." [122] Consequently, incest taboos could not arise among primates incapable of self-other orientation in a web of differentiated moral relationships. In social interaction, the individual could not be held responsible for differentiated responses to kin until the latter were explicitly classified through linguistic or other means. Although precisely the same genealogical relationships existed at a lower level of primate social organization, they could not be consciously identified and utilized as a basis of differential social interaction until the individual "actors" participating in the system developed a personality structure that permitted self-objectification and the use of symbolic means in playing sanctioned roles within a common framework of values.

Further ramifications of the basic significance of normative orientation and its psychological correlate of self-awareness in the evolution of a fully developed mode of cultural adaptation cannot be considered here. But the question can be raised whether the capacity for self-objectification was common to all the Hominidae from the beginning. Perhaps we might venture to say that, although some of the psychological *anlagen* were present at a protocultural stage, a capacity for self-objectification and role differentiation functioning in intimate relations with socially sanctioned value-systems, were sociopsychological developments that only became established in typical form long after the initial steps in hominid anatomical differentiation had taken place. One of the reasons for this, as we shall see, is that these developments were contingent upon a system of communication that was not only socially transmitted but, through symbolic mediation, gave unique and characteristic scope to the novel psychological capacities that had been developing through the expansion of the hominid brain.

EGO AND SELF-OBJECTIFICATION

While it has been widely recognized that self-awareness is a characteristic phenomenon in *Homo sapiens,*[123] the psychological structure that underlies it has been seriously studied only since the rise of a more general interest in personality structure, mainly under the impact of psychoanalytic theories. The evolutionary aspects of the problem have been scarcely touched.[124] Indeed, there have been "many psychologists of the modern period," as Asch says, "who have spoken of the individual organism as of a congeries of capacities and tendencies without a self-character." [125] It has been pointed out, moreover, that "between 1910 and 1940, most psychologists preferred not to mention 'ego' or 'self' in their writings." [126] Nowadays, ego and self are familiar terms, although the connotation given them is not standardized. However, no one uses the ego concept in any substantive sense but rather as a psychological construct useful in conceptualizing a subsystem of the total personality, objectively approached, with reference to its development, structure, and functioning. If we wish to be rigorous, it is best to speak of a group of ego processes or functions, although this is sometimes awkward. Ego functions have a wide range; they are intimately connected with such cognitive processes as attention, perception, thinking, and judgment, because ego processes are involved in determining adjustments to the outer world in the interests of inner needs, particularly in a situation where choice or decision, and hence delay or postponement of action, is required.[127]

On the other hand, the concept of self carries a reflexive connotation: "I" can think of "me." I can discriminate myself from other objects perceptually; I can conceive of myself as an object; I can develop attitudes toward myself. Thus the self is a phenomenal datum, whereas the ego is a construct. "The self can be observed and described; the ego is deduced and postulated. The ego may be conceived in quasi-physiological terms as a sub-system of the organism. . . ." [128] Furthermore, the self does not mirror the ego—the subject's capacity for self-objectification does not imply his objective knowledge of the psychodynamics of his total personality.

Considered in evolutionary perspective ego may be said to be the major "psychological organ" that structurally differentiates the most highly evolved members of the Hominidae from subhominid primates and probably other hominids of lower evolutionary rank. It lies at the core of a human personality structure as we know it in *Homo sapiens*.[129] It permits adaptation at a new behavioral level. Since, in ontogenetic development, the beginnings of ego processes can be identified in the first half-year of life, well before the acquisition of speech, we can say that, while ego development occurs in a context of social interaction, in its initial stages it is not contingent upon the prior existence of either speech or culture. The underlying capacities for ego functioning must have deeper psychobiological roots.[130] This is the area in which the evolutionary problem lies.

Heinz Hartmann has made a most illuminating suggestion as to how this problem may be approached. He says that we must not overlook important relations between animal instinct and human ego functions. His point is that "many functions, which are taken care of by instincts" in the lower animals "are in man functions of the ego." But, he says, we should not identify the nature and role of instincts in animals with "drives" in man; "the id, too, does not appear to be a simple extension of the instincts of lower animals. While the ego develops in the direction of an ever closer adjustment to reality, clinical experience shows the drives, the id-tendencies, to be far more estranged from reality than the so-called animal instincts generally are." [131] In other words, the general evolutionary trend is one in which the role of central cortical functions, acting as intervening variables, becomes increasingly important. Ego processes and functions in *Homo sapiens* would appear to represent the culmination of this trend in the primates, laying the foundation, among other things, for the more psychologically complex "inner world" of man.

Evidence then for the phylogenetic roots of the ego must be sought in the functional equivalents of ego processes and functions at lower primate levels. Although Nissen does not make the inference himself, I think that the examples he gives [132] in support of his assertion that the higher anthropoids are "guided by a delicately balanced system of values," may be taken as evidence of the functioning of rudimentary ego processes:

> The larger and stronger male chimpanzee deferring to his female companion in the division of food, even after the female is pregnant and no longer suitable as a sex partner—the animal "punishing" the misbehavior of his cagemate and in position to inflict serious injury, but contenting himself with merely nipping him painfully—the chimpanzee refusing to expose himself to the frustration of occasional failure in a difficult problem, although he could get a desirable tidbit 50 per cent of the time by merely continuing to make a simple and easy response—these are but a few of many instances of a finely adjusted hierarchy of values. Like man, the chimpanzee has many values only indirectly related to primary needs, as for food, sex, and knowledge.

It need not be inferred, I think, that the values referred to by Nissen were socially sanctioned; nor that the chimpanzee is capable of consciously relating or appraising his own conduct with reference to socially acquired values. These values of the chimpanzee do not represent fully articulated values in the human sense. We are still at a protocultural level of sociopsychological functioning where no normative orientation exists.

However, the intervening variables that appear to be determinative in these situations exemplify the behavioral outcome of the shift from physiological to cortical controls which laid the foundation that enabled the Pongidae and, no doubt, their protohominid relatives, to develop a new level of psychobiological adaptation. I cannot escape the impression, either, that the behavior of the chimpanzees at Orange Park who, seeing visitors arriving, ran quickly to the drinking fountain and, after filling their mouths with water, quietly waited for the closer approach of the visitors before discharging it at them, exemplifies the integration of attention, perceiving, thinking, purposiveness, and the postponement of action in a rudimentary form which are among the ego processes and functions attributed to *Homo sapiens*. Hebb and Thompson, who report this observation,[133] do not refer to ego processes or function but use the episode to illustrate the chimpanzees' capacity for what is called "syntactic behavior," which they consider crucial in phylogenesis. It involves an "increasing independence of the conceptual activity from the present sensory environment, and an increasing capacity for entertaining diverse conceptual processes at the same time." Among other things it "eventually makes speech possible." "At the lowest level, it is the capacity for delayed response or a simple expectancy; at the highest level, for 'building' not only a series of words but also of sentences, whose meaning only becomes clear with later words or sentences." To my mind, Hebb's concept of syntactic behavior falls along the psychological dimension in phylogenesis where we must look for the rudimentary phases of ego processes and functions.[134] At the same time, I do not think that behavioral evidence such as that cited, which appears to indicate the functioning of rudimentary ego processes, allows us to make the further inference that this behavior involves self-objectification.

The capacity for self-objectification represents a level of psychological integration that requires the operation of additional factors. While, on the one hand, self-objectification is rooted in a prior development of rudimentary ego functions, on the other, the representation and articulation of a sense of self-awareness is contingent upon the capacity for the symbolic projection of experience in socially meaningful terms, i.e., in a mode that is intelligible inter-individually. There must be a functional integration of intrinsic representative processes with some extrinsically expressible means of symbolization. An extrinsic mode is necessary in order to mediate socially transmitted and commonly shared meanings in a system of social action. There must become available to an individual some means whereby inwardly as well as outwardly directed reference to his own experience and that of others, and to objects and events in his world that are other than self, can find common ground. Outward behavior can be perceived and imitated through social learning in non-hominid primates. Emotional experiences can become contagious. But what is privately sensed, imaged, conceptualized, or thought cannot be imitated or responded to without an overt sign extrinsic to the experience itself. Working the drinking fountain at Orange Park or nest-building in chimpanzees can be socialized without the mediation of any form of extrinsic representation. There is no evidence to suggest that either the chimpanzee or any other non-hominid has developed a traditional means whereby it is possible for an individual to represent himself and other objects and events to himself as well as to others. Consequently, even though capacities for ego-centered processes may exist, they can attain only a limited functional range.

In phylogenetic perspective there is evidence that intrinsic symbolic processes (i.e., central processes that function as substitutes for or representatives of sensory cues or events that are not present in the immediate perceptual field) occur not only in subhominid primates but in some lower species. But even in the higher apes the functioning of these representative processes appears to be limited, as is a capacity for ego processes. But it is difficult to know precisely what these limits are. Schneirla, making references to Crawford's experiment on the cooperative solving of problems by chimpanzees,[135] says that these animals

were able to learn a gestural form of communication and use it symbolically. [They were enabled] to summon one another by means of self-initiated gestures such as gentle taps on the shoulder. These were truly symbolic, and not merely signals to action. The chimpanzee who tapped was presenting, in anticipation of its social effect, a special cue which had come to symbolize, i.e., to stand for meaningfully, the expected social result. The symbolic, anticipative, and directive nature of this gestural cue was indicated by the fact that, when shoulder taps were insufficient, or slow in producing co-operation, the active animal would turn to pulling alone, or might act forcibly and directly to get the second animal involved in pulling. Although it is not known how far and in what ways such gestural devices may be involved in chimpanzee group communication under natural conditions, their use is probably very limited.

Interpreted in this way the gestures referred to may be considered a rudimentary and highly limited mode of extrinsic symbolization. The function of these gestures was, of course, imposed by the nature and circumstances of the experiment. In this framework conditions were not favorable for the perpetuation of these gestures through social learning and transmission in a wider group.

A unique observation illustrates the presence of intrinsic symbolic processes in chimpanzee, tantalizing because of their incommunicability. It is reported that Viki sometimes played with what appeared to be an imaginary pull-toy which she towed around on an imaginary string.[136] Viki, of course, could not deliberately communicate the content of her experience to ape or man, even if she had so desired. She could only act out her fantasy behaving as she did. Mrs. Hayes could only observe what she saw and guess what the probable image was that motivated Viki's behavior. Viki did not have the capacity to abstract, objectify, and transform the content of her intrinsic symbolic processes into a symbolic form extrinsic to the experience itself. For the same reason we can be certain that she could not think about herself as an object playing with her pull-toy. Because there was no system of extrinsic symbolization available as a means of communication, the world that Viki and Mrs. Hayes could share was very limited psychologically. It may be that one of the major reasons chimpanzees cannot be taught to speak is that they are not capable of manipulating second-order abstractions of the type necessary for extrinsic symbolization even though lower levels of abstraction are possible for them.

The earliest unequivocal proof of the capacity of *Homo sapiens* for extrinsic symbolization in a visual mode is found in the cave art of the Upper Paleolithic. Here we find the graphic representation of such animals as mammoth, rhinoceros, bison, wild horse, reindeer, etc. which could not have been present in the perceptual field of the artist when the drawings were made. The location of them in most of the caves excludes this possibility.[137] The number of human, or humanlike figures, is small in proportion to the hundreds of animal drawings. So far as the figures of wild animals are concerned, we can only infer that the men of this period had highly accurate and vivid memory images of the contemporary fauna (intrinsic symbolization). At the same time their capacity to abstract essential features of their images and represent them in a material medium is demonstrated. When the animals themselves were not present, the drawings of them in a naturalistic style could convey to other men what was "in" the artist's "mind." While the iconic type of symbolization employed required some abstraction, there is a relatively close correspondence in form between the object seen, the memory image, and the graphic symbolization.

But there also seems to be evidence in the cave art of a related human capacity, that is, the ability to project graphically synthetic images of fabulous creatures, animal-like or human-like, which were not objects of ordinary perceptual experience. These belong, rather, to the world of creative imagination. The beast with two horns at Lascaux is the prime example of the representation of a fantastic animal.[138] Many examples of ambiguous human figures—synthesizing both human and animal characteristics—are known, and it is these figures which have proved the most difficult to interpret in the whole repertoire of cave art, since in style they do not fit the realistic tradition of the animal art.[139] The older view that these semi-human figures were the representation of actual human beings wearing masks, or the skins of animals, has been steadily losing ground. In the cave of Trois Frères, the figure originally called a "Sorcerer" by Breuil and Bégouën is now thought by them to be the representation of the "Spirit controlling the multiplication of game and hunting expeditions,"[140] in other words, a god or a personage of an other-than-human class.[141] If the humanly ambiguous figures are thought of as belonging to such a class, I believe that it may be argued that we have evidence which suggests that a system of beliefs is reflected in the art, which makes this category of figures equivalent to the personages that appear in the myths of living primitive peoples. In this case the cave art would offer evidence of a level of imaginative functioning and conceptual creativity that transcended a purely naturalistic reproduction of what was perceived. It could be interpreted as revealing capacities in early representatives of *Homo sapiens* psychologically equivalent to those of living peoples studied in their full cultural context where the details of world-view and religious beliefs have been recorded.[142]

While the symbolism embodied in speech is in a different mode, since sound clusters are given a meaning-content that is unrelated to the form or qualities of the objects or events represented, it seems to me that we must assume that the same basic capacities for extrinsic symbolization are involved. Art forms are as indicative of these capacities as are speech forms. Among other things, graphic art in all its manifestations requires abstraction or else it could not function as a means of representation. In any case, it is hard to believe that the peoples of the Upper Paleolithic did not possess a vocal system of representation (although we have no direct evidence of speech) as well as a fully developed mode of cultural adaptation equivalent to the nonliterate peoples of historic times. Viki and other chimpanzees, if considered as representative of an advanced level of infrahominid behavior, manifest as little capacity for graphic symbolization of an extrinsic type as for vocal symbolization.[143] By the time we reach the Upper Paleolithic, the infrahominids have been left far behind on the ladder of behavioral evolution.

Systems of extrinsic symbolization necessitate the use of material media which can function as vehicles for the communication of meanings. Abstraction and conceptualization are required since objects or events are introduced into the perceptual field as *symbols,* not in their concrete reality. Thus systems of extrinsic symbolization involve the operation of the representative principle on a more complex level than do processes of intrinsic symbolization. In case of *Homo sapiens,* extrinsic symbolic systems, functioning through vocal, graphic, plastic, gestural, or other media, make it possible for groups of human beings to share a common world of meanings and values. A cultural mode of adaptation is unthinkable without systems of extrinsic symbolization.

From a phylogenetic point of view the capacity for individual and social adaptation through the *integral* functioning of intrinsic symbolic processes and extrinsic symbolic systems enabled an evolving hominid to enlarge and transform his world. The immediate, local, time-and-space-bound world of other primates, who lack the capacity for dealing effectively with objects and events outside the field of direct perception, could be transcended. Speech, through the use of personal pronouns, personal names, and kinship terms made it possible for an individual to symbolize, and thus objectify, himself in systems of social action. Self-related activities, both in the past and future, could be brought into the present and reflected upon.[144] What emerged was a personality structure in which ego processes and functions had become salient at a high level of integration—self-awareness. The inner world of private experience and the outerworld of public experience became intricately meshed through symbolic mediation. In all human societies, the self-image became, in part, a culturally constituted variable; self-orientation became integrated with other basic orientations toward the world that enabled the individual to think, feel, and act in a culturally constituted behavioral environment.[145] As a result of self-objectification human societies could function through the commonly shared value-orientations of self-conscious individuals, in contrast with the societies of non-hominid and probable early hominid primates, where ego-centered processes remained undeveloped or rudimentary. In fact, when viewed from the standpoint of this peculiarity of man, culture may be said to be an elaborated and socially transmitted system of meanings and values which, in an animal capable of self-awareness, implements a type of adaptation which makes the role of the human being intelligible to himself, both with reference to an articulated universe and to his fellow men.

The central importance of ego processes and self-awareness that we find distinctive in *Homo sapiens* can be viewed from another angle. Since self-objectification involves self-appraisal in relation to sanctioned moral conduct, we can see the social as well as the individual adaptive value of unconscious psychological processes such as repression, rationalization and other defense mechanisms. Culturally constituted moral values impose a characteristic psychological burden, since it is not always easy, at the level of self-awareness, to reconcile idiosyncratic needs with the demands imposed by the normative orientation of the self. For animals without the capacity for self-objectification no such situation can arise. As Freedman and Roe [146] write,

> Only in man is there simultaneously such a rigidity of social channeling and such a degree of potential plasticity and flexibility for the individual. Incompatible aims and choices which are desirable but mutually exclusive are inevitable conditions of human development. This discrepancy between possibility and restriction, stimulation and interdiction, range and construction, underlies that quantitively unique characteristics of the human being: conflict.

In *Homo sapiens,* unconscious mechanisms may be viewed as an adaptive means that permits some measure of compromise between conflicting forces. They relieve the individual of part of the burden not only forced upon him by the requirements of a morally responsible existence but by the fact that the normative orientation of any human social order permeates all aspects of living. A human level of existence requires an evolutionary price; man as a species has survived despite proneness to conflict, anxiety, and psychopathology.[147] There seems to be little question that one of the crucial areas of individual adjustment turns upon the sensitivity of the self to feelings of anxiety and guilt.

Psychoanalysts, in particular, have come more and more to recognize that psychological maladjustment centers around the structural core of the human personality. David Beres, for example, writes: [148] "There is then in man this unique structure, the ego, which in its full function allows for the expression of those qualities which distinguish the human from the animal and which, in their malfunction, give to his behavior and thought the characteristically human forms of mental illness."

Leopold Bellak [149] has recently reviewed the shift in focus that has occurred in psychoanalytic thinking:

The novelty in psychoanalysis was originally its introduction of the un-conscious in the sense of the unconsciousness of feelings, the unawareness of previously experienced events, the covert nature of motivations, and the hidden meaning of dreams and symptoms. Slowly attention focused on the forces responsible for this unconsciousness, notably repression.

A new era, however, "dedicated to the analysis not only of the uncon-scious but of the ego and its defences," was initiated with Anna Freud's book, *The Ego and the Mechanisms of Defense* (1936). So that now, "the pendulum has swung nearly full cycle, in that there is so much talk about ego psychology today that the forces of the un-conscious are possibly already somewhat in disregard." [149]

Franz Alexander, commenting on the same shift of interest,[150] says,

> Mental disease represents a failure of the ego to secure gratification for subjective needs in a harmonious and reality-adjusted manner and a breakdown of the defenses by which it tries to neutralize impulses which it cannot harmonize with its internal standards and external reality. . . . The highest form of integrative function requires conscious deliberation. Everything which is excluded from consciousness is beyond the reach of the ego's highest integrative functions. . . . Psychoanalytic therapy aims at the extension of the ego's integrative scope over repressed tendencies by making them conscious.

Thus, in the terminology I have been using here, psychological functioning at a level of self-awareness is as important for rational personal adjustment as it is for the functioning of sociocultural sys-tems. Furthermore, as Schneirla points out, it is an error stemming from an inadequate comprehension of the complex nature of a human level of existence to assume "that man's 'higher psychological proc-esses' constitute a single agency or unity which is capable of being sloughed off" even under extreme provocation. On the contrary "so-cialized man even under stress of extreme organic need or persistent frustration does not regress to the 'brute level.' Rather, he shifts to some eccentric and distorted variation of his ordinary personality, which varies from his prevalent socialized make-up according to the degree of integrity and organization attained by that adjustment sys-tem." [151] This is why we find variations in the symptomatology and incidence of mental disorders in man when we consider them in rela-tion to differences in cultural modes of adaptation. These phenomena often have been given a purely relativistic emphasis. But increasing evidence suggests that they probably can be ordered to psychodynamic principles and etiological factors that operate universally.[152] Direct comparison, moreover, between the psychopathology of the "civilized" individual mind and the "primitive mind" savors more than ever of a pseudo-evolutionary problem.

SUMMARY

What we observe in the behavior of *Homo sapiens* is the culmination and distinctive integration of processes and capacities which require analytical discrimination and investigation in a long evolutionary perspective. The nature of man cannot be fully understood outside this framework. A cultural level of adaptation could not arise *de novo*. There were prerequisites of various kinds. Simple forms of learning, some socialization of the individual, a social structure based on role differentiation in organized social groups, the transmission of some group habits and perhaps tool-using, and a "non-syntactic" (Hebb) form of communication [153] may be identified as necessary but not sufficient conditions for a human level of existence. The development of these conditions in combination provided a preadaptive or protocultural stage. But all of them were raised to a new level of functional organization and inclusiveness by the psychological restructuralization that must have occurred during the evolution of the Hominidae when cerebral expansion took place subsequent to the development of bipedal locomotion and readjustment to new ecological conditions. Without this psychological factor, expressed in part by a capacity for the development of extrinsic forms of symbolization, a cultural level of adaptation could not have been reached in the first place and could not be maintained in its characteristic forms.

So far as learned behavior is concerned, its importance in relation to culture has been both exaggerated and over-simplified. "Experience will not make a man out of a monkey," as Nissen says.[154] Learning in the form of simple conditioning is found far down the animal scale.[155] Of equal importance in behavioral evolution is how much is learned and what is learned, considered in relation to the capacities and total life adjustment of the animal.[156] In anthropological writing prior to the culture and personality movement, the connection between learning and culture remained vague because it had not been considered in relation to the development of personality structure. The fact had been overlooked that the only way in which a culture can be perpetuated is through the characteristic psychological structuralization of individuals in an organized system of social action.

What seems to be significant in primate evolution is that social learning became linked with the functioning of social structure and the transmission of habits at the subhominid level. But at this level *what* was learned appears to have been quantitatively limited. In the case of the Japanese macaques the transmission of new food habits has been primarily stressed. In *Homo sapiens* we have a quantitative maximization of social learning which has led to qualitatively distinctive consequences because of the essential role that learning plays in the development of the higher levels of integrative functioning of the human personality.[157] But this is not all. There are other psychological functions manifested at this level that are of paramount importance. We find cognitive processes raised to a higher level of functioning by means of culturally constituted symbolic forms which can be manipulated creatively through reflective thought and expression. Cultural modes of adaptation, or certain aspects of them, learned and transmitted as they may be, also can be objectified, thought about, analyzed, judged, and even remodelled.

The great novelty then, in the behavioral evolution of the primates was not simply the development of a cultural mode of adaptation as such. It was, rather, the psychological restructuralization that not only made this new mode of existence possible but provided the potentialities for cultural *re*-adjustment and change. The psychological basis of culture lies not only in a capacity for highly complex forms of learning but in a capacity for transcending what is learned; a potentiality for innovation, creativity, reorganization, and change.[158]

While self, society, and culture must, of course, be conceptually differentiated for special types of analysis and investigation, they cannot be postulated as completely independent variables. Considered in phylognetic perspective the temporal depth of their intimate connections is brought into focus. Besides this, the significance of these integral connections becomes more apparent, both with respect to the psychological nature of man as a product of evolution and the primary adaptive process inherent in the achievement of a sociocultural level of existence.

Notes

1. Darwin, *Descent* and *Expression of Emotions*. Cf. R. H. Waters in C. P. Stone (ed.), *Comparative Psychology*. In her Preface to a recently published edition of *The Expression of the Emotions,* Margaret Mead relates Darwin's work to the developing interest in "the non-verbal aspects of human communication—the new science of kinesics."

2. Quoted by Eiseley (1955), p. 63.

3. Eiseley (1955), p. 63. Cf. Eiseley (1958), p. 306.

4. His *Animal Intelligence* (1883) "is the first comparative psychology that was ever written, and its author used this term believing that comparative psychology would come to rank alongside of comparative anatomy in importance" (Boring, p. 473).

5. See Yerkes (1943), "Epilogue: The Story of an Idea," pp. 289–301.

6. Nissen (1955), p. 100.

7. Frazer, p. 586. In this paper Frazer expresses a preference for "the more general name of mental anthropology," rather than "social anthropology" for the division of the subject in which he worked.

8. See Hallowell (1954), pp. 167–70; and (1955), chap. 2; De Beer, chap. 1.

9. Wayne Dennis (1951, p. 2) points out that "it would not be inaccurate to say that developmental psychology began with a theory—the theory of recapitulation. Child psychology, the most productive segment of developmental psychology, began shortly after the promulgation of the theory of evolution when all scientific minds were inflamed by this great conceptual achievement." But after the movement had arrived at the "concise hypothesis" that "ontogeny recapitulates phylogeny" its decline was imminent. "The evolutionary viewpoint had seemed to open up wide unconquered vistas to child psychology. But on closer approach these beckoning plains proved to be inhabited only by unsubstantial figures and retreating will-o'-the-wisps. There was not a testable hypothesis in the entire landscape." While some psychologists of an older generation, like G. Stanley Hall and J. M. Baldwin, had adopted the theory of recapitulation and made it an integral part of their thinking, as did Frazer and Freud, this working hypothesis is not a necessary assumption of "developmental psychology." Heinz Werner (1940, p. 3) points out that the concept "is perfectly clear if this term is understood to mean a science concerned with the development of mental life and determined by a specific method, i.e., the observation of psychological phenomena from the standpoint of development." While some psychologists, when they employ this term, refer only to ontogenesis, "the mental development of the individual is, however, but one theme in genetic psychology." Related to it "is the developmental study of larger social unities, a field of interest intimately linked with anthropology and best known by the name of *ethnopsychology*. The question of the development of the human mentality, if not arbitrarily limited, must lead further to an investigation of the relation of man to animal and, in consequence, to an *animal psychology* oriented according to developmental theory."

10. Schneirla (1952), p. 563.

11. Roe and Simpson, p. 1.

12. See LeGros Clark, 1955, 1958, 1959; Howell, 1959; and Washburn and Howell, "Human Evolution and Culture," in *Evolution After Darwin,* vol. 2, pp. 33–56, University of Chicago Press, 1960.

13. Straus (1955a), p. 370.

14. Quoted by LeGros Clark (1958), p. 192.

15. "The confusion of ideas," warns LeGros Clark (1958, p. 193), "to which the loose and uncritical use of the colloquial term 'man' can lead is particularly well shown in those lists of anatomical features which are from time to time enumerated with the intention of demonstrating his uniqueness in the animal world. For example, it has been claimed that 'man' is distinguished from all other Primates by such characters as the structure of the genital organs, the prominence of the calf muscles, the red lips, the shape of the female breast, the comparative nakedness of the body, and so forth. It does not always seem to be realized that features of this kind may be no more than distinctions at the specific or generic level—characteristic of the species *Homo sapiens,* and perhaps of the whole genus *Homo.* But, of course, we have no idea whether they were also

characteristic of extinct hominids such as Neanderthal man, *Pithecanthropus* and *Australopithecus.*" Cf. Schultz, 1957.

16. See Howells on classification of primates (1959), p. 137, p. 351, and Glossary.

17. For bibliography to 1957, see Carpenter, 1958*b.*

18. At the present time experimental research on non-hominid primates is also expanding. See, e.g., Harlow (1956), p. 273.

19. For a guide to culture and personality studies, see Hallowell, 1953, and Honigman, 1954 and 1959.

20. "Intelligence," "reason," and other "mental traits" become specific functions of the total personality structure. Furthermore, whether described as "mind" or "personality structure," the psychological organization of the human being is just as much a function of his membership in an organized social group as it is a function of his inherited organic equipment. John Dewey emphasized this point prior to the time when culture and personality studies were initiated and also before social psychology had assumed its present form. He said (1917), "What we call 'mind' means essentially the working of certain beliefs and desires, and that these in the concrete,—in the only sense in which mind may be said to *exist,*—are functions of associated behavior varying with the structure and operation of social groups." Thus instead of being viewed as "an antecedent and ready-made thing," mind "represents a reorganization of original activities through their operation in a given environment. It is a formation, not a datum, a product and a cause only after it has been produced."

21. Kroeber (1950), p. 87.

22. In a biological frame of reference, LeGros Clark points out (1958, p. 186), "The opposition to Darwin's thesis of the evolutionary origin of man naturally led his critics to search for anatomical characters in which the human body could be said to be 'unique,' thus providing arguments for removing man in any system of classification as far as possible from other mammals (especially the apes). In some cases, indeed, these arguments were pushed to an extreme of absurdity, which today we are apt to find rather astonishing." Reference is made to the wrangle over "hippocampus minor."

23. Carpenter (1955), p. 93.

24. Hebb and Thompson, p. 543.

25. However, in a recent review of "some of the achievements and a few of the problems which characterize present-day physical anthropology," J. S. Weiner directs attention to behavioral evolution when he writes: "There is one large baffling topic on which our evolutionary insight still remains very meagre—the emergence of the peculiar attributes of human intelligence, temperament, and social organization." He quotes Hebb and Thompson (note 24), refers to the work of Carpenter and Zuckerman, and concludes: "It remains an unfortunate fact that of all aspects of physical anthropology this one, which carries so much of promise to the sociologist and social psychologist no less than to the human biologist, should at the present time be the most neglected of all fields of study."

26. Nissen (1955), p. 106. Also Lashley in his Introduction to the classical papers of the ethologists, *Instinctive Behavior,* edited by Claire H. Schiller, notes on page ix: "They have traced patterns of instinctive activity among related species and have shown that behavior may be as clear an index of phylogenetic relationship as are physical structures." In contrast with American psychologists, these zoologists have focused their attention upon instinctive rather than learned

behavior, and their observations have been made in the field rather than the laboratory. The chief animals groups studied so far have been invertebrates and lower vertebrates. See also N. Tinbergen, *Social Behaviour in Animals*. New York: John Wiley & Sons, 1953; also Tinbergen's paper in "The Evolution of Life," vol. 1, University of Chicago Press, 1960, pp. 593–613.

27. LeGros Clark (1950, p. 73): "To say that man differs from the other primates in his capacity for tool-making and language is not very useful," to which Nissen (1955, p. 102) adds "until we have identified the mechanisms and processes which produce these complex end results."

28. Révész (1956), p. 92.

29. Critchley notes that Keith believed that a capacity for speech could be pushed back no further than Neanderthal man, whereas L. S. Palmer, basing "his opinion upon the anatomical characteristics of the mandible," argues that perhaps the australopithecines could speak.

30. Schneirla (1952, p. 582) points out that an adequate comparative study of group communicative behavior "is long overdue, particularly to clarify the relationships of concepts such as 'sign,' 'signal,' and 'symbol,' as well as the criteria of 'language,' all of which appear to suffer from a heavy load of speculation and a minimum of systematic research." Cf. the historical review, "Animal Communication" by Critchley and the discussion of "Animal Languages" in Brown (p. 156 ff.). Perhaps expanding research in the area of "paralanguage" in man, as defined by Trager (1958, may provide some new leads.

31. Hockett (1958), p. 570.

32. *Ibid.*, p. 574.

33. Hockett, "Animal 'Languages' and Human Languages," a paper read at the annual meeting of the American Anthropological Association, Dec., 1957, but not published until 1959 (p. 32).

34. Hockett (1958), p. 581.

35. Hockett (1959, p. 36) says: "A behavior pattern is transmitted culturally if it is not only learned but taught, and if the teaching behavior, whatever it may be, is also learned rather than genetically transmitted." Cf. Hockett (1958), pp. 579–80.

36. *Ibid.*, p. 36.

37. See, e.g., Hayes (1951), chap. 8: "Teaching an Ape to Talk."

38. Oakley, 1950, 1951, 1954, 1956.

39. Pumphrey (1951), pp. 27–28.

40. Bartholomew and Birdsell, pp. 482–83.

41. See, e.g., Thorpe, pp. 109, 332; Nissen, 1946.

42. Harlow (1952, p. 217), referring to Köhler's earlier construct of "insight learning," says "Insightful behavior on instrumentation problems apparently occurs only in animals that have had previous opportunity for experience in related situations."

43. Nissen (1946, p. 562) says: "The nearest thing to the manufacture of tools in the ordinary sense seen in primates is the observation reported by Köhler of a chimpanzee fitting together two short sticks in order to make a long one. This observation has not been repeated."

44. Hallowell, 1956.

45. See White, 1942. In 1927, Grace A. de Laguna argued that "it is scarcely credible, even aside from the more theoretical psychological considerations, that the art of chipping stone implements could have been developed by men who had not yet learned to speak." In a later, unpublished manuscript, de Laguna

has expressed her thought by saying: *"Homo faber* is *Homo cogitans."* Cf.
Révész (1956, pp. 92–93), who equates *Homo faber* with *Homo loquens.* Cf.
Vallois (p. 211), who points out that tool-making, "un phenomène essentiel de
l'hominisation culturelle," undoubtedly was preceded by an earlier stage of utilization . . . "qui n'impliquait encore qu'une hominisation à ses débuts. Les processus qui ont permis la fabrication doivent au contraire correspondre á une
cérébralisation déjà avancée ainsique, peut-être, à uncertain usage de la parole.
Une telle fabrication suppose en effect l'apparition de nouveaux centres corti-
caux et de nouvelles connexions sensitivo-motrices. Elle suppose l'idee d'une
transmission des techniques d'un individu à un autre."

46. Many years ago (1928, p. 336), Kroeber noted the chimpanzee's inability
"outside of posed problems to manufacture tools or lay them aside for the future." And Linton ("Appraisal," p. 266) noted the anticipatory dimension of
the human tool-making situation. "This indicates," he said, "a distinct type of
psychology, the realization of operation in the time stream, which no other
animal shares. I think this is the point, actually, where the human mind emerges,
even more than in the capacity for reorganization of experience we call 'thinking.'" Cf. Straus (1955b, p. 133), who observes "that man is peculiar in the
extent to which he lives in the three dimensions of time. It is this peculiarity
that gives use to his remarkable degree of foresight or anticipation which is
perhaps best expressed in tool-making, to use this term in its broadest sense."

47. Dart, p. 335.
48. Leakey, 1959 and 1960.
49. Howell, 1960, (Comments on the Leakeys' discovery), and 1959.
50. LeGros Clark (1959), p. 312. Cf. Oakley, 1958. Oakley (1957, p. 207)
raises the question whether it is possible that "systematic tool-making arose,
not gradually as most nineteenth century evolutionists led us to imagine, but
suddenly and spread rapidly? . . . The earliest tools and weapons would have
been improvisations with whatever lay ready to hand. Although the hominids
must have begun as occasional tool-users, ultimately they were only able to sur-
vive in the face of rigorous natural selection by developing a system of communication among themselves which enabled cultural tradition to take the place of
heredity. At this point systematic tool-making replaced casual tool-using, and it
may be that this change-over took place in the Australopithecine stage. It would
not be surprising, in view of the close correlation between culture and cerebral
development, if there had been at this stage intense selection in favour of larger
brains, with the result that the transition from the small-brained Australopithecus
to the larger-brained Pithecanthropus took place in a comparatively short space
of time."

51. Washburn (1958), p. 432, and Table 19.5, p. 428.
52. Referred to by Kroeber (1955, p. 198) as "that seed lightly tossed out by
Wissler that has never germinated."
53. Wissler (1923), pp. 264–65.
54. Kluckhohn (1953), p. 511.
55. Murdock (1945), p. 124.
56. Cf. Hallowell (1955), p. 100.
57. See Bidney, 1953; Kroeber, 1955.
58. Spiro (1954), p. 21.
59. *Ibid.,* p. 29.
60. Howells, 1950, and the important paper of Washburn in the same symposium. Cf. Heberer who writes: "Wir dürfen wohl sagen, dass, wie bereits

Nehring (1895) vermutete and heute vielfältig werden kann . . . der Mensch 'zuerst mit den unteren Extremitäten Mensch geworden' ist. Die Erwerbung des Bipedalismus schuf die Vorbedingung für die definitive Hominisation durch Cerebralization. Ein pronogrades Wesen konnte keinen humanen Status erreichen, ebensowenig wie dies einem Brachiator möglich war" (p. 537). And on page 540, "Die Hominisation begann mit dem Eisetzen des evolutiven Trends, der zur Erwerbung des Bipedalism und zur Reduktion des Gebisses mit fortschreitendem Ersatz der Zähne durch die Hände (Instrumentalhilfen) führte. Mit diesen Erwerbungen wurde die kritische Phase erreicht, in der sich der Ubergang vom sub-humanen zur humanen Zustand volbezog." Cf. LeGros Clark (1958), p. 196.

61. Oakley (1954) does not think it necessary to assume that the earliest hominid tool-users, or even tool-makers possessed speech. He likewise believes that a system of gestural communication preceded speech (1951). Cf. Critchley in this volume.

62. Oakley, 1959.

63. Nissen (1955), p. 99, points out: "It might well be that if we had a record of behavior as complete as the fossil record of structures, this would yield as convincing a body of evidence for evolution as does the latter. As a matter of fact, a study of the behaviors of living species alone—together with the paleontological evidence regarding the order in which these forms appeared—provides in itself a substantial basis for postulating a process of evolution."

64. Eggan, p. 746. Cf. Hallowell (1953), p. 600.

65. For background material on animal communication see Scott (1958), chap. 9; Schneirla (1952), p. 582; Hebb and Thompson and Haldane.

66. Manuscript of paper presented to the Conference on the Social Life of Early Man (1959). Carpenter (1952, p. 242) says: "Each known genus of primate has a repertoire of gestures which are employed consistently and which stimulate consistent reactions." Examples are given.

67. See Bourlière, chap. 8 ("The Social Life of Mammals"), in which he discusses the differentiated vocalizations of the howlers, gibbons, and chimpanzee in the general framework of the accoustic signals of mammals. See also Carpenter (1952), p. 242.

68. Oakley (1951), p. 75.

69. See Spuhler, p. 8, and Du Bruhl.

70. For bibliography to 1957, see Carpenter, 1958b; Frisch, 1959 gives a brief review with bibliography of the work that has been done at the Japan Monkey Center.

71. Bourlière (1956), p. 221.

72. Carpenter (1958a), p. 242.

73. See Table 1 ("Habitat and Group Structure in Different Species of Primate") in Chance, 1959.

74. Murdock, 1949.

75. Westermarck, however, was on the right track and must be seen in historical perspective. Hart points out (p. 108), "What had really happened to evolutionary theory between 1859 and 1891 was that, while Huxley had spent his life labouring on the genetic front to get his contemporaries to accept 'the unitary view of organic nature' and to reject the old dualistic view which saw man on one level, the rest of the animal world on another with an impassable gap eternally fixed between, the pass had been betrayed by Spencer and his followers, who, by assuming that society was one thing and biology another, had merely

substituted a new dualism for the older one, and had opened up as big a gap between man and the rest of nature as had been there in pre-Darwinian days. The extraordinary thing is not that this should have happened, but that nobody seems to have been aware of what was happening until Westermarck pointed it out." The latter in his *History of Human Marriage* (p. 9) said: "If we want to find the origin of marriage, we have to strike into another path . . . which is open to him alone who regards organic nature as one continued chain, the last link of which is man. For we can no more stop within the limits of our own species, when trying to find the root of our psychical and social life, than we can understand the condition of the human race without taking into consideration that of the lower animals." Etkin argues for a monogamous protohominid social structure but on quite different grounds than did Westermarck at the turn of the century.

76. Bourlière (1956), p. 147.

77. Chance (1959) points out: "Female macaques and baboons are sexually receptive for approximately 9 out of the 28 days of their reproductive cycle, so that in a group of monkeys where two or more adult females are present, the males will be in the presence of a sexually active female for more than half of the time. And in larger groups there will be continual sexual provocation, a situation found nowhere else in the animal kingdom except for a two-month interval during the mating season of the Pribilof seal."

78. Beach, 1947, and Ford and Beach. Cf. Beach, 1958.

79. Carpenter (1942), pp. 256–57.

80. Beach (1951), p. 426. See also Schneirla (1951, p. 104 ff.) in regard to ontogenetic factors influencing group organization. Cf. Paul H. Schiller, who believed there is evidence that primates have distinctive *manipulative* patterns of activity available that are not derived from experience.

81. Scott (1956), pp. 217, 218.

82. Collias, p. 1087.

83. Imanishi, p. 51.

84. Frisch, p. 589.

85. Nissen (1955), p. 106. See also Note 90.

86. Yerkes, p. 52. Yerkes thought the characterization of chimpanzee as "cultureless" to be "a seriously misleading statement, if not demonstrably false." He believed that "the elements or makings of cultural exhibits are present," but that "they are relatively unimpressive because unstable, fragmentary, variable and seldom integrated into functional relations." See Munn (pp. 120–30) for references to the experimental data on observational learning. He concludes: "It is only in monkeys and apes that anything clearly approximating such observational learning can be demonstrated and even at this level the problems solved by imitation are relatively simple." Instances of spontaneous imitation on the part of Viki were: operating a spray gun, prying off the lids of cans with a screw driver, etc. (Hayes and Hayes, 1955). In the concluding paragraphs of his summary of the observations in the Japanese macaques, Frisch (p. 595) says: "It seems doubtful that definitions [of culture] which strongly emphasize such concepts as social heredity, socially acquired response-patterns, learned traditional behavior, will be able to do justice to what Julian Huxley has called the 'uniqueness of man.' To the extent to which culture is equated with learned, traditional behavior, monkeys appear to have indeed much more 'culture' than anthropologists have often thought." There is a terminological problem, too, since the author discusses some of the case material referred to above under the caption

"acculturation," to which he adds quotes in the text. Imanishi employs the same term without quotes.

87. Bidley (1953), p. 27, says: "The identification of culture with the social heritage is, to my mind, not only a misnomer but also a serious error, since it implies that the essential feature of culture is the fact of communication and transmission, whereas I maintain that the essential feature is the combination of invention and acquisition through habituation and conditioning." Cf. the remarks of Kroeber on the use of the term "social heredity" (1948, p. 253).

88. Voegelin, p. 370. Harlow (1951, p. 127) clearly discriminates between infrahominids and *Homo sapiens* when he says, "In a limited sense . . . any animal living in a group and capable of facile learning must develop a *semblance of culture,* since it must have learned to be influenced in its behavior by the way of its fellows," but, at the same time he points out that "no animal other than man has a *true culture* in the sense of an organized body of knowledge passed down from generation to generation." (Italics ours.)

89. See Hochbaum for a discussion of "tradition" in birds. Dobzhansky (1955, pp. 340–41) discusses "Rudiments of Cultural Transmission among Animals." Several of the concrete instances cited are taken from observations on bird behavior; he does not discuss this phenomena among primates. The major point he stresses, however, involves a fundamental distinction between man and other animals, relative to Bidney's point. "In animals," he says, "the individuals of one generation transmit to those of the next what they themselves learned from their parents—not more and not less. Every generation learns the same thing which its parents have learned. In only very few instances the evidence is conclusive that the learned behavior can be modified or added to and that the modifications and additions are transmitted to subsequent generations."

90. In recent years some observers have used the term "culture" where it appears that certain habits have been socially learned and transmitted. Nissen (1955, pp. 105–6) referring to nest-building in chimpanzees writes: "There is pretty good evidence . . . that this nest-building is not instinctive, as in birds, but is, rather, transmitted by imitation or tuition from one generation to the next; it is, therefore, one of the very few items of behavior seen in these animals which may be classified as cultural." Cf. Nissen (1951a), p. 426. Fuller and Scott (1954, p. 29) write: "The possibility of *cultural* as well as biological inheritance can be tested by raising animals either in complete isolation or in contact with a foster species with very different habits of behavior. The results of such experiments on birds have been described extensively by Lorenz who has found evidence of both *cultural* and biological factors." (Italics ours.) I believe that *proto-culture* is a term which could be used in the context of either quotation or some other word such as *tradition* (employed by ornithologists, see Hochbaum) which clearly indicates that the species referred to does not possess a system of culture that is equivalent to that of *Homo sapiens*. While Bidney (1953, p. 127) says that "all animals which are capable of learning and teaching one another by precept or example are capable of acquiring culture," he makes a distinction between "culture in general" and human or "anthropoculture" (p. 125) which is peculiar to man. He goes on to say that "this implies an evolutionary approach to the concept of culture which recognizes degrees of culture from the sub-human to the human level." Nevertheless, I find a generic concept of culture unsatisfactory for reasons I have indicated in my discussion.

91. Carpenter (1958a), p. 245.

92. Carpenter (1955), p. 98.

93. Frisch, p. 591.

94. We do not know what objective factors underlay the increase in the size and range of early hominid groups. Change to a carnivorous diet and hunting have been suggested. (Washburn and Avis, 1958, p. 434.) But, as Washburn says (*op. cit.*) "whether early man scavenged from the kills of the big carnivores, followed herds looking for a chance to kill, drove game, or followed a wounded animal, his range of operations must have been greatly increased over that of arboreal apes. The world view of the early human carnivore must have been very different from that of his vegetarian cousins. The interests of the latter could be satisfied in a small area, and other animals were of little moment, except for the few which threatened attack. But the desire for meat leads animals to know a wider range and to learn the habits of many animals. Human territorial habits and psychology are fundamentally different from those of apes and monkeys."

95. Fiske (1909, p. 26) says it occurred to him immediately that "if there is any one thing in which the human race is signally distinguished from other mammals, it is in the enormous duration of their infancy"; a point he did not recollect ever seeing any naturalist so much as allude to. But Fiske was not quite as original as he thought. See, e.g., Lovejoy.

96. Fiske (*op. cit.*), p. 28.

97. *Ibid.*, p. 9.

98. *Ibid.*, p. 2.

99. *Ibid.*, p. 11.

100. *Ibid.*, pp. 12–13.

101. Bolk is mainly responsible for this particular term.

102. Carter, 1951, 1953; De Beer.

103. De Beer, pp. 75–76.

104. Schultz (1955), p. 53. And see his 1956 publication for an authoritative comparative treatment of the details of growth and development in various primate species. Schultz concludes that it is erroneous to emphasize retardation exclusively in man's ontogenetic development, since "ontogenetic specializations can consist of accelerations as well as retardations in man as well as in all other primates" (p. 959).

105. Roheim (p. 424) says, "This ultra-Lamarckian point of view is untenable," i.e., Freud's Primal Horde theory.

106. *Ibid.*, p. 424. Roheim (p. 409) says: "It is a curious fact that while man's delayed infancy is univerally admitted hardly anybody uses this fact in the sense that I do. The usual statement is that the delayed infancy makes it possible to condition human beings and that it is why psychology depends on conditioning, i.e., on culture. What culture depends on is then of course the kind of question no well behaved anthropologist should ask, because looking for origins is 'outmoded,' in fact it is nineteenth century, a truly terrible thing, a word loaded with the worst possible kind of *mana*. Quite apart, however, from this aspect of the question, how is it that nobody recognizes that in this one fact we have one of the most important keys to the understanding of human nature?"

107. *Ibid.*, p. 413. Perhaps it should be added that while in *both* man and the anthropoids sexual organs reach maturity earlier than full body growth, in man the time difference is greater.

108. Montagu (1956), p. 90. Cf. (1955), p. 22.

109. Huxley (1954), p. 20. The unkindest cut of all has come from Cuenot

(1945) who has said that man "can be considered a gorilla fetus whose development and growth have been greatly retarded."

110. Bernhard Rensch, who has been investigating the effects of increased body size on the relative size of the brain and its parts, and on higher psychological functions, has advanced the hypothesis (pp. 197–98): "In man's line of descent we may at least consider the increase of the cortex, the relative increase of 'progressive," i.e. more complicated cortex-regions, the absolute increase of the number of neurons and of dendritic ramifications, as . . . selectively advantageous factors. Thus the trend towards the human level of brain organization may be regarded as inevitable. Another important factor here is the prolongation of the juvenile phase found in many large animals. This could only occur where multiple births, and therefore intrauterinal selection for rapidity of development, had been eliminated. But once this had taken place, the prolongation of the juvenile phase was favored by selection because thereby the period of learning, that is to say the period of gaining experience and of exploration by play, is also extended. Thus the evolution of man, too, was inevitable." Cf. Rensch, 1956 and 1959.

111. Keith. See comments by Schultz (1955), pp. 49–50. The Hayeses, however, suggest "the possibility that most of the fourfold increase in cranial capacity from anthropoid to man took place after the appearance of culture and language, and therefore after primate behavior had become essentially human" (1955, p. 116).

112. *Appraisal,* p. 262.

113. Washburn (1959), pp. 27–29.

114. See, e.g., Penfield and Rasmussen; Penfield and Roberts; Bremer *et al.* (eds.); Von Bonin; and Kubie. Penfield and Rasmussen write (p. 204): "It is apparent that there are important connections which conduct both ways between areas of cortex and specific nuclei of the diencephalon, and that in the process of encephalization a varying degree of autonomy has been handed over to the large cortical projections. It does not necessarily follow, however, that all function, either new or old, has been handed over in this way nor that correlation between the activities of the different cortical areas is necessarily carried out in the cortex rather than in the diencephalon. . . . Popular tradition, which seems to be largely shared by scientific men, has taken it for granted that the cortex is a sort of essential organ for the purposes of thinking and consciousness, and that final integration of neural mechanisms takes place in it. Perhaps this is only natural since there has been an extraordinary enlargement of the cortex in the human brain, and, at the same time, man seems to be endowed with intellectual functions of a new order." However, "the whole anterior frontal area, on one or both sides, may be removed without loss of consciousness. During the amputation the individual may continue to talk, unaware of the fact that he is being deprived of that area which most distinguishes his brain from that of the chimpanzee" (pp. 205–6, 226).

115. See Edward C. Tolman, in Parsons and Shils, pp. 344–46; Clyde Kluckhohn and others, "Values and Value—Orientations in the Theory of Action" (pp. 388–433). A value-orientation, whether "held by individuals or in the abstract-typical form, by groups," and varying from explicit to implicit, is defined by Kluckhohn *et al.* (p. 411) as "a generalized and organized conception, influencing behavior, of nature, of man's place in it, of man's relation to man, and of the desirable and non-desirable as they may relate to man-environment and interhuman relations."

116. Jennings (p. 105), assuming a phylogenetic perspective and speaking of infra-human animals, said: "Only if the individuals play different functional roles is there social organization."

117. Cf. the discussion of "role expectations" in Sarbin (p. 226 ff., and p. 255): "Persons occupy positions or statuses in interactional situations. Psychologically considered, positions are cognitive systems of role expectations, products of learning. Role expectations are bidimensional; for every role expectation of other there is a reciprocal role expectation of self. The organized actions of the person, directed towards fulfilling these role expectations, comprise the role."

118. Dobzhansky says, "It is man's moral sense which makes him truly human" (p. 376). And Simpson, asserting that "man is a moral animal," says: "It requires no demonstration that a demand for ethical standards is deeply ingrained in human psychology. Like so many human characteristics, indeed most of them, this trait is both innate and learned. Its basic mechanism is evidently part of our biological inheritance" (p. 294).

119. Consequently, it is thoroughly intelligible why role theorists, more than any other group, as Sarbin points out (*op. cit.,* p. 238) "have developed and used the conception of the self as an intervening variable."

120. For a more extended discussion see Hallowell (1955) chap. 12.

121. Lowie, e.g., in his *Primitive Society* (1920) expressed the view that incest taboos have an instinctive basis. Later, he changed his mind (1933), p. 67.

122. Kroeber (1942), p. 206.

123. For example, Bidney at the outset of his *Theoretical Anthropology,* (p. 3) writes: "Man is a self-reflecting animal in that he alone has the ability to objectify himself, to stand apart from himself, as it were, and to consider the kind of being he is and what it is that he wants to do and to become. Other animals may be conscious of their affects and the objects they perceive; man alone is capable of reflection, of self-consciousness, of thinking of himself as an object." The psychologist David Katz, writing more than twenty years ago, likewise stressed what he called "objectivization" as a human differential (1937, p. 253). More recently, Rollo May has given particular emphasis to human self-awareness. "We can never see man whole," he says, "except as we see him, including ourselves, as the mammal who has a distinctive capacity for awareness of himself and his world. Herein lie the roots of man's capacity to reason and deal in symbols and abstract meaning. And herein lies also the basis for a sound view of human freedom" (1955, p. 313). Cf. May (1953), pp. 84–85. Other comparable opinions could be cited.

124. Stanley Cobb (1957, p. 202), in discussing the papers contributed to the symposium "Brain Mechanisms and Consciousness," says: "Although some of the authors seem to confuse the concepts of 'mind' and 'consciousness,' Fessard seems to agree with me that 'consciousness' is but one attribute of 'mind.' I would say [it is] *that part which has to do with awareness of self and of environment.* It varies in degree from moment to moment in man and from fish to man in phylogeny. It may be that invertebrates and even plants have rudimentary forms of awareness of self." It is difficult, however, to follow Cobb through to this point! Sir Julian Huxley (1956, pp. 558–59) has suggested that since *"mind* and *mental* have various undesirable connotations, it is best to drop them and to speak of awareness. Psychology in the customary sense can then be regarded as part of the general study of awareness and its evolution."

This would include "the way in which new possibilities of awareness are in fact realized, and also of the limitations on their realization. . . . There are two evolutionary prerequisites for a high organization of awareness involving the incorporation of individual experience by learning: (1) a long youth period . . . ; (2) Homothermy, permitting greater uniformity and continuity of awareness. Prerequisites for the further organization of the awareness-system, to enable it to incorporate experiences from other individuals and from past generations, are (1) social life, (2) the capacity to organize awareness in the form of concepts, (3) true speech. These have permitted the evolution of the unique type of awareness-system found in man." Cf. Huxley, 1953.

125. Asch, p. 276.

126. Sargent, chap. 20. The publication of G. W. Allport's article in 1943 initiated a renewed interest in ego and self on the part of social psychologists in particular.

127. Cf. Symonds, p. 4. Hartmann (1950) distinguishes ego, a psychic sub-system of the total personality with functions distinguishable from the id and superego, from self, one's own person.

128. Mac Leod (1951), p. 234. Cf. Asch, chap. 10, "The Ego," and Symonds.

129. See Hall and Lindzey, e.g., who point out that "among the theorists who, in some way, make prominent use of the ego or self concept are Adler, Allport, Angyal, Cattell, Freud, Goldstein, Jung, Murphy, Murray, and Sullivan" (p. 545). Cf. Spiro (1954), pp. 27–28.

130. While there is a considerable literature on the body-image phenomenon, the relations between body-image, ego, and self concepts are still under discussion. See Fisher and Cleveland.

131. Hartmann (1948), p. 379 ff. With reference to ontogenesis, Hartmann has been responsible for stressing an early "undifferentiated phase," in contrast with the notion that the id is chronically older than the ego, and the concept of a "conflict-free ego sphere" (1950). In the early undifferentiated stage of ontogenetic development there are no ego functions and no differentiation of self from the world outside. With respect to phylogenetic development, Hartmann says that while psychoanalysts do "attribute a sort of ego to animals" (1958, p. 48; no species indicated) "we cannot speak, in regard to the animal, of that kind of separation into ego and id which exists in the human adult. The very fact that the concept of instincts as it pertains to the lower animals is much more comprehensive than the concept of instinctual drives as it pertains to man prevents such a separation. It is possible, and even probable, that is just this sharper differentiation of the ego and the id—the more precise division of labor between them—in human adults which on the one hand makes for a superior, more flexible, relation to the outside world and, on the other, *increases the alienation of the id from reality.*" Cf. Hartmann, 1948.

132. Nissen (1955), p. 108.

133. Hebb and Thompson, p. 539.

134. Hebb and Thompson (*ibid.,* p. 544) make a most illuminating comment: "It is probably a common experience to all who have worked at the Yerkes Laboratories to feel that the bare bones of human personality, the raw essentials, are being laid open before his eyes. At the same time, it is hard to convey this to others, and to support it with behavioral evidence."

135. Schneirla (1953), pp. 64–65. In a later publication (1957, p. 102) it is noted that "a child's attainment of sentences marks a new advance from the

stage of unitary verbal symbols, and contrasts sharply with a monkey's inability to master symbolic relationships beyond the simplest abstractions. In a far wider sense, man's capacity for repatterning verbal symbols serially, or for attaining such symbols at all, is qualitatively far above the functional order represented by the gestural symbolic processes to which the chimpanzee seems developmentally limited, although not altogether dissimilar in its ontogenetic basis." I am not concerned here with the introduction of symbolic cues into laboratory investigations by the experimenter. See Harlow (1951), p. 493 ff.

136. Cathy Hayes, chap. 11.

137. In one cave I visited I remember crawling along a low gallery on my knees, with candle in hand, for a considerable distance before reaching the end of it. Discouraged at not finding any drawings, I turned over on my back for a rest. There above me were several drawings of wild horses. Cf. Laming (p. 158), who says: "At Arcy-sur-Cure the engravings are discovered only after a painful crawl of about 80 yards over slippery clay and sharp-pointed calcite. Such remote recesses, difficult of access and laborious of approach, are almost as numerous as the painted and engraved caves themselves. The placing of all these figures in remote parts of dark caverns seems to bear witness to a pursuit of the arduous, the magical, and the sacred."

138. See Breuil (p. 118 and Fig. 89) who writes: "By its massive body and thick legs, it resembles a bovine animal or a Rhinoceros; the very short tail is more indicative of the latter; the flanks are marked with a series of O-shaped oval splashes; the neck and ears are ridiculously small for the body; the head with a square muzzle, is like that of a Feline; two long stiff straight shafts, each ending in a tuft, are like no known animal horns, unless, as Miss Bate suggested, those of the Pantholops of Thibet . . . This is not the only example of a composite unreal animal in Quaternary art but it is the most spectacular." The drawing measures about 5 ft. 6 in.

139. See Saccasyn-Della Santa for illustrations of 250 examples of these figures and a systematic classification and analysis of them.

140. Breuil (*op. cit.*), pp. 176–77.

141. Laming is of the opinion that "the imaginary animals and the semi-human figures are . . . incompatible with the theory of sympathetic magic" which has been applied to the animal art. Considered as a whole, she also finds untenable "the theory that they represent hunting masks or have some connection with ritual hunting dances." "Why should the sorcerers, who were probably the artists of the tribe, depict themselves on the walls of the sanctuary wearing their masks?" she asks; it seems more likely that these drawings "represent mythical beings who were perhaps connected in some way with the history of the ancestors of the group" (pp. 191–92).

142. Cf. the discussion of "persons" of an other-than-human class among Ojibwa in Hallowell, 1958. Persons of this category are reified beings in the behavioral world of the Ojibwa and are equivalent to characters in their myths. Among them these narratives are true stories. Since metamorphosis is possible, a hard and fast line cannot even be drawn between the outward appearance of *human* persons and animals. Persons of the other than human class in particular, appear in myths and dreams in animal form. If the Ojibwa had an art similar to that of the Upper Paleolithic peoples and we had no other evidence, it can be imagined how difficult it would be to interpret the graphic representations they had made of persons of an other-than-human class.

143. See the colored reproductions of Viki's paintings in *Life* (Dec. 3, 1951).

144. Cf. Révész (1956, p. 104), "Without the verbal formulation of subjective experience and ethical standards, self-consciousness is incomplete and self-knowledge and self-control equally so. To be conscious of one's own self, to examine one's own endeavors, motives, resolves, and actions, necessarily presupposes language."

145. See Hallowell (1955), chap. 4.

146. Freedman and Roe, p. 461, in Roe and Simpson.

147. Cf. (*ibid.*), p. 422. Freud's interpretation is to be found in his *Civilization and its Discontents* (p. 123), "The price of progress in civilization is paid for in forfeiting happiness through the heightening of the sense of guilt."

148. Beres, pp. 170 and 231.

149. Bellak, pp. 25–26. Cf. Stierlin, p. 146.

150. Alexander (p. 78 ff.). Cf. Hartmann's remarks on the synthetic or organizing functions of the ego (1948, pp. 383–84).

151. Schneirla (1949), p. 273.

152. Benedict and Jacks; Teicher.

153. Carpenter, (1952, p. 242) says: "The limitations of capacities for communication, especially for symbol communication seem to stop non-human primate social development at the level of limited contemporary social groupings, to preclude the development of tribal kinship and to make it impossible for them to have any except the anlagen of cultural traditions."

154. Nissen (1955), p. 105.

155. Harlow (1958), argues that "there is no evidence that any sharp break ever appeared in the evolutionary development of the learning process" (p. 288); at the same time, "it is quite clear that evolution has resulted in the development of animals of progressively greater potentialities for learning and for solving problems of increasing complexity" (p. 269).

156. Hilgard is not content with the implicit, if not always explicit, generalization from comparative studies that "there are no differences, except quantitative ones, between the learning of lower mammals and man." At the human level, he says (p. 461), "There have emerged capacities for retraining, reorganizing, and foreseeing experiences which are not approached by the lower animals, including the other primates. No one has seriously proposed that animals can develop a set of ideals that regulate conduct around long-range plans, or that they can invent a mathematics to help them keep track of their enterprises. . . . Language in man is perhaps the clearest of the emergents which carries with it a forward surge in what may be learned. It seems plausible enough that other advances in the ability to learn must have come about as the nervous system evolved through successive stages below man. . . . There are probably a number of different kinds of learning which have emerged at different evolutionary periods, with the more highly evolved organisms using several of them. It is quite probable that these different kinds of learning follow different laws, and it is foolhardy to allow our desire for parsimony to cause us to overlook persisting differences."

157. The use of terms like "acculturation" and "enculturation" as well as "superego," without qualification, in reporting observations made on the Japanese macaques seems of dubious value. (See Imanishi, 1957.) If these Old World monkeys already possess culture and have superegos, what does human evolution mean?

158. Cf. Henry (pp. 221–22) who points out that "because his mechanism for

determining personal relations lack specificity" man's unique evolutionary path is set for him "by his constant tendency to alter his modes of social adaptation. Put somewhat in value terms, man tries constantly to make a better society, i.e., one in which he can feel more comfortable. When he makes a 'mistake,' he tries to change. This is one way in which he evolves."

Bibliography

ABERLE, D. F., COHEN, A. K., DAVIS, A. K., LEVY, M. J., JR., and SUTTON, F. X. 1950 "The Functional Prerequisites of a Society," *Ethics*, LX, 100–111.

ADRIAN, E. D., BREMER, F., DELAFRESNAYE, J. F., and JASPER, H. H. (eds.) 1954 *Brain Mechanisms and Consciousness*. Springfield: Charles C Thomas.

ALEXANDER, FRANZ 1950 "The Evolution and Present Trends of Psychoanalysis," *Acta Psychol.*, VII, 126–33. Reprinted in *The Study of Personality: A Book of Readings*, HOWARD BRAND (ed.). New York: John Wiley & Sons.

ALLPORT, GORDON W. 1943 "The Ego in Contemporary Psychology," *Psychol. Rev.*, L, 451–78.

ASCH, SOLOMON E. 1952 *Social Psychology*. New York: Prentice-Hall, Inc.

An Appraisal of Anthropology Today. 1953 Edited by SOL TAX, LOREN C. EISELEY, IRVING ROUSE, and CARL F. VOEGELIN. Chicago: University of Chicago Press.

BARTHOLOMEW, G. A., JR., and BIRDSELL, J. B. 1953 "Ecology and the Protohominids," *Amer. Anthropologist*, LV, 481–98.

BEACH, FRANK A. 1947 "Evolutionary Changes in the Physiological Control of Mating Behavior in Mammals," *Psychol. Rev.*, LIV, 297–315.

—— 1951 "Instinctive Behavior: Reproductive Activities." In *Handbook of Experimental Psychology*, S. S. STEVENS (ed.). New York: John Wiley & Sons.

—— 1958 "Evolutionary Aspects of Psychoendocrinology." In *Behavior and Evolution*, ANNE ROE and G. G. SIMPSON (eds.). New Haven: Yale University Press.

BELLAK, LEOPOLD 1956 "Psychoanalytic Theory of Personality." In *Psychology of Personality: Six Modern Approaches*, J. L. McCARY (ed.). New York: Logos Press.

BENEDICT, PAUL K., and JACKS, IRVING 1954 "Mental Illness in Primitive Societies," *Psychiatry*, XVII, 377–89.

BERES, DAVID 1956 "Ego Deviation and the Concept of Schizophrenia," *The Psychoanalytic Study of the Child*, XI, 164–235.

BIDNEY, DAVID 1953 *Theoretical Anthropology*. New York: Columbia University Press.

BOLK, L. 1926 *Das Problem der Menschwerdung*. Jena: Fischer.

BORING, EDWIN G. 1950 *A History of Experimental Psychology*. New York: Appleton-Crofts.

BOURLIÈRE, FRANÇOIS 1952 "Classification et caractéristiques des principaux types de groupements sociaux chez les Vertébrés sauvages." In *Structure et physiologie des sociétés animales*, pp. 71–79. Paris: Centre National de la Recherche Scientifique.

—— 1956 *The Natural History of Mammals* (2d ed. rev.). New York: Alfred A. Knopf.

254 *A. Irving Hallowell*

BREUIL, H. 1952 *Four Hundred Centuries of Cave Art.* Montignac, Dordogne: Centre d'Etudes et de Documentation Prehistoriques.

BROWN, ROGER 1958 *Words and Things.* Glencoe, Ill.: The Free Press.

CARPENTER, C. R. 1934 "A Field Study of the Behavior and Social Relations of the Howling Monkeys," *Comp. Psychol. Mono.,* Vol. X.

—— 1940 "A Field Study in Siam of the Behavior and Social Relations of the Gibbon (*Hylobates lar.*)," *Ibid.,* Vol. XVI.

—— 1942 "Characteristics of Social Behavior in Non-human Primates," *Trans. New York Acad. Sci.,* Ser. II.

—— 1945 "Concepts and Problems of Primate Sociometry," *Sociometry,* VIII, 55–61.

—— 1952 "Social Behavior of Non-human Primates," pp. 227–45. In *Structure et physiologie des sociétés animales,* Vol. XXXIV. Paris: Centre National de la Recherche Scientifique.

—— 1954 "Tentative Generalizations on Grouping Behavior of Non-human Primates," Human Biol., XXVI, 269–76. Included in *The Non-human Primates and Human Evolution,* arr. by JAMES A. GAVAN. Detroit: Wayne State University Press, 1955.

—— 1958a "Territoriality: A Review of Concepts and Problems." In *Behavior and Evolution,* ANNE ROE, and G. G. SIMPSON (eds.). New Haven: Yale University Press.

—— 1958b "Soziologie und Verhalten freilebender nichtmenschlicher Primaten" in *Handbuch der Zoologie,* Bd. 8, Lief. 18:1–32. Berlin. Walter de Gruyter.

CARTER, G. S. 1951 *Animal Evolution.* London: Sidgwick & Jackson.

—— 1953 "The Theory of Evolution and the Evolution of Man." In *Anthropology Today,* A. L. KROEBER (ed.). Chicago: University of Chicago Press.

CHANCE, M. R. A. 1959 "What Makes Monkeys Sociable," *The New Scientist* (March, 1959).

CHANCE, M. R. A., and MEAD, A. D. 1953 "Social Behavior and Primate Evolution," *Symposia of the Society for Experimental Biology,* Vol. VII.

COBB, STANLEY 1957 "Awareness, Attention and Physiology of the Brain Stem." In *Experiments in Psychopathology,* HOCH and ZUBIN (eds.). New York: Grune & Stratton.

COLLIAS, N. E. 1950 "Social Life and the Individual Among Vertebrate Animals," *Annals N.Y. Acad. of Science,* L, 1074–92.

COUNT, EARL W. 1958 "The Biological Basis of Human Sociality," *Amer. Anthropologist,* LX, 1049–85.

CRAWFORD, MEREDITH P. 1937 "The Cooperative Solving of Problems by Young Chimpanzees," *Comp. Psychol., Mono.,* Vol. XIV, No. 2.

CRITCHLEY, MACDONALD 1958 "Animal Communication," *Trans. of the Hunterian Society of London,* XVI (1957–58), 90–111.

CUENOT, L. 1945 "L'homme ce Neotenique," *Bull. Acad. roy. Belgique* (Brussels), Vol. XXXI.

DART, RAYMOND A. 1956 "Cultural Status of the South African Man-Apes." *Annual Report, Smithsonian Institution (1955),* 317–38. Washington, D.C.

—— 1959 *Adventures with the Missing Link.* New York: Harper & Bros.

DARWIN, CHARLES 1871 *The Descent of Man.* London: Murray.

—— 1873 *The Expression of the Emotions in Man and Animals.* New York: Appleton. (A new edition with Preface by Margaret Mead was published by the Philosophical Library, New York, 1956.)

DE BEER, G. R. 1951 *Embryos and Ancestors.* London and New York: Oxford University Press.

DE LAGUNA, GRACE A. 1927 *Speech: Its Function and Development.* New Haven: Yale University Press.

DENNIS, WAYNE 1951 "Developmental Theories." In *Current Trends in Psychological Theory.* Pittsburgh: University of Pittsburgh Press.

DEWEY, JOHN 1917 "The Need for a Social Psychology," *Psychol. Rev.,* XXIV, 266–77.

DOBZHANSKY, TH. 1955 *Evolution, Genetics and Man.* New York: John Wiley & Sons.

DuBRUHL, E. LLOYD 1958 *Evolution of the Speech Apparatus.* Springfield: Charles C Thomas.

EDINGER, TILLY 1956 "Objects et resultats de la paleoneurologie," *Ann. paleontol.,* XLII, 97–116.

EGGAN, FRED 1954 "Social Anthropology and the Method of Controlled Comparison," *Amer. Anthropologist,* LVI, 743–63.

EISELEY, LOREN C. 1955 "Fossil Man and Human Evolution." In *Yearbook of Anthropology, 1955,* WILLIAM L. THOMAS, JR. (ed.). New York: Wenner-Gren Foundation for Anthropological Research.

—— 1958 *Darwin's Century: Evolution and the Men Who Discovered It.* New York: Doubleday.

ETKIN, WILLIAM 1954 "Social Behavior and the Evolution of Man's Mental Faculties," *Amer. Naturalist,* LXXXVIII, 129–42.

FISHER, SEYMOUR, and CLEVELAND, SIDNEY E. 1958 *Body Image and Personality* New York: D. Van Nostrand.

FISKE, JOHN 1909 *The Meaning of Infancy.* Boston: Houghton Mifflin Co. Reprinting of "The Meaning of Infancy" from *Excursions of an Evolutionist* (1884) and "The Part Played by Infancy in the Evolution of Man" from *A Century of Science, and Other Essays* (1899).

FORD, CLELLAN S., and BEACH, FRANK A. 1951 *Patterns of Sexual Behavior.* New York: Harper & Bros.

FRAZER, JAMES G. 1922 "Scope and Method of Mental and Anthropological Science," *Sci. Progress,* XVI, 580–94.

FREEDMAN, LAWRENCE Z., and ROE, ANNE 1958 "Evolution and Human Behavior." In *Behavior and Evolution.* ANNE ROE and G. G. SIMPSON (eds.). New Haven: Yale University Press.

FREUD, SIGMUND 1930 *Civilization and Its Discontents.* New York: Jonathan Cape and Harrison Smith.

FRISCH, JOHN E. 1959 "Research on Primate Behavior in Japan," *Amer. Anthropologist,* LXI, 584–96.

FULLER, JOHN L., and SCOTT, JOHN PAUL 1954 "Heredity and Learning Ability in Infrahuman Animals," *Eugenics Quart.,* I, 28–43.

GREENBERG, JOSEPH H. 1957 "Language and Evolutionary Theory." In *Essays in Linguistics.* (Viking Fund Publications in Anthropology, No. 24.) New York: Wenner-Gren Foundation for Anthropological Research.

HALDANE, J. B. S. 1955 "Animal Communication and the Origin of Human Language," *Sci. Progress,* XL, 385–401.

HALL, CALVIN S., and LINDZEY, GARDNER 1957 *Theories of Personality.* New York: John Wiley & Sons.

HALLOWELL, A. IRVING 1953 "Culture, Personality, and Society." In *Anthropology Today,* A. L. KROEBER (ed.). Chicago: University of Chicago Press.

―――― 1955 *Culture and Experience*. Philadelphia: University of Pennsylvania Press.

―――― 1956 "The Structural and Functional Dimensions of a Human Existence," *Quart. Rev. Biol.*, XXXI, 88–101.

―――― 1958 "Ojibwa Metaphysics of Being and the Perception of Persons." In *Person Perception and Interpersonal Behavior*, R. TAGIURI and L. PETRULLO (eds.). Stanford, California: Stanford University Press.

HARLOW, HARRY F. 1951*a* "Levels of Integration along the Phylogenetic Scale: Learning Aspect." In *Social Psychology at the Cross Roads*, JOHN H. ROHRER and MUZAFER SHERIF (eds.). New York: Harper & Bros.

―――― 1951*b* "Thinking." In *Theoretical Foundations of Psychology*, HARRY HELSON (ed.). New York: D. Van Nostrand.

―――― 1952 "Primate Learning." In *Comparative Psychology*, CALVIN P. STONE (ed.). 3d ed. New York: Prentice-Hall, Inc.

―――― 1956 "Current and Future Advances in Physiological and Comparative Psychology," *Amer. Psychologist* (June, 1956).

―――― 1958 "The Evolution of Learning." In *Behavior and Evolution*, ANNE ROE and G. G. SIMPSON (eds.). New Haven: Yale University Press.

HART, C. M. H. 1938 "Social Evolution and Modern Anthropology." In *Essays in Political Economy in Honour of E. J. Urwick*, H. A. INNES (ed.). Toronto: University of Toronto Press.

HARTMANN, HEINZ 1948 "Psychoanalytic Theory of Instinctual Drives," *Psychoanal. Quart.*, XVII, 368–88.

―――― 1950 "Comments on the Psychoanalytic Theory of the Ego," *Psychoanalytic Study of the Child*, Vol. V.

―――― 1958 *Ego Psychology and the Problem of Adaptation*. Trans. by DAVID RAPAPORT. (Journal of the American Psychoanalytic Association Monograph Series, No. 1.) New York: International Universities Press.

HAYES, CATHY 1951 *The Ape in Our House*. New York: Harper & Bros.

HAYES, KEITH J., and CATHERINE 1955 "The Cultural Capacity of Chimpanzee." In *The Non-human Primates and Human Evolution*, arr. by JAMES A. GAVAN. Detroit: Wayne State University Press.

HEBB, D. O., and THOMPSON, W. N. 1954 "The Social Significance of Animal Studies." In *Handbook of Social Psychology*, Vol. I, GARDNER LINDZEY (ed.). Cambridge: Addison-Wesley Press.

HEBERER, GERHARD VON 1956 "Die Fossilgeschichte der Hominoidea." In *Primatologia* (edited by H. HOFER, A. H. SCHULTZ, and D. STARK), I, 379–560.

HENRY, JULES 1959 "Culture, Personality and Evolution," *Amer. Anthropologist*, LXI, 221–26.

HERRICK, C. JUDSON 1956 *The Evolution of Human Nature*. Austin: University of Texas Press.

HILGARD, ERNEST R. 1956 *Theories of Learning*. 2d ed. New York: Appleton-Century-Crofts.

HOCHBAUM, H. ALBERT 1955 *Travels and Traditions of Waterfowl*. Minneapolis: University of Minnesota Press.

HOCKETT, CHARLES F. 1958 *A Course in Modern Linguistics*. New York: Macmillan Co.

―――― 1959 "Animal 'Languages' and Human Language." In *The Evolution of Man's Capacity for Culture*. J. N. SPUHLER (ed.). Detroit: Wayne State University Press (and in *Human Biol.*, February, 1959).

HOFER, H., SCHULTZ, A. H., and STARK, D. (eds.). 1956 *Primatologia: Handbuch der Primatenkunde*, Vol. I. Basel and New York: Karger.

HONIGMANN, JOHN J. 1954 *Culture and Personality*. New York: Harper & Bros.

—— 1959 "Psychocultural Studies." In *Biennial Review of Anthropology—1959*, BERNARD J. SIEGEL (ed.). Stanford: Stanford University Press.

HOWELL, F. CLARK 1959 "The Villafranchian and Human Origins," *Science*, CXXX, 2 October.

—— 1960 Commentary on Leakey's "The Newest Link in Human Evolution," *Current Anthropology*, I, 76–77.

HOWELLS, W. W. 1950 "Origin of the Human Stock: Concluding Remarks of the Chairman." *Cold Spring Harbor Symp. Quant. Biol.*, XV, 79–86.

—— 1959 *Mankind in the Making*. Garden City: Doubleday and Co.

HUXLEY, JULIAN 1941 *Man Stands Alone*. New York: Harper & Bros.

—— 1953 *Evolution in Action*. New York: Harper & Bros.

—— 1954 "The Evolutionary Process." In *Evolution as a Process*, J. HUXLEY, A. C. HARDY, and E. B. FORD (eds.). London: Allen & Unwin.

—— 1955 "Evolution, Cultural and Biological." In *Yearbook of Anthropology—1955*, WILLIAM L. THOMAS, JR. (ed.). New York: Wenner-Gren Foundation for Anthropological Research.

—— 1956 "Psychology in Evolutionary Perspective," *Amer. Psychologist*, XI, 558–59.

IMANISHI, KINJI 1957 "Social Behavior in Japanese Monkeys, *Macaca fuscata,*" *Psychologia*, I, 47–54 (English).

—— 1959 "Identification: A Process of Enculturation in the Sub-human Society of *Macaca fuscata,*" *Primates*, I, 1–29 (English summary).

JENNINGS, H. S. 1942 "The Transition from the Individual to the Social Level." In *Levels of Integration in Biological and Social Systems*, ROBERT REDFIELD (ed.). ("Biological Symposia," Vol. VIII.) Lancaster, Pa.: Cattell Press.

KATZ, DAVID 1937 *Animals and Men: Studies in Comparative Psychology*. London: Longmans, Green.

KEITH, ARTHUR 1948 *A New Theory of Human Evolution*. London: Watts & Co.

KLUCKHOHN, CLYDE 1953 "Universal Categories of Culture." In *Anthropology Today*, A. L. KROEBER (ed.). Chicago: University of Chicago Press.

KROEBER, A. L. 1928 "Sub-human Cultural Beginnings," *Quart. Rev. Biol.*, III, 325–42.

—— 1942 "The Societies of Primitive Man." In *Levels of Integration in Biological and Social Systems*, ROBERT REDFIELD (ed.). ("Biological Symposia," Vol. VIII.) Lancaster, Pa.: Cattell Press.

—— 1948 *Anthropology*. New York: Harcourt, Brace & Co.

—— 1950 "Anthropology," *Scientific American*, CLXXXIII, 87–94.

—— 1955 "On Human Nature," *Southwest. Jour. of Anthropology*, XI, 195–204.

KUBIE, LAURENCE S. 1953 "Some Implications for Psychoanalysis of Modern Concepts of the Organization of the Brain," *Psychoanal. Quart.*, XXII, 21–68.

LA BARRE, WESTON 1954 *The Human Animal*. Chicago: University of Chicago Press.

LAMING, ANNETTE 1959 *Lascaux Paintings and Engravings*. London: Penguin Books.

LASHLEY, K. S. 1949 "Persistent Problems in the Evolution of Mind," *Quart. Rev. Biol.*, XXIV, 28–42.

LEAKEY, L. S. B. 1959 "A New Fossil Skull from Olduvai," *Nature*, CLXXXIV, 491–93.

—— 1960 "The Newest Link in Human Evolution: The Discovery by L. S. B. Leakey of *Zinjanthropus boisei*," *Current Anthropology*, I, 76.

LEGROS CLARK, W. E. 1950 *History of the Primates: An Introduction to the Study of Fossil Man*. London: British Museum.

—— 1955 *The Fossil Evidence for Human Evolution: An Introduction to the Study of Paleoanthropology*. Chicago: University of Chicago Press.

LEGROS CLARK, W. E. 1958 "The Study of Man's Descent." In *A Century of Darwin*, S. A. BARNETT (ed.). Cambridge: Harvard University Press.

—— 1959 "The Crucial Evidence for Human Evolution," *American Scientist*, XLIX, 299–313.

LOVEJOY, A. O. 1922 "The Length of Human Infancy in Eighteenth Century Thought," *Jour. Phil.* XIX, 381–85.

LOWIE, ROBERT H. 1920 *Primitive Society*. New York: Boni & Liveright.

—— 1933 *The Family as a Social Unit*. (Papers of the Michigan Academy of Science, Arts and Letters.) Ann Arbor: University of Michigan Press.

MACLEOD, ROBERT B. 1951 "The Place of Phenomenological Analysis in Social Psychological Theory." In *Social Psychology at the Cross Roads*, ed. JOHN H. ROHRER and MUZAFER SHERIF. New York: Harper & Bros.

MAY, ROLLO 1953 *Man's Search for Himself*. New York: W. W. Norton.

—— 1955 "The Historical Meaning of Psychology as a Science and Profession," *Trans. N.Y. Acad. of Sciences*, Ser. II, XVII, 312–14.

MONTAGU, M. F. ASHLEY 1955 "Time, Morphology, and Neoteny in The Evolution of Man," *Amer. Anthropologist*, LVII, 13–27.

—— 1956 "Neoteny and the Evolution of the Human Mind," *Explorations*, No. 6, pp. 85–90.
(Both Montagu articles reprinted in *Anthropology and Human Nature*. Boston: Porter Sargent, 1957.)

MUNN, NORMAN L. 1955 *The Evolution and Growth of Human Behavior*. Boston: Houghton Mifflin Co.

MURDOCK, GEORGE P. 1945 "The Common Denominator of Cultures." In *The Science of Man in the World Crisis*, RALPH LINTON (ed.). New York: Columbia University Press.

—— 1949 *Social Structure*. New York: Macmillan Co.

NISSEN, H. W. 1931 "A Field Study of the Chimpanzee: Observations of Chimpanzee Behavior and Environment in Western French Guinea," *Comp. Psychol. Mono.*, No. 1, p. 8.

—— 1946 "Primate Psychology." In *Encyclopedia of Psychology*, P. L. HARRIMAN (ed.). New York: Citadel Press.

—— 1951*a* "Phylogenetic Comparison." In *Handbook of Experimental Psychology*, S. S. STEVENS (ed.). New York: John Wiley & Sons.

—— 1951*b* "Social Behavior in Primates." In *Comparative Psychology*, C. P. STONE (ed.). New York: Prentice-Hall, Inc.

—— 1955 "Problems of Mental Evolution in the Primates." In *The Nonhuman Primates and Human Evolution*, arr. by JAMES A. GAVAN. Detroit: Wayne State University Press.

OAKLEY, KENNETH P. 1950 *Man the Tool-Maker*. London: British Museum.

—— 1951 "A Definition of Man," *Science News*, No. 20 (Penguin Books).

———— 1954 "Skill as a Human Possession." In *History of Technology*, Vol. I, C. J. SINGER *et al.* (eds.). Oxford: Oxford University Press.

———— 1956 "The Earliest Tool-Makers," *Antiquity*, XXX, 4–8.

———— 1957 "Tools Makyth Man," *Antiquity*, XXXI, 199–209. (Reprinted in *Annual Report, Smithsonian Institution, 1958*, 431–45.)

———— 1958 "Tools or Brains. Which Came First?" *Archeological News Letter* (London), VI, 48.

———— 1959 "Early Man's Use of Fire." *Conference on the Social Life of Early Man*, Wenner-Gren Foundation. (Summer, 1959.)

PARSONS, TALCOTT, and SHILS, EDWARD A. (eds.). 1951 *Toward a General Theory of Action.* Cambridge: Harvard University Press.

PENFIELD, W., and RASMUSSEN, T. 1950 *The Cerebral Cortex of Man.* New York: Macmillan Co.

PENFIELD, W., and ROBERTS, LAMAR. 1959 *Speech and Brain-Mechanisms.* Princeton: Princeton University Press.

PUMPHREY, R. J. 1951 *The Origin of Language.* Liverpool: University Press. (Reprinted in *Acta Psychol.,* IX (1953), 219–39.)

RENSCH, BERNHARD. 1954 "The Relation Between the Evolution of Central Nervous Functions and the Body Size of Animals." In *Evolution as a Process*, J. HUXLEY, A. C. HARDY, and E. B. FORD (eds.). London: Allen & Unwin.

———— 1956 "Increase of Learning Capability with Increase of Brain Size." *American Naturalist*, XC, 81–95.

———— 1959 *Homo Sapiens Vom Tier zum Halbgott.* Göttingen: Vandenhoeck und Ruprecht.

RÉVÉSZ, G. 1953–54 "Is There an Animal Language?" *Hibbert Jour.,* LXX, 141–43.

———— 1956 *The Origins and Prehistory of Language.* New York: Longmans, Green.

ROE, ANNE, and SIMPSON, GEORGE GAYLORD (eds.). 1958 *Behavior and Evolution.* New Haven: Yale University Press.

ROHEIM, G. 1950 *Psychoanalysis and Anthropology.* New York: International Universities Press.

ROMANES, G. J. 1883 *Animal Intelligence.* New York: Appleton.

———— 1888 *Mental Evolution in Man.* New York: Appleton.

SACCASYN-DELLA SANTA, E. 1947 *Les figures humaines du paléolithique supérieur Eurasiatique.* Antwerp: De Sekkel.

SAHLINS, MARSHALL D. 1959 "The Social Life of Monkeys, Apes and Primitive Man." In *The Evolution of Man's Capacity for Culture*, J. H. SPUHLER (ed.). Detroit: Wayne State University Press.

SARBIN, THEODORE R. "Role Theory." In *Handbook of Social Psychology*, Vol. I, GARDNER LINDZEY (ed.). Cambridge: Addison-Wesley Press.

SARGENT, S. STANFIELD. 1950 *Social Psychology.* New York: Ronald Press Co.

SCHILLER, CLARE H. (ed.). 1957 *Instinctive Behavior.* New York: International Universities Press.

SCHILLER, PAUL H. 1957 "Innate Motor Action as a Basis of Learning: Manipulative Patterns in the Chimpanzee." In *Instinctive Behavior*, CLAIRE H. SCHILLER (ed.). New York: International Universities Press.

SCHNEIRLA, T. C. 1949 "Levels in the Psychological Capacity of Animals." In *Philosophy for the Future*, R. W. SELLARS, V. S. McGILL, and M. FARBER (eds.). New York: Macmillan Co.

———. 1951 "The 'Levels' Concept in the Study of Social Organization of Animals." In *Social Psychology at the Cross Roads,* JOHN H. ROHRER and MUZAFER SHERIF (eds.). New York: Harper & Bros.

——— 1952 "A Consideration of Some Conceptual Trends in Comparative Psychology," *Psychol. Bull.,* XLIX, 559–97.

——— 1953 "The Concept of Levels in the Study of Social Phenomena." In *Groups in Harmony and Tension,* M. SHERIF and G. W. SHERIF (eds.). New York: Harper & Bros.

——— 1956 "Interrelationships of the 'Innate' and the 'Acquired' in Instinctive Behavior." In *L'instinct dans le comportement des animaux et de l'homme.* (Foundation Singer-Polignac.) Paris: Masson et Cie.

——— 1957 "The Concept of Development in Comparative Psychology." In *The Concept of Development,* DALE B. HARRIS (ed.). Minneapolis: University of Minnesota Press.

SCHULTZ, ADOLPH H. 1955 "Primatology in Its Relation to Anthropology." In *Yearbook of Anthropology, 1955,* WILLIAM L. THOMAS, JR. (ed.). New York: Wenner-Gren Foundation for Anthropological Research.

——— 1957 "Past and Present Views of Man's Specialization," *The Irish Journal of Medical Science* (August, 1957).

——— 1959 "Some Factors Influencing the Social Life of Primates." *Conference on the Social Life of Early Man,* Wenner-Gren Foundation. (Summer, 1959.)

SCOTT, JOHN PAUL. 1956 "The Analysis of Social Organization in Animals," *Ecology,* XXXVII, 213–21.

——— 1958 *Animal Behavior.* Chicago: University of Chicago Press.

SIMPSON, GEORGE G. 1950 *The Meaning of Evolution.* New Haven: Yale University Press.

SPIRO, MELFORD E. 1954 "Human Nature in Its Psychological Dimensions," *Amer. Anthropologist,* LVI, 19–30.

SPUHLER, J. N. 1959 "Somatic Paths to Culture." In *The Evolution of Man's Capacity for Culture,* J. N. SPUHLER (ed.). Detroit: Wayne State University Press.

STIERLIN, HELM. 1958 "Contrasting Attitudes toward the Psychoses in Europe and in the United States," *Psychiatry,* XXI, 141–47.

STONE, CALVIN P. (ed.). 1951 *Comparative Psychology.* 3d ed. New York: Prentice-Hall, Inc.

STRAUS, WILLIAM L. J. 1955a "The Great Piltdown Hoax," *Annual Report, Smithsonian Institution, 1954.* Washington, D.C.

——— 1955b "Closing Remarks." In *The Non-Human Primates and Human Evolution,* arr. by JAMES A. GAVAN. Detroit: Wayne State University Press.

SYMONDS, PERCIVAL M. 1951 *The Ego and the Self.* New York: Appleton.

TEICHER, MORTON I. 1954 "Three Cases of Psychoses among the Eskimo," *Jour. Ment. Sci.* C, 527–35.

THORPE, W. H. 1956 *Learning and Instinct in Animals.* London: Methuen.

TINBERGEN, N. 1953 *Social Behaviour in Animals.* New York: John Wiley & Sons.

TRAGER, GEORGE L. 1958 "Para-Language- a First Approximation," *Studies in Linguistics,* XIII, 1–12.

VALLOIS, HENRI V. 1958 "Le problem de l'hominisation." In *Les processus de l'hominisation.* Paris: Centre National de la Recherche Scientifique.

VOEGELIN, C. F. 1951 "Culture, Language, and the Human Organism," *Southwest. Jour. Anthropol.,* VII, 357–73.

VON BONIN, GERHARD9. 1950 *Essay on the Celebral Cortex.* Springfield: Charles C Thomas.

WASHBURN, S. L. 1950 "The Analysis of Primate Evolution with Particular Reference to the Origin of Man," *Cold Spring Harbor Symp. Quant. Biol.,* XV, 67–78.

—— 1959 "Speculations on the Interrelations of the History of Tools and Biological Evolution." In *The Evolution of Man's Capacity for Culture,* J. N. SPUHLER (ed.). Detroit: Wayne State University Press.

WASHBURN, S. L., and AVIS, VIRGINIA. 1958 "Evolution of Human Behavior." In *Behavior and Evolution,* ROE, ANNE and SIMPSON, G. G. (eds.). New Haven: Yale University Press.

WEINER, J. S. 1957 "Physical Anthropology . . . An Appraisal," *Amer Scientist,* XLV, 79–87. (Reprinted in *Evolution and Anthropology: A Centennial Appraisal.* The Anthropological Society of Washington, 1959).

WERNER, HEINZ. 1940 *Comparative Psychology of Mental Development.* New York: Harper & Bros.

WESTERMARCK, EDWARD. 1903 *History of Human Marriage.* London: Macmillan & Co., Ltd.

WHITE, LESLIE A. 1940 "The Origin and Nature of Speech." In *Twentieth Century English,* WILLIAM S. KNICKERBOCKER (ed.). New York: Philosophical Library.

—— 1942 "On the Use of Tools by Primates," *Jour. Comp. Psychol.,* XXXIV, 369–74.

WISSLER, CLARK. 1923 *Man and Culture.* New York: Thomas Y. Crowell.

YERKES, ROBERT M. 1943 *Chimpanzees: A Laboratory Colony.* New Haven: Yale University Press.

ZUCKERMAN, SOLLY. 1958 "L'hominisation de la famille et des groupes sociaux." In *Les Processus de l'hominisation.* Paris: Centre National de la Recherche Scientifique.

The Multiple Bases of Human Adaptability and Achievement: A Species Point of View

BENSON E. GINSBURG AND

WILLIAM S. LAUGHLIN

I. THE PROBLEM OF POLYMORPHISM—
GOALS AND PRIORITIES FOR BIOLOGICAL RESEARCH ON THE HUMAN SPECIES

The possibilities inherent in a genuinely international biological program keyed to economic productivity and improved human welfare can effectively help to accomplish many scientific and social goals unattainable within the confines of more circumscribed national programs. It is essential that a species point of view should prevail, and therefore the ecosystem of the entire human species must be studied. There should be no major missing links in the intensive multidisciplinary approach that has been recommended for the study of human adaptability, or the predicted chain of future broadly conceived researches will not be forged. An element of urgency intrudes in cases of disappearing peoples who represent in an important degree the conditions under which mankind has spent the major part of its evolutionary history. Many of our present characteristics and diseases represent responses to past environments, and a scientific understanding of these depends upon a comprehensive knowledge of the genetics of such groups of hunters that have remained in the environmental context in which all mankind evolved (Neel, 1958; WHO, 1964). Simultaneously, all mankind is undergoing changes with respect to health and fitness deriving from new selection pressures. Changed mating patterns reflected in new nations are constantly promoting the genetic restructuring of all populations, some at a relatively rapid pace (Goldschmidt, 1963). The assessments of these changes in a wide range of habitats, economies, ethnic groups, and cultures are needed to enhance our basic knowledge of the biology of human adaptability

NOTE: The authors gratefully acknowledge the support of several NIH grants supporting their individual research, and that of the Center for Advanced Study in the Behavioral Sciences, which made their study and collaboration possible.

From *Eugenics Quarterly*, Vol. 13, No. 3, September 1966, pp. 240–57. Reprinted by permission.

and to provide information directly applicable to many problems of human health and welfare.

Whether mankind's greatest threat is that posed by fallout from future explosions of hydrogen bombs or by fallout from the population explosion that has already taken place and is currently exacting a heavy toll in childhood death and disease, is scarcely a scientific question. Fundamental studies of human adaptability may help to prevent or ameliorate the undesirable consequences of either of these very real hazards. A signal point that we should like to emphasize is that human adaptability has multiple bases and that it is expressed in a variety of ways and achieved by a variety of routes in subpopulations of our species. We should like to underscore the fact that any fair-sized population (whose lower numerical limits remain to be determined) contains sufficient genetic variability to replace the entire human species with genotypically well-adapted populations. Stated another way, it is our contention that any reasonably large population contains sufficient genetic variability to move its adaptive topography by restructuring itself genetically without the introduction of new mutations or of genes from other populations.[1] No population has a monopoly on genetic variation essential to future evolution. The recombination of existing variation is more than adequate for the foreseeable future (Crow, 1961). As Ernst Mayr (1963) has remarked: "The essential genetic unity of species cannot be doubted. Yet the mechanisms by which this unity is maintained are still largely unexplored." A major goal of an international biological program should be to obtain precise information that bears directly upon the ways in which our diverse species has maintained its essential unity.

Within the ecosystem of the human species, there is a biobehavioral reticulum whose interdependencies are receiving more attention each year. Some of what we choose to call the intradependencies, however, are neglected both in theory and in application. The congruences of morphology, physiology, and behavior in Eskimo adaptation to cold stress and to glare contains genetically based intradependencies within a biobehavioral reticulum rather than interdependencies between disparate entities. In contrast, interdependence between Eskimos and their dogs is empirically based upon a practical knowledge of breeding and behavior. This in itself, and similarly with other groups of hunters, is an important part of their adaptive system (Laughlin, 1964). The intellectual achievements of primitive groups have been consistently underestimated and underreported (Laughlin, 1963); and to the extent that these constitute an integral part of their adaptive system, they should form a focus for more intensive studies.

The achievements of groups separated by distances and diffusion barriers too great for detectable gene flow attest to the enormous plasticity and potential for achievement inherent in populations generally. Thus, the Maya Indians of Guatemala and Mexico who generated a concept of zero, mathematics, astronomy, writing, monumental architecture, etc., developed these expressions of biobehavioral abilities on their own from a population base of primitive hunters who had entered the New World no more than 15,000 years ago. The fact that populations as remote from each other as Eskimos and Mayas can adapt to environments that are exceptionally diverse, with differences in intellectual interests, growth rates, disease patterns, nutritional regimes, population densities, mating practices, etc., and yet remain similar in many marker genes, suggests that, in fact, we know very little about the epigenetic systems and homeostatic devices shared by diverse populations that place limits on their genetic and phenotypic change and thus maintain the genetic unity of the species.

The genetically diverse populations inhabiting similar habitats, together with the genetically similar populations inhabiting diverse habitats, provide a natural comparison matrix in which research can be efficiently pursued. The basic problems posed by human polymorphisms require that many kinds of groups be studied, for neither the processes nor the parameters of human adaptability can be generalized from any single division of the species. With careful attention to the integrity of the individual and the community of which he is a member, the immediate practical benefits of being studied by teams of dentists, serologists, cardiologists, childgrowth specialists, virologists, nutritionists, behavior geneticists, et al., as well as the expense of undertaking field operations, laboratory tests, statistical analyses, and training of students and other personnel, should be easily justified when added to the long-range benefits and understanding to be derived from such basic information.

II. ANALYSES OF HUMAN DIVERSITY

A broad question such as that of man's place in nature cannot be treated at the research level by a single person or a single discipline. Nevertheless, the evidence that is collected by differently trained and oriented workers must be assembled and interpreted. The utilization of a variety of evidence, drawn from different fields, is a generic problem that poses special difficulties when we attempt to examine ourselves. The *zeitgeist* in which we operate is one dominated by a preoccupation with ethical considerations in which one hopes that dispassionate investigation will yield results that are consonant with our moral notions. Where there is an apparent danger of conflict between science and ethic, three modes of operation have been adopted with respect to the areas that interest us here.

The Dichotomy-Dismissal Approach. Here the two major procedures have been:

1. To dismiss the subject of heritable human variability that may extend to behavioral capacities by pointing out that present methodologies and information permit only tentative conclusions to be drawn in this area, and that these are vulnerable to misinterpretation and fraught with political danger (Mead, 1958, 1962).

2. To dichotomize the biobehavioral continuum, dismissing the biological aspects and, assigning to culture the role of determining all that is meaningful in human behavior. Thus, "In general, human variability seems to have had no proven effect on culture" (Steward and Shimkin, 1962, p. 72).

The practical results, in terms of training students or integrating different kinds of materials, are especially the same: a serious stultification. For example, Margaret Mead (1958, p. 487) states:

The artificial distinction between culture—as a purely human process—and all forms of learning through experience—in the rest of the biological sector—may have been a necessary device to dispose of theories of racial difference which assumed a racial factor in "Gallic wit" or "Negro musical ability."

This view had a tremendous influence upon the directions and priorities of anthropological and sociological investigations of the thirties and forties and was given further impetus by the elevation of the pseudoscientific racist writings of Gobineau and Chamberlain to the role of official dogma for the Third Reich. Indeed, the heat generated by the recent suggestion of concerted biological research in the area of human population differences as set forth by Ingle (1964) came partly from the crematoria of Auschwitz and Bergen-Belsen and partly from our own segregationist practices in this country. It is as though the recognition of significant biological differences among human population groups necessarily implies immutable distinctions in behavioral capacities that arrange themselves on a superiority-inferiority axis, and that studies of such differences can only lend themselves to racist doctrines. The ethical scientist, afraid of what he might let loose upon the world should he open this Pandora's box, is therefore better advised to turn his attention to other variables and to focus upon the social determinism of important human differences.

The latter view has been well epitomized by Baker (1962), who states that, "The concept of culture, as defined by some, almost precludes the biology of man from a significant role in his behavior." Biologically speaking, the species Man is the text so far as the identicist is concerned—the genetically partitioned subgroups are merely commentary. Hence, all distinctly human qualities, of whatever degree, become species attributes by definition, and are attainable by any human group under appropriate conditions of the surround.

The Unlike but Equal Approach. Here, the existence of biological differences unequally partitioned among various subpopulations within the human species is taken as a demonstrated fact, but the extension of these differences to include fundamental behavioral capacities is denied or minimized. As Dobzhansky (1964) points out:

Equality does not mean identity. Equality means equality of opportunity. . . . Race is a category of classification applied to subdivisions of mankind—there are races of man and of animals and plants . . . regardless of whether there is someone who wishes to classify them.

The apposition of competent taxonomy and population genetics to problems of human systematics attempted by many workers has not yet produced a synthesis. Instead, the biology-culture dichotomy is invariably reinstated; and the conclusion, though arrived at on other grounds, is that of the cultural determinist. Human population differences are analyzed in terms of beanbag genetics and referred to as "more" differences in frequency distributions of genes (although these may include frequencies of 0 to 100% as well as very different probabilities for achieving particular combinations, where intermediate values obtain). The implication is that such differences are nonqualitative and that any gene can get to any population, as there are no impenetrable barriers to genetic exchange between any groups within the species. Man's psyche, together with his intellectual capacities are, again, taken to be properties of the entire species, and no significant biological differences in behavioral capacities are therefore reasonable expectations among human subgroups, however classified. Individual differences occur in all populations, but these are, in this view, not selectively arrayed according to geography, pigmentation, or marriage customs. It is as though no genetic changes have occurred in the human species since the dawn of civilization and cultural factors have had no selective influence on the human genotype in almost 200 generations.

This view is, perhaps, most dramatically illustrated in the recent UNESCO report (1965) in which 22 scientists representing 17 nations agreed that:

The genetic capacity for intellectual development, like certain major anatomical traits peculiar to the species, is one of the biological traits essential for its survival in any natural or social environment. The peoples of the world today appear to possess equal biological potentialities for attaining any civilizational level. Differences in the achievements of different peoples *must be attributed solely to their cultural history.* [Our Italics.]

Thus, the matter has been resolved by resolution and the issue of the equality of all peoples made to rest on the premise of genetic non-involvement where differences in significant behavioral capacities are concerned. The very description of these differences in the report gives them a hierarchical value and implies that were they to have any genetic basis, some human groups would then be at least statistically inferior to others, a situation that would be philosophically and ethically intolerable to the authors of the report.

The Holistic Synthesis. On this view, "all aspects of any organism may be thought of as 100 per cent genetic but not 100 per cent determined" (Ginsburg, 1958). The genetic endowment of any organism, which includes its behavioral capacities, represents a potential, the actualization of which involves a series of interactions with environmental factors that restrict the degrees of freedom of this potential. The expressed phenotype at various stages of development, though dependent on what has been encoded in the genome, is not entirely determined by it. To be sure, there are varying degrees of liability between gene and character, but even at the highest level of lability, that of intellectual behavior, limits are set by the genotype. There is no aspect of any organism that is exempted from these biological effects (Ginsburg, 1963).

Turning from the individual to the group, the human species is seen as a population reticulum in which genetic exchange is much more probably within aggregates united by a common biological and cultural history than between them. Despite the intergradations and diversity that occur in all widely distributed and variable species, there are identifiable phenotypic population clusters resulting from a common breeding history under the influence of selective factors. These coadapted genotypes cannot be thought of as simply the sum of their component parts and are, therefore, not adequately represented by a table listing the frequency of occurrence of each gene. The genomes constituting a population are intradependent environmentally regulated servomechanisms assimilated to an evolved set of phenotypic norms. As such, they are buffered and able to absorb genes from other populations without undergoing a phenotypic change proportional to the amount of genetic infusion. It has, for example, been estimated that American Negroes have an admixture of Caucasian genes that is, minimally, on the order of 30% (Glass and Li, 1953). Although this contributes to the variability of the population, this infusion is continually being assimilated to the prevailing phenotype, which is not obliterated by it. The corollary to this phenomenon is that a population of sufficient size harbors a great deal more genetic variability than its current phenotypic census would suggest and that, given a selective impetus, such a population can move to other phenotypic norms in a relatively short time using its own genetic resources. These resources are probably most meager with respect to those genes that serve as phenotypic markers, on the basis of which assortative mating occurs, and that are, therefore, under extreme selective pressure for phenotypic constancy. Given a multiplicity of genetic ways of achieving similar phenotypic expression, convergence on the part of genetically diverse partial isolates within a species is to be expected under a common and sustained selection pressure. Man's culture, while an expression of his genetic endowment, also affects it via the assortative mating patterns that result, thus constituting part of a feedback system whose components are continually interacting.[2] To attribute the achievements of peoples solely to their cultural histories, which may be the products of differences as well as similarities in their biological endowments, is, in a dramatic sense, to dispense with the people. The student of culture thereby becomes a paleontologist of behavior, whose fossils are the books, music, technology, and other leavings of human organisms taken as groups—except that most hypotheses regarding the significance of biological factors as contributors to similarities or diversities that might be entertained by the student of fossil behavior of other organisms when he finds consistent differences in the nests built by different species of termites or of birds, for example, are excluded *a priori*.

III. THE SPECIES RETICULUM APPROACH

Biobehavioral Monism. The holistic synthesis that we are attempting here admits to no genetical-cultural dualism, nor does it array biologically based clusters of capacities that may differ statistically among subpopulations in any necessary hierarchical order. Evidence from the fields of behavior genetics and ethology provide ample documentation of the biological contributions to behavioral capacities ranging from intelligence to temperament to instinct (Ginsburg, 1958, 1963; Fuller and Thompson, 1960; Erlenmeyer-Kimling and Jarvik, 1963; Gardner, 1966; Thorpe, 1956; Shields and Slater, 1960). Freud faced up to the problem of biological determinism in relation to individual differences, but in practical terms he homogenized these differences and left biology primarily at the instinctual level (Freud, 1935).

Contemporary comparative psychologists, among them Beach and Lehrman, have gone back to the genome, and have, as Thiessen (1965) has summarized, ". . . forcefully argued and demonstrated that *behavior is the outcome of genotype developing within a milieu of environmental and social influences.* Instincts, as a result, are translated into species-specific behaviors with unique heritable and experiential components." The mind and the body have thus again become aspects of each other, not only in the sense of traveling in the same conveyance, but also of occupying the same seat.

Wright (1953), in an intensely provocative article, has pointed out that the organization of a species is that of a network, or reticulum, and that the human social organism includes domesticated animals, cultivated plants, and products of technology. In going from gene to society, his successive levels of involvement include the theory of the gene itself; physiological genetics at the cellular level; developmental genetics at the level of the individual; population genetics at the species level; and genetics of behavior at the societal level. At this societal level of organization, cultural anthropology and history deal with human behavior descriptively; while sociology and certain aspects of philosophy deal with it dynamically, and behavior genetics, theoretically. On his analysis, these disciplines are embedded in a matrix whose axes and dimensions are biological, and from which aspects of individual and group behavior are emergent.

Analysis by Comparison. All people belong in museums, Philadelphia lawyers and Eskimo shamans alike, for they are equally exotic to each other. It is a truism derivable both from experience and as a consequence of the practically infinite field for genetic variability attributable to Mendelian recombination under biparental reproduction that no two persons derived from separate ova are genetically alike, nor is it probable that the genetic duplicate of such a person has occurred or will occur throughout the history of life on earth. Still, Eskimos, as we know them, are not infinitely variable but are distinguishable from other populations. There exists a cluster of traits by which they can be recognized. Those that are not manifest and subject to convergent selection are often used as "tracers." Those that serve as the hallmarks of recognition may be termed "markers" and are of prime importance in assortative mating. As long as these markers remain within normal limits of variability, a great deal of genetic variation for other characters may be carried by the population. In view of the fact that there is a multiplicity of genetic ways of achieving similar phenotypic expression, selective mechanisms can and have acted to buffer or assimilate this variability to the prevailing phenotypic norms. In domestic animals, the practical breeder has taken advantage of this latent variability to create new color varieties, body types, and behavioral constellations through selective inbreeding (Lush, 1945).

Given the nonpanmictic structure of the human population, in which groups are maintained in partial, and in some cases total, genetic isolation from each other over long periods of time, it is extremely improbable that such subgroups within our species should be genetically alike as populations. Indeed, our evolutionary strength as a species lies precisely in this fact. Such a reticulum of subpopulations within which there is free genetic exchange and between which such genetic exchange is restricted to varying degrees depending upon distance, cultural diffusion barriers, and biological dissimilarities expressed primarily via combinations of marker genes, provides a set of excellent conditions whereby different genetic constellations can be "tried out" in a variety of environmental circumstances and conforms to the conditions that, according to Wright (1939), may be expected to provide the most favorable opportunities for evolutionary advance.

The environments that served as selective agencies by means of which directive effects have been exerted have been consistently dissimilar over considerable periods of time not only with respect to such variables as temperature, altitude, and sunlight, but also with respect to the selective effects of diverse cultures, some of which have placed a premium on attributes having to do with literary, musical, and artistic ability over some 160 or more generations in some genetic stocks, while detecting and selecting for quite different constellations of traits in others. The results of selection experiments with other mammals would suggest, not that populations under such differential pressures would generally develop unique constellations of genotypes (although they might in certain circumstances), but rather than genetic combinations that are adaptive in terms of the demands and opportunities of particular cultures are detected within such cultures and maintained as well as augmented by an assortative mating system that places a premium on these abilities. The frequencies of these genetic combinations are thereby increased.

The differential selective effects of the physicocultural environmental complex are themselves dependent on the biological (i.e., biobehavioral) potential of the population, not only in the ordinary sense of constituting a differential sieve for existing phenotypes, which impose limits upon the selective mechanisms, but also in a very special sense of crossing a biocultural threshold. In order to accomplish the latter, it is necessary for a population to be able to generate enough individuals possessing special and unusual abilities at a particular time and place to make a discovery that has the potential for changing the conditions of life for the group and to translate this potential into actuality. Once such a threshold is crossed, new selective forces are set into motion that extract and fix genetic combinations that would otherwise not be favored, and thereby produce genetic differences that were, in turn, generated by genetic differences that permitted such a threshold to be crossed in the first place.

The detection of such differences, especially when behavioral capacities are involved, can be accomplished only through comparative studies that do not rest on the assumption that the portion of the species reticulum from which the scientists are drawn and with which they are familiar is an adequate sample of the variation existing in the total species reticulum. Otherwise, we are in danger of using the criteria developed in a given culture as measures of abilities for all people in all cultures. Our so-called "intelligence tests" measure attributes that are predictors of success in a certain kind of schoolroom and in other situations requiring verbal and symbolic abilities, relational manipulations, and various other factors that can be identified and listed. When we make such a test "culture free," we free it (to the extent that we are successful) from dependence on particular kinds of experiences but attempt to specify it to the same ends. If our test may be analogized to a prism, which analyzes light in the visible spectrum, then we can make our prism work for light from various sources and of differing intensities. It does not, however, analyze the nonvisible spectrum. This requires a wholly different instrument in addition to the appreciation that the nonvisible spectrum exists. Comparative studies must attempt to sample the total range of human capacities and should include both similar and dissimilar genotypes in as widely varying environments as possible. Otherwise, we are looking through our instruments at a mirror.

The Meaning of Correlation. Studies of attributes of different peoples provide an important test of the degree to which correlated characteristics are causally related. From the genetic point of view, six major possibilities are apparent:

The first is that where the correlated characteristics are attributable to a common agency. Thus, on the hypothesis put forward by Stockard (1941) that the genotype controls the endocrine balance and that this, in turn, is responsible for both body form and behavior, a consistent relationship between somatotype and behavior is to be expected. The second possibility is that the same relationship would hold if the associated effects were determined by the same genes but dependent on different mechanisms. Thirdly, a less invariant relationship would be expected if separate but linked genes were involved, depending upon the degree of linkage. Coadapted mechanisms resting on a more complex genetic base constitute a fourth possibility, as in the case of the AB and Rh blood groups (Parsons, 1964). As a fifth possibility, the pairing of genes through independent selection for their separate effects may also occur; or, as a sixth alternative, such pairing may occur by chance through the vicissitudes of sampling. Data on the invariant occurrence of particular associations of traits in widely different populations as against the possibility of their occurrence in different associations in diverse populations (as well as within a single, variable population) are needed to help eliminate the range over which speculation may occur and also to identify, by means of the differences emerging from such comparative studies, what the traits are that may be considered to be natural units of variation for human beings and how they are distributed in the context of the reticular organization of the human species.

IV. CONTAINERS AND CONTENTS

The tremendous field for variation afforded by Mendelian recombination in a sexually reproducing species provides an apparatus whereby some aspects of the phenotype may be held relatively constant (as in the case of marker genes on which assortative mating patterns are often based), while others vary widely. Should selection favor a complex of independently heritable characteristics, these may come to be associated in a given population although they have no other dependent connections. In another population some elements of this complex may appear in association with quite different characteristics. As mentioned above, comparisons of populations based on such similarities and differences may be expected to provide clues regarding the natural evolutionary units involved.

Two complications must be considered in relation to the interpretation of such clues: The first is that those morphological, physiological, and behavioral properties that attract our attention constitute only an aspect of the phenotypic expression of the genes on which they depend. To discover the total phenotype resulting from the possession of these genes requires further research (Clausen and Ginsburg, 1958). The second is that there is no invariant relationship between genotype and phenotype (Ginsburg, 1958). Whether one is considering amino acid sequences or behavior, there is more than one genetic route to the same end result. In addition, environmental manipulations may produce similar results (phenocopies) by nongenetic means; and, conversely, genetic deficiencies may be compensated for by environmental intervention (i.e., the administration of insulin to genetic diabetics). The phenotypic topography of a population is, therefore, dynamically complex. Its traits and their associations must be considered from the point of view of a context matrix in which correlations may be due to any of the six relationships to the genetic substratum outlined in the previous section. When one adds the considerations just described to the context matrix (namely, that similar phenotypes may arise convergently from different genetic bases, that any given genotype may be variably expressed depending upon environmental conditions, and that phenocopies can mimic particular genotypes), it is evident that comparative studies must include genealogies, mechanisms, and developmental histories in order to arrive at any sensible interpretation of observed phenomena.

In the genetic sense, both populations and individuals may be considered to be container units with reference to the great variety of genetic materials that can be added or deleted with no perceptible change in the continuity of the population over a span of generations, or, put the other way around, in the external appearances of the range of individual organisms comprising the population. Among the important differences between these kinds of units is the fact that natural selection operates only through populations, not through individuals or types; and populations are what really evolve. Variation for physiological and behavioral characteristics can occur within individuals of a given physical constitution or somatotype (see Rin-Tin-Tin complex, Section VI), and spurious correlations may be secured by comparing constitution with various physiological and behavioral traits as discussed in Section III.[3]

Just as traits cannot be adequately treated without a knowledge of the context matrix in which they occur, neither can a sample of individuals be treated without a knowledge of the population context in which they occur. An important part of a population is the matrix of pathways connecting the individuals. Populations consist of related individuals, not separate units such as beans in a bag. The sampling of a population should reflect the nature of this population matrix which may enhance redundancy as a consequence of inbreeding, or of assortative mating, large family size, or the many other conditions that structure the genetic distance between individuals. It is efficient and necessary to define isolates and small populations with reference to the fact that they are intrabreeding communities. Thus, a population is a cluster of genetic pathways whose intersections recombine molecular units of inheritance, some of which develop into living organisms that reproduce.[4] Too much attention has traditionally been given to the end products of the reproductive system of a population, the developed traits of adult males and females most commonly used for morphological, physiological, and serological sampling.

Genetic populations are clusters of individuals who more frequently mate with other individuals within the group than outside. Geographical and cultural boundary-maintaining devices limit the genetic exchange between groups which, if random, would of course dissolve the groups. No two populations are identical, and they may vary in any trait used to characterize the populations. The common definition of a population as an intrabreeding community differing in the frequency of one or more genes from other such communities is uninformative. The stipulation of differing from others is extraneous and raises a multitude of questions such as, in how many genes they should differ and from whom they should differ. The study of migrant and hybrid groups is especially valuable for obtaining information on processes, even though physical differentiation of isolates separated by only one generation is minor compared with groups that have been separated for 8 or 80 generations. There is little point in collecting data on characteristics of people, be they morphological, physiological, serological, or behavioral, unless the genetic relationships between the individuals are known and means for testing hypotheses can be developed. The relationship of sample to population provides an equally valid reason for genealogical study. In small isolates this constitutes no theoretical problem, though it is tedious and time consuming. In metropolitan studies, where assortative mating is a more important factor and various kinds of subgroups are included, theoretical problems require more attention, and various models such as those based upon isolation by distance may be more relevant (Spuhler and Clark, 1961).

There are many ways of making comparisons between populations, all of which are vitiated if the original population unit is not adequately characterized. The construction of a species standard to which each population can be compared is efficient and objective (Penrose, 1950). The construction of clines or character gradients is still another useful method of comparison, and formal classification involving the estimation of biological distance (numerical taxonomy) between three or more groups is a third major category for describing between-group variation. All of these methods of relational systematics are useful for estimating degrees of similarity and difference, for assessing the distribution of variation, and for testing hypotheses. It should be noted that the explanation of similarity between groups (reflected in comparisons) is not automatically provided by the distributional maps or tables of relative degrees of similarity. The correspondence between similarity and affinity is a problem in relational systematics of populations for which there is a rich body of theory. Confusion between the procedures of defining or delimiting a population, identifying individuals who belong to a population, characterizing a population, and then making comparisons between populations (of which classification is only one method) are common. The enumeration of the number of populations is often more of an inventory than a classification. Classification consists of arranging the populations in a meaningful system. The problem of how many there are to be arranged is a separate and prior problem. All human populations intergrade to some extent, though there are many traits that are confined to a single continent and completely missing in another. Since we are dealing with variation within a single, nonpanmictic species, rather than with different species or with ideal types, intergradation is the rule. The lack of watertight compartments offers no theoretical block to study, though this is sometimes conceived to be so because of the confusion that exists between identifying individuals, on the one hand, and comparing populations, on the other. Paleontologists who work with genera between which there is a decided morphological gap, where identifying individuals and arranging them into series is no problem, have no fewer difficulties in assessing the relational systematics of the taxons with which they work. In the case of human populations, improvement in understanding degrees of relationship between populations is not automatically achieved by the substitution of gene frequency data for morphological data. The classificatory containers can remain the same with change only in the kind of data to be poured into them. Tabulation of gene frequencies is one way of characterizing a limited portion of the variability of a population. The frequency of a gene is not a necessary measure of the significance of that gene in that population. A gene may have the same frequency in two different populations and yet differ in its functional significance in each population because of the frequency of other genes or because of differences in environmental conditions. The trait complex matrix and the population matrix must both be known in order to interpret the significance of the frequency of a gene.

V. MAN: THE SELF-DOMESTICATING SPECIES

Principles and directions may often reveal themselves clearly in a simplified context where they are difficult to detect in a more complex one. Darwin found it useful to outline the principles of his theory of evolution on the basis of what could be seen and demonstrated with domesticated forms where man himself was the selecting agency. The analogy to domestic animals, and especially to breed formation, is often extended to man but is as often disputed. Dobzhansky (1964), for example, considers the analogy misleading, because selection in dogs, horses, and cattle has included behavioral attributes such as "temperament," "disposition," "intelligence," and "trainability," whereas selection for behavioral attributes in human beings has, on his view, not been parallel. In advancing this point of view, proponents of this concept are assuming the heritability of these aspects of an organism and sufficient genetic variability with respect to these qualities to make them amenable to relatively rapid selection by man but are denying that man, whose behavioral attributes are the most critically adaptive of any mammalian species and form the basis for his ability to live in groups and generate culture, can have developed these behavioral adaptations by similar means.

The position of biobehavioral monism formulated here precludes such a point of view. Most students of evolution would agree with Simpson (1964) that "Behavior is subject to particularly strong selection, and it is probably farthest removed from the genes and also most elaborately polygenic as a rule. Some single-gene determinants of behavior are known, but they are exceptional."

Washburn and Shirek (1966) have identified the bridge between behavior and its selection, including man's selection of his own behavior, by pointing out that "there is feedback between behavior and its biological base, so that behavior is both a cause of changing gene frequencies and a consequence of changing biology." Culture, which is a consequence of man's genetic endowment, is also a selective agency. It helps to determine the extent to which assortative mating will occur on the basis of obvious physical genetic markers. It also detects genetic combinations capable of specialized behavioral performances involved in the evolution of civilization, such as artistic, musical, and mathematical ability, as well as the types of intelligence that are necessary for the production of literature, technology, and art. As these detecting mechanisms improve through the universalization of education, more efficient use can be made of the genetic resources of the population in these regards. By providing attractive niches for the development and execution of these talents, cultures not only detect and develop them, but siphon them off and provide opportunities and impetus for assortative matings, consanguineous and otherwise, based on these criteria, thereby composing and perpetuating useful coadapted gene complexes. Tht cultures from which ours has evolved have been doing this for upwards of 150 generations—certainly time enough to have exerted selective genetic effects.

These genetic effects have been a source of worry to many students of human population who are concerned that the more intellectually capable segments of a society are outbred by the less capable segments. This is a needless worry on two grounds. The first is minor and is simply that favorable genotypes for the values existing in our culture are constantly being generated from the less advantaged segments of the population. The second is that the numerical proportion of creative minds with specialized capabilities need not be large in order to maintain and advance civilization. They form the keystone of a bio-behavioral arch; and as long as there is sufficient sustained assortative mating on the basis of these qualities to keep such a genetic track going, the possibility for shifting its numerical representation as cultural demands change is a potential that the population possesses.

Man as a self-domesticating species may take advantage of a large variety of relatively simple devices in order to exert increasing control over his own genetic potential, on a voluntary basis. These include birth control, abortion, adoption (including prenatal adoption), sperm donor programs (the genetic data from which should be kept on a worldwide basis), and genetic counseling in relation to particular pedigrees, to inbreeding, and to minimizing radiation hazard. These devices can, in turn, provide data on the basis of which more intelligent assessment of alternatives will become increasingly possible and useful, especially as social strictures change. What is important here is that as cultures become more specialized and complex, they provide a multiple-track system demanding different though overlapping biological capacities. While detecting and developing these from an existing genetic base, cultures also encourage assortative matings within these tracks, thereby leading to the formation and retention of particular kinds of genetic combinations on preferential bases. Thus, genetic variability has a demonstrable effect on culture, which, in turn, organizes the genetic pool on the basis of assortative mating systems relevant to the culture.

VI. THE GENOTYPES OF RACE AND CULTURE

The genetic parsing of experimental animal populations has revealed that they differ markedly with respect to behavioral capacities (Ginsburg, 1958, 1963). Emotionality and aggressiveness in mice, for example, are profoundly affected by infantile manipulation. Both the direction and magnitude of the effects vary according to strain or genotype. Whether there is a critical period or the maximal effectiveness of the applied stimulation and when it occurs, are also strain-specific. A mouse population from which these diverse response patterns to identical stimulation may be extracted is a reticulum whose measures of central tendency have a misleading biological meaning. Selection can quickly extract diverse styles, magnitudes, and directions of responses from such a population, all of which can be assimilated to a variety of physical marker genes. Thus one could, by genetic manipulation, create a population of black mice having a uniform set of responses to the manipulations described, although there is no causal relationship between the coat color and the behavior. One could as easily have associated the color with another behavioral profile. Similarly, the temperament, disposition, and various other behavioral qualities of dogs can be assimilated to one or another physical type. One of us has been associated with a project that produces dogs to lead the blind, where, possibly because of the image of Rin-Tin-Tin, the demand has been primarily for the German shepherd breed. Many of the foundation animals from which the present stocks on this particular project are derived, although intelligent and highly trainable, were also of a protective and mistrustful disposition and did not transfer easily from one person to another. These qualities, while admirable in a guard dog, are not suitable to one who must be a guide. Neither are they sufficiently reliably modified by conditions of rearing and training. Over approximately 10 generations of selective line-breeding, it has been possible to change the behavioral predisposition within this population while maintaining the characteristic appearance without resorting to cross-breeding, an indication that a good deal of genetic variability had been assimilated to the prevailing phenotype and could be extracted from it to conform to a different set of behavioral norms while retaining the identifying physical marker genes.

Such clusters of buffered genotypes that can assimilate a high degree of potential genetic variability to a prevailing phenotypic profile are typical of natural populations as well, and, as suggested by data on white and Negro populations, between which there is considerable genetic exchange in this country, are also characteristic of man. He is not panmictic either within or between population subgroups variously designated as racial or ethnic. The use of culture as a scanning mechanism that identifies and repackages the bits and pieces of heredity are, in a longer time, analogous to what may be accomplished with mice and dogs in a much shorter time span of more rigorous selection. The recombined genetic constituents are not entirely independent and may be expected to exhibit secondary interaction effects with other factors in the trait context matrix. Thus, the species reticulum, consisting of subpopulations that differ in marker genes and in the probabilities with which particular genetic combinations expressing themselves as identifiable phenotypes are encountered, is partially and flexibly partitioned. No part of it adequately represents the whole, and every substantial part undoubtedly has sufficient genetic resources to move to a new set of phenotypic norms under appropriate selection pressures. These new norms most probably include any phenotype now represented in the species reticulum with the probable exception of those dependent upon marker genes, which may be relatively fixed where the history of selection with respect to the phenotypes they control has narrowed the range of variability.

If one views the entire species reticulum at a given instant in time, it is not to be expected that the nature-nurture or genetic-cultural feedback mechanisms have resulted in convergent clusters of phenotypes at all nodal points. Styles and rates of response to environmental agencies as well as over capacities may differ as well as overlap. Just as the critical period at which early trauma has the greatest effect in a population of mice is genotype-dependent, as are the directions and magnitudes of the effects in question, so the rates, sensitivities, and outcomes of the far more sensitive interactions of human genotypes with respect to emotion, learning, and other behavioral attributes of importance to a social species are probably also biologically variable. Nor must it be taken for granted that the capacities measured by tests extrapolated from the capacities and cultures of one part of the species reticulum are adequate measures for all—either in scaling, or in the definition of what is to be measured. Readiness for assimilating particular kinds of experience may easily vary, as may the capacity for sequential ordering—i.e., objects before symbols, for example. What is an optimal early educational procedure in terms of the prevailing phenotypes of European caucasoids, is not necessarily optimal for Aleuts in order to achieve exactly the same goals. Analogy to animal behavior-genetics would lead us to expect such differences. Parallel hypotheses need to be entertained and investigated in relation to our own species where, precisely because we have confined ourselves to particular measures on particular scales and attempted to homogenize our educational procedures, hierarchical value judgments have been made where none necessarily exist. Instead of investigating a problem in a manner that would best enable us to take advantage of the differences offered by varying portions of our species reticulum, we have, out of misguided condescension involving apology for the fact that some of us measure up better than others in proportion as the scale we use was constructed expressly for us, shut ourselves off from the possibility of both understanding and making better use of the rich and varied resources of our species.

VIII. SPADE VERSUS GEOTOME: ETHICAL CONSIDERATIONS

The ethical obligations of a research team to the population being studied should be prominently reiterated in the training of personnel as well as in the actual prosecution of studies. These include respect for the dignity and privacy of subjects; compensation for their time and participation; medical, dental, and related services; consultation and exchange of information with learned men; an appreciation of the impact a research team may have on a community; an assessment of the values that remain after the research team departs; and, of course, cooperation with the officials and agencies of the national authority to which the people are responsible (WHO, 1964, pp. 24–25). The immediate practical benefits of being studied by teams of dentists, serologists, child-growth specialists, geneticists, nutritionists, anthropologists, et al., is often enhanced by the opportunity to train a member of the community who may continue some data collection and who may use this skill as a source of future compensation or entry to an academic institution. Genetic information as well as general health information is sometimes sought by members of the community as well as local government officials, and the same standards of accuracy and discretion should be applied to all.

A second area in which an ethical obligation is apparent is in the training of the students and other personnel for participation in an international program. Education in human biology of the species, where the genetic unity of the species and understanding of all the variation contained within it is the frame of reference, is an honest and scientifically unqualified undertaking. One of the effective by-products is dissipation of fallacious concepts emerging from the typological models still in use, treatment of human variation in a nonhierarchical reticulum, or the implication that various populations must undergo mixture in order to advance. It is far more effective and much faster to insert scientific and testable ideas into peoples' heads than to delete erroneous ideas already lodged there. The positive facts of evolutionary species biology and the methods for securing and testing them are of value to all members of the species, and they provide the only known basis for intelligently counteracting the arguments of racists and environmentalists.

A third area is that of the reactions to a false dilemma posed by belief in hierarchy and by our egalitarian ethic. The common tendency to read hierarchy into phenomena that are nonhierarchical, and our existing corpus of literature and beliefs in which this "Great Chain of Being" is applied to humans within the species, coupled with the simultaneous espousal of a belief in the worth of all individuals, should not induce us to eschew biobehavioral studies dealing with differences in maturation rates, various kinds of learning, and other special aptitudes. Variation in aptitudes does not indicate position on an ascending scale, any more than underpigmentation indicates position on a hierarchical phylogenetic scale. It does indicate that different populations have emphasized different as well as similar foci in the biobehavioral reticulum as these have been relevant to their adaptive needs and evolutionary history—a reticulum common to the entire species, whose basic elements are found in all groups. An isomorphic analogy is the difference between males and females, ranging from the molecular to the derivative behavioral characteristics. The differences may be considered minor, but there is cause for rejoicing that they exist at all. It would obviously be inapplicable to configure a study of males and females in terms of an ascending scale of nature.

No single scale or frequency is adequate to characterize a population, and tests designed for one population may be inapplicable to all others. All groups need the information resident in other groups, because no single population or national unit contains an adequate sample of the variability of the entire species in forms that we can presently study. The answers to many fundamental biological questions cannot be secured by more intensive study of one or even several populations.

VIII. GUIDELINES FOR INTERNATIONAL BIOLOGICAL RESEARCH AND TRAINING

A meaningful study of those parameters of the human species with which we are here concerned must include its total range of physical environments, genetic partitioning, and conditions of rearing and culture. As presently conceived, the International Biological Program is potentially a major compiler of the history of the human species. Its wider role depends upon the productivity of all the sections in the program, for they will all provide information relevant to the understanding of human adaptability. Competent researchers are already at work in the various participating nations on important problems. A major problem will be to attract and develop new ideas and projects in the face of a real shortage of scientists and facilities for training them. Much help may be expected from international agencies such as UNESCO and WHO, which have considerable experience in international research. In the final analysis, the actual research will be supported by particular nations and individuals. The momentum of international research may exceed the number of individuals not already committed and the number of persons who already have adequate training. We would suggest that priorities should go to new ideas involving genuinely international collaboration and cooperation, with special attention given to those elements of urgency arising from both conservational exigencies and from the crucial nature of fundamental problems. These may be epitomized simply as (1) hypothesis testers, (2) hypothesis generators, and (3) studies investigating poorly known parts of the human biobehavioral reticulum which require development of instrumentation and interpretation free of the two common biases: (a) population bias, reflected in limitation of tests or observations that have optimum reliability only on the population for which they were developed, and (b) interpretative bias, in which inaccurate and inapplicable ideas of hierarchical arrangement persist.

Basic questions are multitudinous and can best be posed by the researchers who are concerned to answer them. Is an increase of homozygosis harmful per se or only for particular loci? Under what conditions may hybrid vigor be manifested? What is the evidence of actual deterioration reflected in consanguinity models? What are the genetic effects, as well as the ecological ones, of impulsive breeding or relaxation of birth control measures? Is there significant genetic variation in length of gestation and in maturity of the human infant at birth? Do conditions of very early rearing have important differential effects on later behavior of humans, as they do in other mammals; and do similar conditions of rearing produce differing outcomes depending on both the genotype and later cultural influences? Are somatotype-morbidity data congruent in populations between which there has been negligible gene flow? Are there indigenous differences in incidence and patterns of mental illness among diverse ethnocultural intersects? Are there differences in perceptual and motor abilities between populations, and if so, have these resulted in effective differences in educational practices that exploit such variation in abilities? Are the basics of human behavior so predetermined biologically that variations in cultural practices have little influence upon them? If not, do cultural practices compensate for the normal range of variability in order to homogenize human social behavior? Can a child from a primitive culture, if raised from infancy in a highly specialized one, become an effective member of the latter, behaviorally—and is the Tarzan of popular lore a reasonable probability?

Many other questions could be formulated, and most suggest the societies and circumstances in which they can best be studied. Most are feasible for study. In fact, numerous social and educational practices both here and abroad (i.e., the Headstart program, hospital nursery procedures for normal and premature infants, sperm donor programs, and many other conditions of human husbandry) are either based on assumed answers to the above questions or provide conditions under which scientific studies of these problems could be carried out if the right investigating teams were fielded.

In addition to the need for well worked out human data dealing with the range of behavioral capacities of genetically diverse groups in various social contexts, there is a need for more comparative data on the infrahuman origins of intelligence, emotionality, and social behavior. In this comparative realm there has been a temptation to forget what has been learned with respect to the evolution of morphological adaptation and to infer homologies from similarities in behavior among taxonomically related groups. The gorilla, the baboon, and the rhesus monkey are all highly specialized primates whose social behavior may as easily represent specialized side branches of the evolutionary tree to which we humans trace our biobehavioral capacities, as to the main stem. Studies of other social species such as wolves, dogs, sea otters, and even rats and mice, may add as much of relevance for the understanding of human behavior to the comparative picture as primate studies. Similarities in behavior between various representatives of the primates, where adaptive, may represent convergence rather than common origin, so that, fascinating and excellent as many of these researches have been in their own right, their utility for the evaluation of the origins of human behavior remains to be determined in the context of further comparative studies—including studies of human primitives, additional primate groups under both natural and laboratory conditions, and other social mammals.

Notes

1. A discussion of this point on the basis of experimental evidence obtained by Dobzhansky and Pavlovsky with *Drosophila pseudoobscura* is especially pertinent. See T. Dobzhansky, 1962, *Mankind Evolving*. Yale University Press, New Haven and London, p. 283.

2. This relationship is beginning to receive systematic attention under the rubric of "social genetics."

3. This area is discussed and illustrated in a kinescope tape entitled "Repackaging People" made by the authors in May 1966 and is available through the University of Wisconsin educational television station, WHA, Elizabeth Bailey, producer.

4. This is the genetic definition of "race."

References

BAKER, PAUL T. 1962 The application of ecological theory to anthropology. *Amer. Anthropologist*, 64 (1) Part 1:15–22.

CLAUSEN, J. A., and B. E. GINSBURG 1958 Genetic and cultural characteristics. *Eugen. Quart.*, 5 (2):95–104 (see p. 101).

CROW, J. F., 1961 Mechanisms and trends in human evolution. *Daedalus*, 90 (3):416–431.

DOBZHANSKY, T. 1964 *Heredity and the Nature of Man*. Harcourt, Brace and World, Inc., New York.

ERLENMEYER-KIMLING, L., and L. F. JARVIK 1963 Genetics and intelligence: A review, *Science*, 142:1477–1479.

FREUD, S. 1935 *A General Introduction to Psychoanalysis*. Garden City Publishing Co., Garden City, New York (see p. 22 and lecture 10).

FULLER, J. L., and W. R. THOMPSON 1960 *Behavior Genetics*. John Wiley and Sons, Inc., New York and London.

GARDNER, R. W. 1966 "Genetics and Personality Theory." *In* S. G. Vandenberg (ed.), *Methods and Goals in Human Behavior Genetics*. Academic Press, New York.

GINSBURG, B. E. 1958 Genetics as a tool in the study of behavior. *Perspectives in Biology and Medicine*, 1 (4):397–424.

——— 1963 "Genetics and Personality." *In* J. M. Wepman and R. W. Heine (eds.), *Concepts of Personality*. Aldine Pub. Co., Chicago, Ill., pp. 63–78.

GLASS, H. B., and C. C. LI 1953 The dynamics of racial intermixture: An analysis based on the American Negro. *Amer. J. Hum. Genet.*, 5:1–20.

GOLDSCHMIDT, E. (ed.) 1963 *The Genetics of Migrant and Isolate Populations*. Williams and Wilkins Co., New York.

INGLE, D. 1964 Racial differences and the future. *Science*, 146 (3642):375–379.

LAUGHLIN, W. S. 1963 "Primitive Theory of Medicine: Empirical Knowledge." *In* I. Galdston (ed.), *Man's Image in Medicine and Anthropology*. Monograph IV, Institute of Social and Historic Medicine, pp. 116–140.

——— 1964 Races of mankind: Continental and local. *Anthropological Papers of the University of Alaska*, 8 (2):89–99. Reprinted in G. W. Lasker (ed.), *Physical Anthropology 1953–1961, Year Book of Physical Anthropology*, Vol. 9.

Lush, J. L. 1945 *Animal Breeding Plans.* Iowa State College Press, Ames, Iowa (see esp. chap. 21).

Mayr, Ernst 1963 *Animal Species and Evolution.* Harvard University Press, Cambridge.

Mead, M. 1958 "Cultural Determinants of Behavior." *In* A. R. Simpson and G. G. Simpson (eds.), *Behavior and Evolution.* Yale University Press, New Haven, pp. 480–503.

——— 1962 "Retrospects and Prospects." *In* Thomas Gladwin and William C. Sturtevant (eds.), *Anthropology and Human Behavior.* The Anthropological Society of Washington, pp. 115–149.

Neel, J. 1958 The study of natural selection in primitive and civilized human populations. *Hum. Biol.,* 30 (1):43–72.

Parsons, P. S. 1964 Interaction within and between chromosomes. *J. Theoret. Biol.,* 6 (2):208–216.

Penrose, L. S. 1950 "Genetics of the Human Race." *In* L. C. Dunn (ed.), *Genetics of the 20th Century.* Macmillan, New York, pp. 393–399.

Shields, J., and E. Slater 1960 Heredity and psychological abnormality. *In* H. J. Eysenck (ed.), *Handbook of Abnormal Psychology.* Pitman Medical Publishing Co., Ltd., London, pp. 298–343.

Simpson, G. G. 1964 Organisms and molecules in evolution. *Science,* 146 (3651):1535–1548.

Spuhler, J. N., and P. J. Clark 1961 Migration into the human breeding population of Ann Arbor, Michigan, 1900–1950. *Hum. Biol.,* 33 (3):223–236.

Steward, J. H., and D. B. Shimkin 1962 "Some Mechanisms of Sociocultural Evolution." *In* H. Hoagland and R. W. Burhoe (eds.), *Evolution and Man's Progress.* Columbia University Press, New York and London, pp. 67–87.

Stockard, C. R. 1941 *The Genetic and Endocrine Basis for Differences in Form and Behavior.* Wistar Institute of Anatomy and Biology, Philadelphia.

Thiessen, D. D. 1965 Stickleback zigzags to monomorphic marking. *Contemp. Psychol.,* 10 (6): 246–248.

Thorpe, W. H. 1956 *Learning and Instinct in Animals.* Harvard University Press, Cambridge, Mass.

UNESCO 1965 UNESCO Conference Report, August 18, 1964. Proposals on the biological aspects of race. *UNESCO Courier,* April 1965, pp. 8–11.

Washburn, S., and W. Shirek 1966 "Human Evolution." *In* J. Hirsch (ed.), *Genetics and Behavior.* McGraw-Hill, New York.

WHO 1964 *Research in Population Genetics of Primitive Groups.* World Health Organization Technical Report Series No. 279, Geneva.

Wright, S. 1939 *Statistical Genetics in Relation to Evolution.* Herman and Cie, eds., Paris (see esp. pp. 58–60).

——— 1953 Gene and organism. *Amer. Natur.,* 87 (832):5–18.

Cultural Selection of Human Psychological Types

R. KUTTNER

It is generally recognized that civilization insulates man from selective forces in his physical environment. This insulation does not prevent evolutionary change but rather shifts the focus of activity. It is within man's cultural dimension that selective pressures are found that shape his development. The task of identifying, tracing, and analyzing these forces is made extremely difficult by the fact that man alters his social environment by interacting with it.

G. V. de Lapouge (discussed and evaluated in Sorokin [1]) listed eight cultural and institutional factors that modified the biological composition of human populations. These were: war, politics, law, religion, morality, economics, occupation, and urbanization. Modern thinking on this subject has been considerably refined. Lapouge's categories were so mechanistically obvious that they tended to conceal the operation of more subtle forces. Current theoretical work has placed less emphasis on sharply focused eugenic and dysgenic factors and has started to probe the influence of sociocultural agencies on psychological and personality types.

Illustrative of this new trend are the suggestions and speculations of Lasswell. [2] He develops the hypothesis that there is a necessary congruence between government and the institutions by which individual character is formed. For a political constitution to endure, an appropriate temperament must be inculcated into the citizenry. Stable governments with stable constitutions exist because they rest on a stable citizenry. Recent history amply demonstrates that nations which suddenly adopt democratic rule all too often fail to support the experiment. A span of time is required before the masses adjust to their new government. Where this adjustment has been gradual, and the people shaped by the political philosophy, as in most West European states, then great stability is found. Where constitutions are abruptly imposed, little observance is given them and they have little permanence. The fitting of national character to socio-political forms is a process of mutual adaptation, and it is evident that over a period of time those

From *Genus*, Vol. XVI, No. 1–4, 1960, pp. 3–6. Reprinted by permission.

who cannot assimilate themselves to the developing pattern are eliminated by exile, emigration, or some means of social attrition.

Lasswell suggests that bureaucratization is one process for introducing personality changes in a population. A growing bureaucracy is the means by which a modern state copes with the complexities of civilized society. The multiplication of the administrative apparatus of a government involves a selection from the very outset. Bureaucratic organizations exert a strong attraction for compulsive neurotic types. It has been reported that obsessive-compulsive personalities rarely receive medical discharges from military service, and it is assumed that such individuals find an atmosphere of regimentation congenial to their temperaments.[3] While it is true that normal, well-integrated individuals, because of their flexibility and adaptability, can compete successfully for the top posts in an hierarchy, this alone does not protect an organization from ultimate domination by deviant types. Normal personalities are sufficiently adaptable to be able to work well with non-typical colleagues, and they may recruit into the upper echelons as successors men who are markedly compulsive or rigidly formalistic. This recruitment is not likely to be reciprocated. Once lodged at the power centers of an institution, neurotics tend to surround themselves with similar personalities. Neurotics create or select others in their own image. Such a selective phenomenon serves, in the end, to neuroticize an entire organization, even a government, and may stamp its collective character on vast numbers of people.

Another mechanism for injecting non-typical individuals into the character-forming organs of a social body is through the democratic elective system itself. Bluemel[4] points out that representative government is a psychological fallacy. A sorting of personality types occurs the moment some individuals offer themselves for nomination. Willingness to hold office already distinguishes a candidate from the self-effacing majority. This kind of representation is by substitute, not by equivalent. When the higher posts of a government or institution are held by dynamic, dominant, or aggressive persons, the pattern of social life may change for all others. Some temperaments will find themselves in harmony with the new climate; many others may experience damaging maladjustments or express resentments that lead to purges, exile, or political reconditioning. Every student of history knows of men who created an "age" or a "period" that reflected their own personalities. The selective influence of such a period should not be underestimated merely because the psychological transmutation of the population takes place by slow, submerged, and cumulative processes.

The Russian character, according to one analysis, is the result of centuries of Tartar, Czarist, and Communist oppression.[5] Human qualities that were incompatible with a continuing autocracy were eliminated by a very efficient program of mass banishment and genocide. Radzinski notes a polarization of the Russian people into a wolf-like class of oppressors and a mass of submissive, robotized workers. Perhaps Lenin's famous judgment that the proletariat could never develop enough self-consciousness to spark a revolution was an intuitive recognition of the inbred passivity of the Russian people.

The link between the somatic aspects of personality and biological selection is aptly expounded by Henry.[6] Poor social adaptation results in stresses that have physiological repercussions. Tensions may be so severe that organic consequences ensue. These are the diseases of adaptation that have come into prominence in recent medical literature. Psychosomatic illnesses induced by socio-cultural stress have as one of their chief targets the reproductive functions. Susceptible individuals suffer a diminished fertility that operates to eliminate them from the breeding population. Different societies and cultures generate different tensions. By the elimination of those individuals who are most vulnerable to the stresses peculiar to a culture, biological selectivity alters the composition of a population in the direction of greater compatibility with the existing socio-cultural environment.

The above discussion has attempted to elucidate two processes: the concentration and entrenchment of non-typical personalities in the culture-regulating and culture-transforming instruments of society, and the resulting anxiety and stress that afflicts the normal majority when it tries to adjust to an environment created by a dominant elite that differs significantly from the psychological average.

Eugenicists have been long concerned over the possible physical degeneration of humanity through the suspension of selective forces that removed the weak and inferior from the breeding population. Modern medicine is presumably keeping alive many genetically defective individuals who in the past would not have survived long enough to leave progeny. An analogous problem exists with aberrant personality and psychological types. In this area, however, it is far more difficult to detect deleterious changes since the definition of normalcy is based on traits possessed by the majority. If the majority itself is being selectively modified by socio-cultural stresses set in motion by a small group of self-perpetuating, deviant types, then there is no permanent standard by which normalcy can be defined. The psychological quality of a population may deteriorate without external signs of change. It would seem wise if some objective concept of normality could be devised so that statistical data on sociopathy could be correlated with the hypothesized accumulation of neurotic and aberrant types in the general population.

References

1. PITRIM SOROKIN, *Contemporary Sociological Theories* (New York: Harper & Bros., 1928) pp. 238–242.
2. HAROLD D. LASSWELL, "Political Constitution and Character," *Psychoanalysis and the Psychoanalytic Review,* 46:1–18.
3. J. J. MICHAELS & R. T. PORTER, "Psychiatric and Social Implications of Contrasts Between Psychopathic Personality and Obsessive Compulsion Neurosis," *Journal of Nervous & Mental Diseases,* 109:122–132.
4. C. S. BLUEMEL, *War, Politics, and Insanity* (Denver: World Press, 1950) pp. 101–102.
5. JOHN M. RADZINSKI, "Phrenophagia: A Form of Human Artificial Selection," *American Journal of Psychiatry,* 113:312–318.
6. JULES HENRY, "Culture, Personality and Evolution," *American Anthropologist,* 61:221–226.